M. Daughty          Room 303
The Lovett School

# Review Course in Algebra

BY

## W. E. SEWELL, Ph. D.

*Assistant Professor of Mathematics*
*Georgia School of Technology*

D. C. HEATH AND COMPANY

BOSTON

# PREFACE

This text contains sufficient and appropriate material for a thorough review course in algebra. It is therefore adapted for use in the latter part of the high school curriculum, or in any situation where the usual high school unit requirements in algebra have been completed but need to be reviewed.

It is the author's observation and experience that pupils leave high school having forgotten much of the algebra learned, and go into life or college unable to apply successfully the algebraic principles necessary to the solution of practical problems or to future mathematical or scientific work. *Review Course in Algebra* is designed to correct these deficiencies.

While the text is essentially a review course, it covers the entire field, beginning with the first principles of algebra. Although some of the explanatory material found in first year texts is omitted, each topic is fully treated on a level with the more mature pupils who will take the course. Special attention is given to those topics and principles which are most troublesome.

The text contains all the definitions, examples, and explanations necessary for such a course. The exercises are ample to insure mastery, and are arranged in the order of increasing difficulty. The problems are largely practical, many of them relating to the actual life experiences of the pupil. Careful instructional helps and illustrative examples precede each type of problem introduced.

The first seven chapters cover the subject from the basic definitions through systems of quadratic equations and must be taken consecutively. The last four chapters, however, are independent of each other and may be taught in any order. For example, a knowledge of functions and graphs is helpful to an understanding of the solution of systems of equations and may well be taught in conjunction with the chapter on quadratic systems or even earlier. The review problems at the end of the book are arranged to cover various topics: Part A covers Chapter II; Part B, Chapter III; Part C, Chapters IV, V, VI, VII; Part D, Chapter VIII; and Part E, Chapters IX, X, XI. In addition part F affords a general review of the entire book, and many of the problems are typical of those appearing on college entrance examinations.

In the preparation of this book the author acknowledges his indebtedness to his colleagues at the Georgia School of Technology for their generous assistance, especially to Ballou, Coleman, Holton, Hook, Steen, and Webb. He is particularly grateful to Dr. D. M. Smith, Head of the Mathematics Department, for his encouragement and many valuable suggestions.

Finally, the author wishes to thank the many high school teachers of mathematics, too numerous to name, for their wise guidance and direction in determining both the scope and gradation of the text.

W. E. SEWELL

# CONTENTS

CHAPTER                                                          PAGE

I. INTRODUCTION . . . . . . . . . . . . . . . . . . . .   1

II. EXPONENTS AND RADICALS . . . . . . . . . . . . . .   9

III. ALGEBRAIC REDUCTIONS . . . . . . . . . . . . . . .  18

IV. LINEAR EQUATIONS . . . . . . . . . . . . . . . . .  52

V. LINEAR SYSTEMS . . . . . . . . . . . . . . . . . .  65

VI. QUADRATIC EQUATIONS . . . . . . . . . . . . . . .  81

VII. SYSTEMS INVOLVING QUADRATICS . . . . . . . . . . .  96

VIII. FUNCTIONS AND GRAPHS . . . . . . . . . . . . . . . 110

IX. RATIO, PROPORTION, AND VARIATION . . . . . . . . . 116

X. PROGRESSIONS . . . . . . . . . . . . . . . . . . . 123

XI. THE BINOMIAL THEOREM . . . . . . . . . . . . . . . 128

REVIEW EXERCISES . . . . . . . . . . . . . . . . . 134

INDEX . . . . . . . . . . . . . . . . . . . . . . . 144

# REVIEW COURSE IN ALGEBRA

## CHAPTER I

### INTRODUCTION

**1. Arithmetic and algebra.** Algebra, like arithmetic, deals with numbers and the same fundamental operations, addition, subtraction, multiplication, and division, are used in both. The primary difference lies in the fact that in arithmetic the numbers themselves appear in the expressions whereas in algebra symbols are used to represent numbers. Through this use of symbols algebra gains much power in the writing down concisely of valuable formulas and in the solving of problems. The expression $7 - 5$ is purely arithmetic, while $x - y$ is an algebraic expression which becomes $7 - 5$ when $x$ is put equal to 7 and $y$ to 5. Consequently, results in algebra can be applied to arithmetic by the substitution of specific numbers for the symbols involved.

### EXERCISES

**1.** If $x = 5$ and $y = 4$, find the number which is represented by
(a) $x + y$, (b) $x - y$, (c) $\frac{x}{y}$, and (d) $\sqrt{x + y}$.

*Repeat the substitutions using in the above expressions the values:*

| | | |
|---|---|---|
| **2.** $x = 3, y = 2$ | **3.** $x = 6, y = 1$ | **4.** $x = 13, y = 7$ |
| **5.** $x = 8, y = 4$ | **6.** $x = 101, y = 37$ | **7.** $x = 226, y = 1$ |
| **8.** $x = 80, y = 1$ | **9.** $x = 15, y = 10$ | **10.** $x = 12, y = 4$ |

**11.** If $a = 2, b = 1$, find $\frac{a^2 - ab}{3b}$.

**2. Classification of the real numbers.** Since the symbols of algebra represent numbers an understanding of the various types of numbers is of prime importance. **The positive integers are**

$$1, 2, 3, 4, 5, 6, \cdots ;$$

these are also called the **natural numbers** or **whole numbers**. A **rational number is one which can be expressed exactly as the quotient of two integers**, e.g., $\frac{1}{2}$, $\frac{3}{5}$, etc.; since $\frac{a}{1} = a$ the positive integers are rational numbers. **A number which is not rational is called an irrational number**, e.g., $\sqrt{2}$, $\pi$,* and $e$.† The indicated root of an integer is either an integer or an irrational number, e.g., $\sqrt{4} = 2$, an integer; $\sqrt{2}$ is irrational.

All of the above numbers are positive and a + (plus) sign is understood before each one. In algebra negative numbers are used, in addition to the positive numbers. The negative numbers are the numbers of arithmetic preceded by − (minus) signs, e.g., − 5, − 17, − 2, − $e$. For every positive number there is a corresponding negative number, e.g., 6 and − 6, $\frac{1}{2}$ and − $\frac{1}{2}$.

The positive and negative rational and irrational numbers and the number zero are called **real numbers** and constitute all the real numbers of algebra. Every real number has a decimal representation. Such a representation is said to terminate if every digit after a certain one is zero, e.g., $\frac{1}{4} = .25000$ terminates with 5. A decimal representation is said to repeat if the succeeding digits after a certain one can be determined from the preceding digits, e.g.,

$$\tfrac{1}{7} = .14285714285714 \cdots$$

is a repeating decimal. The decimal representation of a rational number either terminates or repeats; the decimal representation of an irrational number neither terminates nor repeats.

### EXERCISES

*Classify as integer, rational number, or irrational number:*

1. $\sqrt{5}$, $\frac{e}{2}$, − 17, $\frac{26}{2}$, $\sqrt[3]{27}$, $\sqrt[3]{28}$, $3\pi$, .257, $\frac{3}{5}$

2. 1.75, $\sqrt[3]{176}$, $4\frac{1}{2}$, $\pi + 2$, − $\frac{5}{4}$, 132.2, $\sqrt{25}$, 1.489732

*Find the decimal representation of:*

| | | | |
|---|---|---|---|
| 3. $\frac{1}{3}$ | 4. $\frac{1}{13}$ | 5. $\frac{8}{7}$ | 6. $\frac{14}{15}$ |
| 7. $\frac{1}{8}$ | 8. $\frac{25}{10}$ | 9. $\frac{4721}{1000}$ | 10. $2\frac{1}{4}$ |

* The number $\pi$ represents the ratio of the circumference of a circle to its diameter and its *approximate* value is 3.14159.

† The number $e$ represents a number which has its origin in the calculus and its *approximate* value is 2.71828.

**11.** $4\frac{1}{7}$     **12.** $17\frac{2}{10}$          **13.** $2\frac{3}{4}$          **14.** $\frac{2.2}{100}$

**15.** Which of the decimals in exercises 3 to 14 terminate?

**16.** Which of the decimals in exercises 3 to 14 repeat?

**17.** Designate in each the block of digits which repeats.

**3. Graphical representation of the real numbers.** If on a line $l$ of unlimited length we choose an **initial point** $O$, a **positive direction,** to the **right,** and a **unit of length** $OA$, every real number can be represented by a point on $l$. Let $O$ represent the number zero. Since the direction to the right has been chosen as positive, the direction to the left is negative. Thus the number $+1$ is represented by the point $A$ one unit to the right of $0$, the number $-2$ by the point $B$ two units to the left of $0$, the number $\pi$ by the point $C$ approximately 3.1 units to the right of $0$, etc. On the other hand, the number corresponding to the point $D$ is $-4$, because $D$ is four units to the left of $0$; and for the point $E$ it is

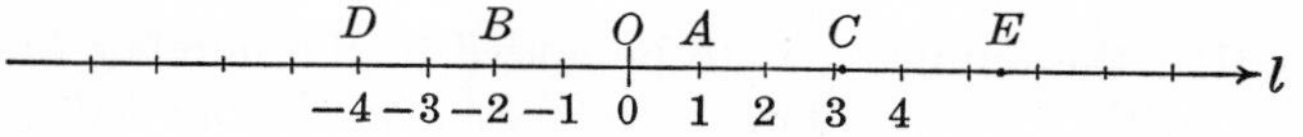

$$D \quad B \quad O \quad A \quad C \quad E$$
$$-4 \; -3 \; -2 \; -1 \quad 0 \quad 1 \quad 2 \quad 3 \quad 4$$

Fig. 1.

$5\frac{1}{2}$. It can be shown that *to every real number there corresponds one and only one point on $l$, and, conversely, to every point on $l$ there corresponds one and only one real number.* The process of marking the point on $l$ corresponding to a real number is called **"plotting the point."**

**"The point $a$,"** where $a$ is any real number, means **"the point corresponding to the number $a$."** *Of two numbers $a$ and $b$, if the point $a$ is to the right of $b$, we say that* $a > b$ (the symbol $>$ is read **"is greater than"**), *or* $b < a$ (the symbol $<$ is read **"is less than"**). Thus

$$5 > 2, \; -3 < -2, \; 0 > -1, \; \tfrac{1}{2} < \tfrac{3}{4}.$$

*The number $b$ is between $a$ and $c$ if $a > b > c$, or $a < b < c$.* The absolute value or magnitude of a number is the number of units (regardless of direction) of the corresponding point from $0$; the symbol $|\,a\,|$ is read **"absolute value of $a$."**

Thus     $|\,2\,| = 2, \quad |-5\,| = 5, \quad |\,0\,| = 0, \quad |-\tfrac{3}{5}\,| = \tfrac{3}{5}.$

## EXERCISES

**1.** Plot on a line the points corresponding to the following numbers:

$$2, \; -\frac{1}{2}, \; \frac{7}{3}, \; \pi, \; 2\tfrac{1}{2}, \; \frac{e}{2}, \; 1.4, \; \frac{2}{7}, \; 0, \; -e, \; \left|\frac{3}{4}\right|, \; 7, \; \left|-5\right|, \; \frac{1}{3}, \; 2\pi, \; |-e|.$$

**2.** Arrange the numbers in exercise 1 in order of increasing magnitude.

**3.** Find a rational number between $e$ and $\pi$, $\tfrac{1}{2}$ and $\tfrac{1}{3}$, 0 and $-\tfrac{1}{5}$, 1.4 and 1.5, 3 and $\pi$.

**4. The fundamental laws of algebra.** Let $a$, $b$, and $c$ represent any three numbers. The symbols of grouping in algebra are the *parentheses* ( ), *brackets* [ ], *braces* { }, and the *vinculum* ‾. Thus either

$$(a + b), \; [a + b], \; \{a + b\}, \; \text{or} \; \overline{a + b}$$

indicates that the sum $a + b$ is to be treated as a *single number*, e.g.,

$$c + (a + b)$$

means that the number $c$ is to be added to the number $(a + b)$.

As in arithmetic, addition is indicated in algebra by $+$, and subtraction by $-$. The product of $a$ by $b$ may be written in several ways

$$c = ab = a \cdot b = a \times b = (a)(b) = a(b);$$

here $a$ is the multiplicand, $b$ the multiplier, and $c$ the product. The quotient of $a$ by $b$ may be written

$$c = a \div b = \frac{a}{b}, \text{ if } b \neq 0.$$

(The symbol $\neq$ is read **"is not equal to."**) Since division by zero is impossible, this restriction on $b$ is necessary. Here $a$ is the dividend, $b$ the divisor, and $c$ the quotient. In the fraction $\frac{a}{b}$, $a$ is the numerator and $b$ the denominator.

In applying the four fundamental operations the following laws are observed:

I. **Addition and multiplication are commutative,**

i.e., $$a + b = b + a,$$
and $$ab = ba.$$

II. **Addition and multiplication are associative,**

i.e., $a + (b + c) = (a + b) + c = a + b + c,$
and $a(bc) = (ab)c = abc.$

III. **Multiplication is distributive with respect to addition,**

i.e., $a(b + c) = ab + ac.$

### EXERCISES

*By applying the above laws rewrite the following:*

**1.** $5 \cdot 3$      **2.** $4 + x$      **3.** $a + (2b + 3)$

**4.** $2(3y + 7)$      **5.** $xyz$      **6.** $(4x)5$

**7.** $3x + (4 + y)$      **8.** $2(a + b)$      **9.** $17x + 5y + 4$

**5. Operations and signs.** In this paragraph $a$, $b$, $c$, and $d$ will represent positive numbers, while negative numbers will be written as $(-a)$, etc. In applying the fundamental operations the following rules are observed:

I. **To add two numbers with like signs,** *add their absolute values and prefix the common sign.*

$$5 + 3 = + (5 + 3) = 8$$
$$(-5) + (-3) = - (5 + 3) = -8$$
$$(-a) + (-b) = - (a + b)$$

II. **To add two numbers with unlike signs,** *take the difference of their absolute values and prefix to it the sign of the number having the larger absolute value.*

$$5 + (-3) = + (5 - 3) = 2$$
$$(-5) + 3 = - (5 - 3) = -2$$
If $|a| > |b|,$ $\quad (-a) + b = - (a - b),$
$$a + (-b) = + (a - b).$$

III. **To subtract a number $a$ from a number $b$,** *change the sign of $a$, and add.*

$$5 - 3 = 5 + (-3) = 2$$
$$3 - 5 = 3 + (-5) = -2$$
$$b - a = b + (-a)$$
$$b - (-a) = b + (+a) = b + a$$

IV. *The product or quotient of two numbers having* **like signs** *is* **positive,** *and the product or quotient of two numbers having* **unlike**

**signs** *is* **negative.** *The absolute value of the product or quotient is found as in arithmetic.*

$$6 \div 2 = 3$$
$$(- 6) \div (- 2) = 3$$
$$6 \div (- 2) = - 3$$
$$(- 6) \div (2) = - 3$$
$$(- a) \div b = - (a \div b)$$

$$(6)2 = 12$$
$$(- 6)(- 2) = 12$$
$$6(- 2) = - 12$$
$$(- 6)(2) = - 12$$
$$(- a)(b) = - (ab)$$

V. *A single parenthesis preceded by a* **plus sign** *may be removed without changing the sign within the parenthesis; a single parenthesis preceded by a* **minus sign** *may be removed upon changing the sign of each number in the parenthesis.*

$$5 + (2 - 1) = 5 + 2 - 1 = 6$$
$$5 - (2 - 1) = 5 - 2 + 1 = 4$$
$$a + (b + c - d) = a + b + c - d$$
$$a - (b - c + d) = a - b + c - d$$
$$a - \{b + (c - d)\} = a - b - (c - d) = a - b - c + d$$

The following rules are observed in algebra as in arithmetic:

VI. *The sum of any number and* 0 *is the number itself.*

$$a + 0 = a - 0 = a$$
$$(- b) + 0 = - b$$

VII. *The product of any number and* 0 *is* 0.

$$a \cdot 0 = 0 \cdot a = 0$$
$$(- b)0 = 0$$

VIII. 0 *divided by any number not* 0 *equals* 0.

$$0 \div a = 0, \text{ if } a \neq 0,$$
$$0 \div (- b) = 0, \text{ if } b \neq 0.$$

IX. *Division by* 0 *is meaningless.* Thus $a \div b$ has no meaning if $b = 0$.

We apply the above rules in solving the following problems:

EXAMPLE I.   Remove all symbols of grouping in

$$a - \{3b + (c - \overline{4d + e} + 2x - [7y + 3z - (2 + w)] + 6u) + 2f\} - 5g.$$

**Solution.**   (Remove the innermost symbols first.)

$$a - \{3b + (c - 4d - e + 2x - [7y + 3z - 2 - w] + 6u) + 2f\} - 5g =$$
$$a - \{3b + (c - 4d - e + 2x - 7y - 3z + 2 + w + 6u) + 2f\} - 5g =$$
$$a - \{3b + c - 4d - e + 2x - 7y - 3z + 2 + w + 6u + 2f\} - 5g =$$
$$a - 3b - c + 4d + e - 2x + 7y + 3z - 2 - w - 6u - 2f - 5g \quad \text{(Ans.)}$$

EXAMPLE II.   Remove all symbols of grouping in

$$\{7 - [3 + 2(1 - \overline{5 - 3}) - 4] + 2\} \text{ and simplify.}$$

**Solution.**   The work is shortened here by adding and subtracting the numbers within a single symbol of grouping.

*Note.*   $a(b + c - d) = ab + ac - ad.$

$$\{7 - [3 + 2(1 - 2) - 4] + 2\} = \{7 - [3 + 2(-1) - 4] + 2\} =$$
$$\{7 - [3 - 2 - 4] + 2\} = \{7 - [-3] + 2\} = \{7 + 3 + 2\} = 12$$

(Ans.)

EXAMPLE III.   Inclose the last three numbers (or products) of

$$3x + 4xy - 7y + 6yz - 5$$

in parenthesis preceded by (**1**) a minus sign; (**2**) a plus sign.

**Solution.**   (**1**)  $3x + 4xy - (+ 7y - 6yz + 5)$

The signs of the last three numbers must be changed so that if the parenthesis were removed according to rule V we would get the same expression as the original.

(**2**)  $3x + 4xy + (- 7y + 6yz - 5)$   No signs are changed in this case.

## EXERCISES

*Perform the following operations:*

**1.** $(- 5)(- 3)$
**2.** $4(- 1)$
**3.** $2(3x)$
**4.** $(- x)(- y)(- z)$
**5.** $(- a) - (- 3b)$
**6.** $2 \div (- 5)$
**7.** $2 + (- 7)$
**8.** $(- x) \div (- y)$
**9.** $x + 0$
**10.** $(5y)(0)$
**11.** $5 - 0$
**12.** $0 \div 6$
**13.** $6 \div 0$
**14.** $(a)(1)$
**15.** $6 \div 1$
**16.** $2 \div (- 7)$
**17.** $(- 3)(8)$
**18.** $- 13 - (- 12) + 1$

*Remove all symbols of grouping:*

**19.** $2a + (x - c)$
**20.** $3 + \{2x - \overline{4y + 7}\}$
**21.** $a + 3b - [2c + (- d)]$
**22.** $1 + \{7 - [2c + d]\}$
**23.** $x + [(- a)y + z]$
**24.** $a + [- bx - 7c]$
**25.** $a + [7 - 4(c + d)]$
**26.** $12 - [3c + 5 + (- 2)]$
**27.** $24x - \{3y + \overline{8 - 7c}\}$
**28.** $- x + \{3y - (a - [u + 2 - \overline{3 + v}] - z + 4) + w\}$
**29.** $- 12 + 4\{3 - 7(2 - 3[5 - \overline{6 + 4 - 15}] - 4)\}$
**30.** $3(- 5 - 4\{8[2 - 7 \cdot \overline{3 - 1}] + 15 - 6 \cdot 2\} + 6) - 12$
**31.** $3\{a + 2b(6 - 4) - (c + 2a) + 8 - 5c - (8 + b)\}$
**32.** $(8 - 3)(2 - 5)(- 3 + 1)\{2 - (3 + 7)\}$
**33.** $a - \{b - [c + (d - \overline{e - f})]\}$
**34.** $3x - (5y - [7z + 9a - 4] - 3b)$
**35.** $- [a - (- b - 1 + c) - d]$
**36.** $2 + (3 - [7 + \overline{2 - 3}] + 5)$

*Inclose the last three numbers (or products) of each exercise in parenthesis preceded (1) by a plus sign, and (2) by a minus sign:*

**37.** $a^2 + b^2 + c^2 - ab - bc - ca$

**38.** $63x^4 + x^3 + 49x^2 - 16x + 20$

**39.** $x^3 + 2x^2y - 3xy^2 + 4x - 7y^2$

**40.** $a + b - c + d - e$

**41.** $x^2 - y^2 + z^2 - 3$

**42.** $3x^2 - ax + c + bx + y^2 - 3x$

**43.** $a^2 + 2ab + b^3 - c^2 + d^2$

**44.** $a^4 + 3b^2d^2 + 2bd - c$

**45.** $x^5 - 5xy^4 + 6xy^3 - 7x + 3$

**46.** $ax + 2bcy - 3ay + 2z$

**47.** $3x^2 + 7x - 2y + z$

**48.** $2x + 7y - 4z + 6$

# CHAPTER II

## EXPONENTS AND RADICALS

**6. Positive integral exponents.** Let $a$, $b$, $c$, and $d$ be any positive numbers. The product $a \cdot a$ is written $a^2$. This is the second power of $a$ and is read **"$a$ square."** *Here $a$ is called the base*, and 2, the power of $a$, *is called the exponent;* $a^1 = a$. Similarly, $a \cdot a \cdot a = a^3$, **"$a$ cube,"** or **"$a$ to the third power."** In fact, let $m$ be any positive integer then

$$a \cdot a \cdot a \cdots m \text{ times} = a^m, \text{ read "}a \text{ to the } m\text{th power."}$$

With this definition of $a^m$ the laws of exponents follow where $m$ and $n$ are positive integers.

I. $a^m \cdot a^n = a^{m+n}$.

For $a^m a^n = (a \cdot a \cdots m \text{ times})(a \cdot a \cdots n \text{ times})$
$$= (a \cdot a \cdots m + n \text{ times}) = a^{m+n}.$$

Thus $a^n \cdot a^{m-n} = a^m$, $m > n$.

II. $(a^m)^n = a^{mn}$.

For $(a^m)^n = (a^m \cdot a^m \cdots n \text{ times})$
$$= (a \cdot a \cdots m \text{ times}) (a \cdot a \cdots m \text{ times}) (\cdots)$$
$$\cdots n \text{ times}$$
$$= (a \cdot a \cdots mn \text{ times}) = a^{mn}.$$

It should be observed that $(a^m)^n$ **is not the same as $a^{m^n}$**; e.g., $(2^3)^2 = 2^6$, whereas $2^{3^2} = 2^9$.

III. $(a \cdot b \cdot c)^m = a^m b^m c^m$.

In multiplying fractions we have

$$\left(\frac{a}{c}\right)\left(\frac{b}{d}\right) = \frac{ab}{cd}.$$

IV. $\left(\dfrac{a}{b}\right)^m = \dfrac{a^m}{b^m}$.

*Laws III and IV apply to products and quotients, but not to sums and differences,* $(x + y)^m \neq x^m + y^m$, $(a - b)^m \neq a^m - b^m$, $m \neq 1$.

V. $a^m \div a^n = \dfrac{a^m}{a^n} = a^{m-n}, \; m > n.$

VI. $a^m \div a^n = \dfrac{a^m}{a^n} = \dfrac{1}{a^{n-m}}, \; n > m.$

For     $\dfrac{a^m}{a^n} = \dfrac{a^m \cdot 1}{a^m a^{n-m}} = \left(\dfrac{a^m}{a^m}\right)\left(\dfrac{1}{a^{n-m}}\right) = \dfrac{1}{a^{n-m}}.$

EXAMPLE I. Simplify: $2^3 \cdot 2^4$.
**Solution.** $2^3 \cdot 2^4 = 2^{3+4} = 2^7$

EXAMPLE II. Simplify: $(2^3)^2$.
**Solution.** $(2^3)^2 = 2^{3 \cdot 2} = 2^6$

EXAMPLE III. Simplify: $(2 \cdot 3)^4$.
**Solution.** $(2 \cdot 3)^4 = 2^4 \cdot 3^4$

EXAMPLE IV. Simplify: $(\tfrac{2}{3})^4$.
**Solution.** $\left(\dfrac{2}{3}\right)^4 = \dfrac{2^4}{3^4}$

EXAMPLE V. Simplify: $2^5 \div 2^3$.
**Solution.** $2^5 \div 2^3 = 2^{5-3} = 2^2$

EXAMPLE VI. Simplify: $2^3 \div 2^5$.
**Solution.** $2^3 \div 2^5 = \dfrac{1}{2^{5-3}} = \dfrac{1}{2^2}$

EXAMPLE VII. Simplify: (1) $x^3 \cdot x^2$, (2) $(x^4)^2$, (3) $(xy)^2$, (4) $x^4 \div x^3$, (5) $(2x + 3y)^5$.

**Solution.**    (1) $x^3 \cdot x^2 = x^{3+2} = x^5$
           (2) $(x^4)^2 = x^{4 \cdot 2} = x^8$
           (3) $(xy)^2 = x^2 y^2$
           (4) $x^4 \div x^3 = x^{4-3} = x^1 = x$
           (5) $(2x + 3y)^5 = (2x + 3y)^5 \neq (2x)^5 + (3y)^5$

EXAMPLE VIII. If $2^x = 4^4$, find $x$.
**Solution.** $4^4 = (2^2)^4 = 2^8$

Hence   $2^x = 2^8$, consequently $x = 8$.
*Note that* $x^2 y^3 \neq (xy)^5$.

## EXERCISES

*Apply the laws of exponents to evaluate the following:*

| | | |
|---|---|---|
| **1.** $(-3)^2$ | **2.** $2^3$ | **3.** $2^3 \cdot 2^2$ |
| **4.** $2^3 \cdot 3^2$ | **5.** $2^3 \cdot 4^2$ | **6.** $(2^3)^1$ |

**7.** $\dfrac{(16)^2}{4^3}$    **8.** $\{(-1)^3\}^2$    **9.** $[-1^3]^2$

**10.** $-(1^3)^2$    **11.** $2^2 \div 2^3$    **12.** $\dfrac{3^5}{3^2}$

**13.** $x^5 x^3$    **14.** $(x^2)^3$    **15.** $x^5 \div x$

**16.** $x^3 x^{n-3}$    **17.** $\left(\dfrac{x}{y}\right)^4$    **18.** $(a+b)^5 \div (a+b)^7$

**19.** $\left(\dfrac{x^2}{y^3}\right)^4$    **20.** $\dfrac{(2+x)^8}{(x+2)^5}$    **21.** $\dfrac{(x+3y-7)^6}{(x-7-3y)^4}$

**22.** If $x = 5$, find $\dfrac{2x^2}{(2x)^2}$.    **23.** If $x = -1$, find $2x \cdot 4x^3$.

**24.** If $a = 2$, $b = -3$, find $(a^3b) \div a^2$.    **25.** If $x = 2$, find $2^x + 1^x + 0^x$.

**26.** If $2^x = (-2)^6$, find $x$.    **27.** If $2^x = 4^5$, find $x$.

**7. Fractional exponents.** We define $a^{\frac{1}{m}}$ where $m$ is a positive integer and $a$ is positive in such a way that Law I of § **6** will hold. Thus, $a^{\frac{1}{m}}$ *is that number which when multiplied by itself m times gives a.*

$$a^{\frac{1}{m}} \cdot a^{\frac{1}{m}} \cdots m \text{ times} = (a^{\frac{1}{m}})^m = a.$$

Then it follows immediately that *the remaining laws of exponents are valid for fractional exponents.* For example $a^{\frac{r}{m}} = (a^{\frac{1}{m}})^r$.

The number $a^{\frac{1}{m}}$ is called an **"mth root of a,"** and may be written $\sqrt[m]{a}$, $a^{\frac{1}{m}} = \sqrt[m]{a}$. A number $a \neq 0$ has $m$ different $m$th roots, e.g.,

$$4^{\frac{1}{2}} = +2, \quad \text{and} \quad 4^{\frac{1}{2}} = -2,$$

because $2 \cdot 2 = 4$ and $(-2)(-2) = 4$. We shall, however, assume here that $a^{\frac{1}{m}}$ represents the arithmetical or positive value of $a^{\frac{1}{m}}$, where $a$ is a positive number.

EXAMPLE I.  Simplify: **(1)** $(2^{\frac{2}{3}})^{\frac{3}{4}}$, **(2)** $(27)^{\frac{2}{3}}$, **(3)** $\left(\dfrac{x^3}{y^2}\right)^{\frac{1}{3}}$, **(4)** $x^{\frac{1}{2}} x^{\frac{1}{3}}$.

**Solution.**  **(1)** $(2^{\frac{2}{3}})^{\frac{3}{4}} = 2^{\frac{2}{3} \cdot \frac{3}{4}} = 2^{\frac{2}{4}} = 2^{\frac{1}{2}} = \sqrt{2}$

**(2)** $(27)^{\frac{2}{3}} = (27^{\frac{1}{3}})^2 = (\sqrt[3]{27})^2 = 3^2 = 9$

**(3)** $\left(\dfrac{x^3}{y^2}\right)^{\frac{1}{3}} = \dfrac{(x^3)^{\frac{1}{3}}}{(y^2)^{\frac{1}{3}}} = \dfrac{x}{y^{\frac{2}{3}}}$

**(4)** $x^{\frac{1}{2}} x^{\frac{1}{3}} = x^{\frac{1}{2}+\frac{1}{3}} = x^{\frac{5}{6}}$

## EXERCISES

*Simplify:*

**1.** $x^{\frac{1}{3}}x^{\frac{2}{3}}$

**2.** $(x^{\frac{1}{2}})^{\frac{1}{2}}$

**3.** $x^{\frac{5}{2}} \div x^{\frac{3}{2}}$

**4.** $\left(\dfrac{x}{y}\right)^{\frac{3}{4}}$

**5.** $y^{\frac{2}{3}}y^{\frac{1}{2}}$

**6.** $x^{\frac{3}{4}} \div x^{\frac{4}{3}}$

**7.** $a^{\frac{5}{3}}x^{\frac{2}{5}}a^{2}x^{3}$

**8.** $\left(\dfrac{x^{\frac{1}{2}}}{a^{\frac{1}{3}}}\right)^{\frac{2}{5}}$

**9.** $(ax)^{\frac{3}{4}} \div (ay)^{\frac{1}{3}}$

**10.** $(a^2 + b^4)^{\frac{1}{2}}$

**11.** $(a^3 - b^3)^{\frac{1}{3}}$

**12.** $\dfrac{x^3(a + b)^6}{[x^5(a+b)^{10}]^{\frac{1}{5}}}$

**13.** $\left[(a^2)(a+b)^2\right]^{\frac{1}{2}}$

**14.** $\dfrac{(x^2y^3z^{\frac{1}{2}})^6}{x^{12}(y^3 + z^{\frac{1}{2}})^2}$

**15.** $\dfrac{(x^{\frac{1}{2}} + z^{\frac{3}{4}})y^3}{[y(x^{\frac{1}{2}} + z^{\frac{3}{4}})^{\frac{1}{2}}]^2}$

**16.** $\dfrac{a^2(-2b)^2}{a^{\frac{3}{4}}[-2b^2]}$

**17.** $\dfrac{x^{\frac{1}{2}}y^{\frac{3}{2}}(x + y)^{\frac{1}{2}}}{x^{\frac{1}{2}}y^{\frac{2}{3}}(x^{\frac{1}{2}} + y^{\frac{1}{2}})}$

**18.** $\dfrac{(x^3y^{\frac{1}{2}})(z^2)^{\frac{1}{3}}}{(xz)^{\frac{2}{3}}y^{\frac{5}{2}}}$

**8. The exponent 0.** In order that Law I may hold for zero exponents it is necessary that

$$a^0a^m = a^{0+m} = a^m,$$

or
$$a^0 = 1, \ a \neq 0.$$

Thus any number $a \neq 0$ with 0 exponent is equal to 1. *With this definition all the laws of exponents hold for the exponent* 0.

EXAMPLE I. Simplify: **(1)** $2^0$, **(2)** $5^2 \cdot 3^0 \cdot 2^2$, **(3)** $(2x)^0$, **(4)** $2x^0$ **(5)** $(x + y)^0$.

**Solution.**    **(1)** $2^0 = 1$
           **(2)** $5^2 \cdot 3^0 \cdot 2^2 = 25 \cdot 1 \cdot 4 = 100$
           **(3)** $(2x)^0 = 1$
           **(4)** $2x^0 = 2 \cdot 1 = 2$
           **(5)** $(x + y)^0 = 1$

## EXERCISES

*Simplify:*

**1.** $a^3 \div a^3$

**2.** $a^mb \div 2ba^m$

**3.** $a^{\frac{1}{2}}x \div xya^{\frac{1}{2}}$

**4.** $x^{\frac{3}{2}}y^{\frac{5}{3}} \div x^{1\frac{1}{2}}y^{\frac{2}{3}}$

**5.** $3^1 \cdot 2^0 \cdot 5$

**6.** $(4x)^0$

**7.** $4x^0$

**8.** $x^0 + y^0$

**9.** $(x + y + 5)^0$

**10.** $\dfrac{x^{\frac{1}{2}}y^{\frac{1}{3}}z^3}{(x^{\frac{1}{2}})^0(y^0)^{\frac{1}{3}}z^0}$

**11.** $5a^0 + (y^{\frac{2}{3}})^0$

**12.** $2x^0 + (2x)^0$

**13.** $\dfrac{x^3y^5x^{\frac{1}{2}}z^4(a + b)^2}{(a + b)x^{\frac{5}{2}}y^3z^{\frac{3}{2}}x(a + b)}$

**14.** $\dfrac{(2x)^0 + yx^0}{(2y)^0 + xy^0}$

**15.** $\dfrac{(x+3y)^{\frac{1}{2}}(a-2b)^{\frac{3}{4}}x^3y}{(x+3y)^{\frac{1}{4}}(a-2b)^{\frac{1}{2}}x^2(x+3y)^{\frac{1}{4}}(a-2b)^{\frac{1}{4}}}$

**16.** If $x = 0$, find $\dfrac{a^{-2x}+5+a^{2x}}{a^{-x}+a^{x}}$.    **17.** If $x = 0$, find $x^2 + 3^x + 4x$.

**18.** If $x = 0$, find $2^x + x^2 + 5x - 7$.

**9. Negative exponents.** In order that Law I may hold for negative exponents we must have

$$a^m \cdot a^{-m} = a^{m-m} = a^0 = 1,$$

or $$a^{-m} = \frac{1}{a^m}, \; a \neq 0.$$

Thus, in a fraction any number may be transferred from the numerator to the denominator, or vice versa, by changing the sign of the exponent.

*With these definitions the six laws of § 6 are valid for all types of exponents.*

EXAMPLE I. Change to forms having only positive exponents:

$$\textbf{(1) } 2^{-2}, \textbf{ (2) } 3^{-\frac{1}{2}}, \textbf{ (3) } (x^2)^{-2}, \textbf{ (4) } (x^{-2}y)^{-3}, \textbf{ (5) } \frac{1}{x^{-2}}.$$

**Solution.**   **(1)** $2^{-2} = \dfrac{1}{2^2}$

          **(2)** $3^{-\frac{1}{2}} = \dfrac{1}{3^{\frac{1}{2}}}$

          **(3)** $(x^2)^{-2} = x^{-4} = \dfrac{1}{x^4}$

          **(4)** $(x^{-2}y)^{-3} = x^{(-2)(-3)}y^{-3} = \dfrac{x^6}{y^3}$

          **(5)** $\dfrac{1}{x^{-2}} = x^2$

EXAMPLE II. Simplify and change to form having only positive exponents:

$$\left[\frac{(x^{-\frac{1}{2}}y^{-\frac{1}{3}})^2 x^{-\frac{1}{2}}y}{(xy^{-\frac{4}{3}})^2 x^{\frac{3}{2}}y^{-1}}\right]^3.$$

**Solution.** Consider the innermost parenthesis first.

$$\left[\frac{(x^{-\frac{1}{2}}y^{-\frac{1}{3}})^2 x^{-\frac{1}{2}}y}{(xy^{-\frac{4}{3}})^2 x^{\frac{3}{2}}y^{-1}}\right]^3 = \left[\frac{x^{-1}y^{-\frac{2}{3}}x^{-\frac{1}{2}}y}{x^2 y^{-\frac{8}{3}}x^{\frac{3}{2}}y^{-1}}\right]^3 = \left[\frac{x^{-\frac{3}{2}}y^{\frac{1}{3}}}{x^{\frac{7}{2}}y^{-1\frac{1}{3}}}\right]^3 = \left[\frac{y^4}{x^5}\right]^3 = \frac{y^{12}}{x^{15}} \quad \text{(Ans.)}$$

## EXERCISES

*Simplify and change to forms having only positive exponents:*

**1.** $a^{-\frac{1}{2}}a^{\frac{3}{4}}$     **2.** $(2a)^{-\frac{3}{4}}2a^{-\frac{3}{4}}$     **3.** $4^{-\frac{1}{2}}$

**4.** $4^{-\frac{1}{2}} \cdot 8 \cdot 2^{-4}$     **5.** $(x^{-5})^2$     **6.** $(x^{-\frac{1}{2}})^{-\frac{3}{4}}$

**7.** $(xy)^{-\frac{5}{2}}x^{\frac{4}{5}}y^{-\frac{2}{3}}$     **8.** $x^3 3^{-2} x^{-3} 9$     **9.** $\left(\dfrac{x^{-\frac{1}{2}}}{y^{\frac{3}{2}}}\right)^{-\frac{3}{4}}$

**10.** $\left(\dfrac{x^2 y}{64 x^{-3} y^{\frac{1}{3}}}\right)^{-\frac{1}{3}}$     **11.** $\dfrac{(u^6 v^3 c^{-2})^{\frac{1}{3}}}{2^0 (u^2 v^{-2} w^3)^{-\frac{1}{2}}}$     **12.** $\left[\dfrac{2y^{\frac{4}{5}}}{3a^{-2}b^2}\right]^{-5}$

**13.** $\left[\dfrac{(64x^3)^{-\frac{1}{3}}}{27^{-1}c^{-3}}\right]^2$     **14.** $\dfrac{(3x^{\frac{1}{2}})^2 \cdot 5(xy)^{-1}}{15(x^2 y^{-1})^{\frac{1}{2}}}$

**15.** $\left(\dfrac{xy^0 z^{-3}}{x^{-3} y^2 z^3}\right)^{-\frac{1}{2}}$     **16.** $(ab^{-2}c^3)^{\frac{1}{2}}(a^3 b^3 c^{-2} a^3)^{\frac{1}{3}}$

**17.** $\left[\dfrac{a^{-3}}{b^{-\frac{2}{3}}c}\right]^{-\frac{3}{2}}\left[\dfrac{a^2 c^{-1}}{a^{-\frac{1}{4}}b^{\frac{1}{2}}}\right]^2$     **18.** $\left\{\left[\dfrac{(a^{-\frac{2}{3}}x^{\frac{1}{6}})^3}{(x^{-\frac{1}{2}}a^{\frac{3}{8}})^{\frac{1}{2}}}\right]^{-2}\right\}^{-\frac{1}{4}}$

**19.** $\left[\dfrac{y^{-3}}{x^{\frac{2}{7}}z^{-1}}\right]^{\frac{3}{2}}\left[\dfrac{y^{\frac{14}{3}}}{xz^{-\frac{21}{4}}}\right]^{\frac{2}{7}}$     **20.** $\left(\dfrac{a^{-\frac{4}{3}}b^{-\frac{1}{3}}}{a^2 b^{\frac{1}{2}}}\right)^{\frac{3}{8}}\left(\dfrac{a^{\frac{1}{2}}b^{\frac{2}{3}}}{a^{-\frac{2}{3}}b^{\frac{3}{4}}}\right)^{-6}$

**21.** $\left[\dfrac{a^{-\frac{1}{2}}y^{-\frac{1}{3}}(ay)^{-3}}{a^{-\frac{1}{6}}y^{-1}a^{-2}y^{-2}}\right]^{-3}$     **22.** $\left\{\left[\dfrac{a^{-3}b^{-\frac{2}{3}}c^2(ac)^{-\frac{1}{2}}}{a^3 b^{-1}(ab)^{-2}c^3}\right]^{-3}\right\}^{-\frac{1}{3}}$

**10. Radicals.** The symbol $\sqrt[m]{\phantom{a}}$ (see § **7**) is called a radical and $m$ is the **index** of the radical; here $m$ is a positive integer. In $\sqrt[m]{a}$ the number $a$ is called the **radicand**. For $m = 2$ the index is omitted.

$$\sqrt[2]{4} = \sqrt{4}, \quad \text{read “square root of 4.”}$$
$$\sqrt[3]{5}, \quad \text{read “cube root of 5.”}$$

Since $a^{\frac{1}{m}} = \sqrt[m]{a}$ the rules of operations with radicals follow immediately from the laws of exponents. (Here $a$ and $b$ are positive.)

I. $(\sqrt[n]{a})^n = a$

II. $\sqrt[m]{a}\,\sqrt[m]{b} = \sqrt[m]{ab}$

III. $\dfrac{\sqrt[m]{a}}{\sqrt[m]{b}} = \sqrt[m]{\dfrac{a}{b}}$

IV. $\sqrt[m]{\sqrt[n]{a}} = \sqrt[mn]{a}$

*Note.* $\sqrt[m]{a+b} \neq \sqrt[m]{a} + \sqrt[m]{b},\ m > 1.$

EXAMPLE I. Simplify: (1) $\sqrt{4 \cdot 16}$, (2) $\sqrt{\sqrt[3]{5}}$, (3) $\sqrt[4]{\frac{1}{2}}$.

Solution.   (1) $\sqrt{4 \cdot 16} = \sqrt{64} = 8$

　　　　　　(2) $\sqrt{\sqrt[3]{5}} = \sqrt[6]{5}$

　　　　　　(3) $\sqrt[4]{\frac{1}{2}} = \dfrac{1}{\sqrt[4]{2}}$

EXAMPLE II.   Change to radical form: (1) $2^{\frac{1}{3}}x^{\frac{1}{3}}$, (2) $a^{\frac{2}{3}}b^{\frac{1}{2}}$, (3) $(a^2 + b^2)^{\frac{2}{3}}$.

Solution.   (1) $2^{\frac{1}{3}}x^{\frac{1}{3}} = \sqrt[3]{2}\sqrt[3]{x} = \sqrt[3]{2x}$

　　　　　　(2) $a^{\frac{2}{3}}b^{\frac{1}{2}} = (a^2)^{\frac{1}{3}}\sqrt{b} = \sqrt[3]{a^2}\sqrt{b}$

　　　　　　(3) $(a^2 + b^2)^{\frac{2}{3}} = [(a^2 + b^2)^2]^{\frac{1}{3}} = \sqrt[3]{(a^2 + b^2)^2}$

EXAMPLE III.   Change to exponential form:

$$(1)\ \sqrt{xy^3},\ (2)\ \sqrt[3]{a}\sqrt{b},\ (3)\ \sqrt{a^2 + b^2}.$$

Solution.   (1) $\sqrt{xy^3} = (xy^3)^{\frac{1}{2}} = x^{\frac{1}{2}}y^{\frac{3}{2}}$

　　　　　　(2) $\sqrt[3]{a}\sqrt{b} = a^{\frac{1}{3}}b^{\frac{1}{2}}$

　　　　　　(3) $\sqrt{a^2 + b^2} = (a^2 + b^2)^{\frac{1}{2}}$

## EXERCISES

*Change to radical form:*

1. $2^{\frac{1}{2}}$        　2. $3^{\frac{1}{3}}2^{\frac{2}{3}}$        　3. $x^{-\frac{1}{5}}$

4. $(x^5)^{\frac{1}{2}}$        5. $8^{\frac{2}{3}}$        　6. $5^{\frac{1}{6}}x^{\frac{1}{3}}$

7. $a^{\frac{1}{2}}x^{-\frac{2}{3}}$        8. $(x^2)^{\frac{1}{4}}y^{\frac{1}{2}}$        9. $x^{\frac{4}{5}}$

10. $2a^{\frac{1}{2}} + b^{\frac{1}{2}}$        11. $(4a^2 + b^2)^{\frac{1}{2}}$        12. $(x^3y^5)^{-\frac{3}{2}}$

*Change to exponential form:*

13. $\sqrt{x^3}$        14. $\sqrt[3]{x^2y}$        15. $\sqrt{3a^2 + b^2}$        16. $\sqrt{\dfrac{a^3}{b^5}}$

17. $(\sqrt{a^4})^{-3}$        18. $\sqrt{a^{\frac{1}{3}}}$        19. $\sqrt[5]{\sqrt[3]{x^{10}}}$        20. $\sqrt[3]{x^6y^9}$        21. $\sqrt[4]{x^2}$

*Evaluate to three decimals:*

22. $3^2 + 2^0 + \sqrt[3]{8^2}$        　23. $81^{\frac{1}{2}} + 81^{-\frac{1}{4}} + 3^0$

24. $(-27)^{\frac{1}{3}}$        　25. $10(4)^{\frac{5}{2}} + 27^{\frac{2}{3}}$

26. $\dfrac{9^{\frac{1}{2}}16^{\frac{1}{4}}2^2}{8^{\frac{2}{3}}6^0}$        　27. $5^0 + 4^{\frac{1}{2}} - \dfrac{1}{2} + \dfrac{1}{\sqrt[3]{-64}} + 8^{\frac{2}{3}}$

28. $8^{\frac{2}{3}} - 3x^0 + 27^{-\frac{1}{3}} - 1^{\frac{1}{5}}$        29. $12^0 + 4^{\frac{1}{2}} - \dfrac{1}{9} + \dfrac{1}{\sqrt[3]{-64}} + (\sqrt[3]{27})^2$

**30.** $3^0 + 8^{-\frac{2}{3}} - (\frac{1}{5})^{-1}$     **31.** $\sqrt{\frac{1}{25}} + (-343)^{\frac{2}{3}}$

**32.** $8^{-\frac{2}{3}} + (16^3)^{\frac{1}{4}}$     **33.** $[(10,000)^{-3}]^{\frac{1}{4}}$

**34.** $(\frac{1}{27})^{-\frac{2}{3}} + (-8)^{\frac{1}{3}} - \dfrac{\sqrt{8}}{2^{\frac{1}{2}}} + (81)^{-\frac{1}{4}} - \sqrt{12} + \sqrt{8} + (\frac{2}{3})^0 - 4^{\frac{1}{2}}$

*Simplify:*

**35.** $\dfrac{a^{\frac{1}{3}}\sqrt{b^{-\frac{2}{3}}}}{\sqrt[4]{b^3}\sqrt[3]{a^{-1}}}$     **36.** $\dfrac{\sqrt[3]{xb^2\sqrt{z}}}{\sqrt[3]{x^2ba^0\sqrt{z}}}$

**37.** $\sqrt{2}(8x^3)^{\frac{2}{3}}\sqrt{xy^4}$     **38.** $\left[\dfrac{3^{-3}y^6\sqrt{x^{-3}}}{2^43^4}\right]^{-\frac{1}{3}}$

**39.** $\left[\dfrac{2^3a^2}{27a^{-3}y^{\frac{1}{3}}x^0}\right]^{-\frac{1}{3}}$     **40.** $\dfrac{u^{-2}v^{-3}w^{-4}}{u^{-5}v^{-6}w^{-7}\sqrt[3]{u^9}\sqrt[4]{v^{12}}\sqrt[5]{w^{15}}}$

**41.** $\left\{\dfrac{\sqrt[3]{x^2}\sqrt{z^{-3}}y^{-\frac{1}{4}}\sqrt[3]{x}}{\sqrt[4]{y^{-1}}x^{\frac{1}{3}}z^{-1}}\right\}^{-6}$     **42.** $\dfrac{\sqrt[5]{a^{\frac{1}{2}}x^{-2}(a\sqrt{x})^{\frac{1}{3}}}}{[(x^{-1}\sqrt{a})^2]^{\frac{1}{6}}(x^{\frac{1}{2}}a^{-2})^{\frac{1}{5}}}$

**43.** $\left\{\dfrac{\sqrt[3]{-27x^8y^{-5}z}\sqrt{\sqrt[3]{x^{-1}}yz^4}}{(49x^3y\sqrt{z})^{\frac{1}{2}}}\right\}^{-2}$     **44.** $\left[\dfrac{\sqrt[3]{a^{-2}\sqrt{x}}\sqrt[4]{x^{-1}\sqrt[3]{a^{-2}}}}{\{(x^{-1}\sqrt{a^{-1}})^{\frac{1}{6}}\}^2(a^{-2}\sqrt{x^{-3}})^{\frac{1}{4}}}\right]^{-1}$

**11. Imaginary numbers.** No real number multiplied by itself will give a negative number because the product of numbers with like signs is a positive number. Consequently, the square root of a negative number is a new type of number which we call an imaginary number. By letting $i$ denote $\sqrt{-1}$, $i^2 = -1$, we can express any imaginary number as the product of $i$ and a real number.

EXAMPLE I.  Change to forms involving $i$:

(1) $\sqrt{-5}$, (2) $\sqrt{-3x^2}$, (3) $(-x^2)^{\frac{1}{2}}$.

**Solution.**  (1) $\sqrt{-5} = \sqrt{5}\sqrt{-1} = \sqrt{5}i$

(2) $\sqrt{-3x^2} = \sqrt{3x^2}\sqrt{-1} = \sqrt{3}xi$

(3) $(-x^2)^{\frac{1}{2}} = \sqrt{-x^2} = \sqrt{x^2}\sqrt{-1} = xi$

EXAMPLE II.  Simplify:  (1) $i^4 - 1$, (2) $4i^2 + 2$, (3) $i^{16}$

**Solution.**  (1) $i^4 - 1 = (i^2)^2 - 1 = (-1)^2 - 1 = 1 - 1 = 0$

(2) $4i^2 + 2 = 4(-1) + 2 = -4 + 2 = -2$

(3) $i^{16} = (i^2)^8 = (-1)^8 = 1$

## EXERCISES

*Change to forms involving $i$:*

**1.** $\sqrt{-7}$ 　　　　　 **2.** $\sqrt{-16}$ 　　　　　 **3.** $(-a^2)^{\frac{1}{2}}$

**4.** $\sqrt{-4x^2}$ 　　　　 **5.** $a + \sqrt{-b^2}$ 　　　 **6.** $\sqrt{-a^2} + \sqrt{(-b)^2}$

**7.** $2\sqrt{-25}$ 　　　　 **8.** $(-x^2)^{-\frac{1}{2}}$ 　　　 **9.** $a + b\sqrt{-1}$

*Simplify:*

**10.** $i^2 + 2$ 　　　　　 **11.** $3 + i + 2i^2$ 　　　 **12.** $4(2i^2)$

**13.** $i^2 \div i$ 　　　　 **14.** $i^4 + i^2$ 　　　　 **15.** $i^8$

**16.** $(i^4)^n$ 　　　　 **17.** $(i^2)^{2n}$ 　　　 **18.** $i^{-4}(\sqrt{-1})^{\frac{8}{2}}$

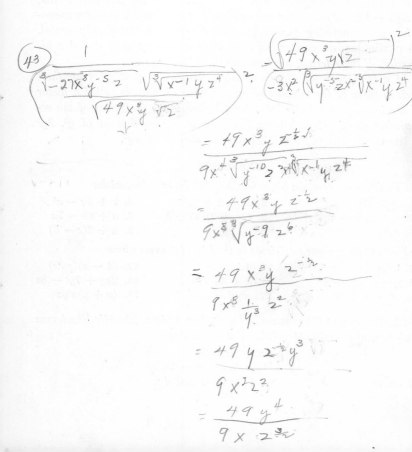

# CHAPTER III

## ALGEBRAIC REDUCTIONS

**12. Algebraic expressions.** *An algebraic expression is a symbol or combination of symbols representing a number.* Thus, $x^2 - 3y + 7$, $3a + 2d$, and $4\pi r^2$ are algebraic expressions. The expression $x^2 - 3y + 7$ is the sum of three numbers $x^2$, $-3y$, and 7; *each of these numbers with its sign is called a term of the expression.* Thus, $3a + 2d$ consists of two terms $3a$ and $2d$; $4\pi r^2$ consists of only one term. The expression $a - 2b = a + (-2b)$ has two terms, $a$ and $-2b$. *An expression consisting of one term is called a monomial; one consisting of more than one term is called a polynomial.* In particular, *an expression consisting of two terms is called a binomial, of three terms, a trinomial.*

*If a term consists of two or more quantities multiplied together, each of them or the product of any number of them is called a factor of the term. Any factor of a term is called the coefficient of the remaining part.* In the term $3ay^2$, $3a$ is the coefficient of $y^2$, $3y^2$ is the coefficient of $a$, and 3 is the coefficient of $ay^2$.

### EXERCISES

*Classify as monomials, binomials, trinomials, or polynomials:*

**1.** $3x + 2y$      **2.** $x^2 - 5 + 4y^2$     **3.** $x + 4y - x^2$
**4.** $a + 3a^2b + 4ab^2 + b^3$     **5.** $(3a + 2)(4b + 5)$     **6.** $a + 6b - 7x$
**7.** $3x^2y^3z$     **8.** $z(a + x)$     **9.** $a + 3(z - 5)$

*Pick out the various coefficients in the following expressions:*

**10.** $3xyz$     **11.** $4x^2yz^2$     **12.** $(3 - x)(xy^2z)$
**13.** $3xy - 7x^2 + 4$     **14.** $a + 3b - c$     **15.** $2xy + 7y^3 - 8z$
**16.** $a^2 - b^2 + 2c$     **17.** $x^3yz^2 - 3xy^2$     **18.** $(x + y)x^2yz$

**13. Sums and differences.** *In algebra as in arithmetic like terms may be added and subtracted.* For example,

$$x + 2x = 3x$$
$$x + 3y - 5x = 3y - 4x.$$

Of course,     $x + 3y \neq 4x \text{ nor } 4y.$

18

EXAMPLE I.   Remove all symbols of grouping and combine like terms

in        $10x - (3y - 4x) - \{2y - \overline{3y + x}\} - \{3y - (2x + y)\}.$

**Solution.**  Remove the symbols of grouping from the inside and combine like terms.

$10x - 3y + 4x - \{2y - 3y - x\} - \{3y - 2x - y\}$
$$= 14x - 3y - \{- y - x\} - \{2y - 2x\}$$
$$= 14x - 3y + y + x - 2y + 2x$$
$$= 17x - 4y \quad \text{(Ans.)}$$

### EXERCISES

*Remove all symbols of grouping and combine like terms:*

1. $3a + 7b - 4b + 2a$      2. $6x + 3xy - 4x - 5xy$
3. $2a + 3b + 5c - (a + b)$      4. $2x + (3x - y)$
5. $3y - (7 + 3y - x)$      6. $(a + 3b - c) + (2b - 4c + a)$
7. $a + \{3y - [7z + (a - 2y - \overline{3 + z})]\}$
8. $a + \{2x - (4c + 2a - \overline{x + 2}) + 7\} - 2c$
9. $- (3ax + 7x^2) - (x^2 + 2ax + 8)$
10. $[a - \{a + (b - a) - (b - a) - a\} - 2a]$
11. $(9x - 4y) - ((5x - \overline{3z - 4y}) - 3z)$
12. $(6x^2 - 11xy - 10y^2) - (6x^2 - 12xy) + 11y^2$
13. $8a^2 - 9b - (5a^2 - \overline{3a + 2}) + (6a^2 - \overline{4a - 7})$
14. $2\{3 - (x + 2) - (a^2 - 2a + 1) - 2[2 + (2 - a)]\}$
15. $7x - 3y - \{(4a - c) - [5a - c - (3x - 2y) - 3c] + 4x + 2y\}$
16. $7a^2 - \{3b - [2 + 5a^2 + (2b - \overline{5 - 3a^2}) - 7b^3] - (3a^2 - 7)\}$
17. $x - (b - c) - [x - \{b + c - (b + c - x) + (x - b) + (c - x)\}]$
18. $a - [2c - (- b + 6a) - \{c - \overline{5a + 2b} + 5a + \overline{6a - 3b}\}]$
19. $2x + (3z - \{2x - [z + \overline{4x - (3z - x)}] - 2z\} - \overline{x + z})$
20. $4x - \{(7x + 5z) - [- 6z + (- 2z - x - z)]\}$
21. $2x - [3x - \{x - (2x - \overline{3x + 4})\} - (5x - 2)]$
22. $4x - 3y - \{(2x + 4y) + 3x + [y - 9x - (2y - x) + (x - y)]\}$
23. $a + 2b + (14a - 5b) - \{6a + 6b - (5a - 4a + 4b)\}$
24. $3c^3 - 2b^2 - \{x - c^3 - [b^2 - 2c^3 - (3b^2 - x)] - 4\} - (2c^3 - 4b^2)$
25. What is the sum of three consecutive odd integers of which the middle one is $2n + 1$?

**14. Products.**  *To find the product of two polynomials multiply each term of one (the multiplicand) by each term of the other (the multiplier) and add the partial products.*

EXAMPLE I.   Multiply   $x + 3y$ by $x - y$.
Solution.

$$x + 3y$$
$$\underline{x - \phantom{3}y}$$
$$x^2 + 3xy$$
$$\underline{\phantom{x^2 + 3xy} - \phantom{x}xy - 3y^2}$$
$$x^2 + 2xy - 3y^2 \quad \text{(Ans.)}$$

EXAMPLE II.   Multiply   $(a^2 - ab + b^2)$ by $(a + b)$.
Solution.

$$a^2 - ab + b^2$$
$$\underline{a + b}$$
$$a^3 - a^2b + ab^2$$
$$\underline{\phantom{a^3} + a^2b - ab^2 + b^3}$$
$$a^3 + \phantom{0}0\phantom{0} + \phantom{0}0\phantom{0} + b^3 = a^3 + b^3 \quad \text{(Ans.)}$$

To find the product of three or more polynomials multiply the first two and then multiply this product by the third, etc.

### EXERCISES

*Perform the following indicated multiplications:*

**1.** $(x + y)(x - y)$     **2.** $(x - 3)(x + 4)$     **3.** $(2x + 5)(x - 7)$
**4.** $(x + 4y)(x - 2y)$     **5.** $(ax + b)(2x)$     **6.** $(x + 3y - 4z)(x - 7)$
**7.** $x^2(3y^2 + 5)(3x^2 + 9)$     **8.** $2(x - 3)(x + 4)(x - 7)$     **9.** $(4xy^2z)(-3x^3y^2z^2)$
**10.** $(2x + 5y - 7z + w)(3x - 8y + 4z - 3w)$
**11.** $(x^3 + 3x^2 - 7x + 12)(x - 3)$
**12.** $(x^3 + 8x^2y - 7xy^2 + 3y^3)(2x)(x - 3y)$
**13.** $(x + y - 2)(x + y + 2)$     **14.** $(2a + 3b - 4c + d)(a + 2d - 3c + 5)$
**15.** $(1 - a - a^2)(a^2 - a - 1)$     **16.** $(x + y + z)^2$     **17.** $(x + y + z)^3$
**18.** $(y - a)(y - b)(y - c)(y - d)$
**19.** $(13a - 12ab - b + 3)(5a - 3b + ab + 5)$
**20.** $(x^2 + y^2 + z^2 - xy - xz - yz)(x + y + z)$
**21.** $(x^2 + 2xy + y^2)(x^2 + 2xy + y^2)$     **22.** $(x + y)^4$
**23.** $2(x + y)(x - y)(x^2 - y^2)3$     **24.** $(3a + 2b)^2 2(a - 3b)^2$

**15. Quotients.** *To divide a polynomial by a monomial divide each term of the polynomial by the monomial and add the quotients.*

EXAMPLE I.   $(6x^2 - 15x + 12) \div 3$.
Solution.   $(6x^2 - 15x + 12) \div 3 = (6x^2 \div 3) + (-15x \div 3)$
$+ (12 \div 3) = 2x^2 - 5x + 4 \quad \text{(Ans.)}$

EXAMPLE II.   $(6x^3 - 8x^2 + 10x + 4) \div 2x$.

**Solution.**   $(6x^3 - 8x^2 - 10x + 4) \div 2x$

$$= (6x^3 \div 2x) + (- 8x^2 \div 2x) + (- 10x \div 2x) + (4 \div 2x)$$

$$= 3x^2 - 4x - 5 + \frac{4}{2x} \quad \text{(Ans.)}$$

Here the quotient is $3x^2 - 4x - 5$ and the remainder is 4.

*To divide two polynomials* (see Example III):

*Arrange both dividend and divisor in descending powers of some common letter.*

*Divide the first term of the dividend by the first term of the divisor. Write the result as the first term of the quotient.*

*Multiply all the terms of the divisor by the first term of the quotient. Subtract the product from the dividend.*

*If there is a remainder, consider it as a new dividend and proceed as before.*

*Continue in this manner until a remainder is obtained which is either zero or an expression whose first term does not contain the first term of the divisor as a factor.*

*If the remainder is zero, the divisor is a factor of the dividend.* The following relation affords a check:

$$\text{dividend} = \text{divisor} \times \text{quotient} + \text{remainder}.$$

EXAMPLE III.   $(a^3 + 28b^3 + 9a^2b + 27ab^2) \div (3b + a)$.

**Solution.** We arrange dividend and divisor in descending powers of $a$

(dividend) $a^3 + 9a^2b + 27ab^2 + 28b^3$ | $a + 3b$ (divisor)

$\underline{a^3 + 3a^2b}$ | $a^2 + 6ab + 9b^2$ (quotient)

$\qquad 6a^2b + 27ab^2$

$\qquad \underline{6a^2b + 18ab^2}$

$\qquad\qquad 9ab^2 + 28b^3$

$\qquad\qquad \underline{9ab^2 + 27b^3}$

$\qquad\qquad\qquad b^3$ (remainder)

Thus,

$$(a^3 + 9a^2b + 27ab^2 + 28b^3) \div (a + 3b) = a^2 + 6ab + 9b^2 + \frac{b^3}{a + 3b}.$$

*Check.*                                                                 (Ans.)

$a^2 + 6ab + 9b^2$

$\underline{a + 3b}$

$a^3 + 6a^2b + 9ab^2$

$\underline{\qquad 3a^2b + 18ab^2 + 27b^3}$

$(a^3 + 9a^2b + 27ab^2 + 27b^3) + b^3 = a^3 + 9a^2b + 27ab^2 + 28b^3 \checkmark$

## EXERCISES

*Perform the following divisions and check:*

**1.** $(x^2 - y^2) \div (x + y)$

**2.** $(x^2 - 2xy + y^2) \div (x - y)$

**3.** $(x^3 + 8y^3) \div (x + 2y)$

**4.** $(6a^2b^2 - 7a^4 - 7a^3b + b^4 - ab^3) \div (b^2 - a^2 - ab)$

**5.** $(x^2 - 5x + 4) \div (x - 1)$

**6.** $(x^2 - 5x + 5) \div (x - 1)$

**7.** $(4x^4 + 7a^2x^2 + 16a^4) \div (2x^2 + 4a^2 + 3ax)$

**8.** $(15y^3 - 30y - 8 - 19y^2) \div (3y^2 - 2 - 5y)$

**9.** $(4a^4 - ab^3 - 8a^3b + 5a^2b^2) \div (ab - 2a^2)$

**10.** $(a^5 + 50 - 70a + 37a^2) \div (10 - 2a + a^2)$

**11.** $(x^2 - y^2 - z^2 - 2yz) \div (x - y - z)$

**12.** $(6a^2y^2 - 4aby^2 - 3a^2 + 5ab - b^2) \div (3a - 2b)$

**13.** $(16y^2 + 9a^2b^2 - 4a^2 - 36b^2y^2) \div (3ab + 6by - 2a - 4y)$

**14.** $(y^2 + 6y - 25x^2 + 9) \div (y - 5x + 3)$

**15.** $(x^5 + 32y^5) \div (x + 2y)$

**16.** $(7u^3 - 3u^4 - 13u^2 + 7u - 6) \div (2 + 3u^2 - u)$

**17.** $(\frac{1}{3}x^5 + \frac{11}{15}x^4y - \frac{73}{30}x^3y^2 - \frac{31}{15}x^2y^3 + \frac{7}{10}xy^4 - 3y^5) \div (\frac{2}{3}x^2 - \frac{2}{5}xy - 4y^2)$

**18.** $(2x^4 - 5x^3y + 6x^2y^2 - 4xy^3 + y^4) \div (x^2 - xy + y^2)$

**19.** $(x^3 - y^3 + z^3 + 3xyz) \div (x^2 + y^2 + z^2 + xy + yz - xz)$

**20.** $(a + 2a^2 - 3a^3 + 4a^4) \div (a - a^2 + a^3 - a^4)$

**21.** $(x^4 - 3x^3 + 7x^2 - 15x + 10) \div (x^2 + 5)$

**22.** $(3x^4 - 7x^3 + 7x^2 - 7x + 4) \div (x^2 + 1)$

**23.** $(4x^4 - 16x^3 + 16x^2 - 24x + 15) \div (2x^2 + 3)$

**24.** If the divisor is $x - 3$, the quotient is $x - 4$, and the remainder is $- 7$, find the dividend.

**16. Equations and identities.** The algebraic expression $x^2 - y^2$ represents a number; this number depends upon the values assigned to $x$ and $y$. For example, if we put $x = 3$ and $y = 2$, we have $x^2 - y^2 = (3)^2 - (2)^2 = 9 - 4 = 5$, whereas, if we put $x = 5$ and $y = 4$, we have $x^2 - y^2 = (5)^2 - (4)^2 = 25 - 16 = 9$. Thus, it is clear that the value of $x^2 - y^2$ depends upon the values assigned to $x$ and $y$. The equality

$$x^2 - y^2 = 9$$

holds good for $x = 5$ and $y = 4$, but it does not hold good for $x = 3$ and $y = 2$. *If the two sides (or members) of an equality are equal for certain particular values of the symbols, but not for all values, the equality is called a* **conditional equality** *or an* **equation.**

Thus, $x^2 - y^2 = 9$ is an equation.

On the other hand, in § **14** we see that the product $(x + y)(x - y)$ is $x^2 - y^2$, thus

$$(x + y)(x - y) = x^2 - y^2$$

holds good for every value of $x$ and $y$. *If the two members of an equality are equal for all values of the symbols for which the members are defined * the equality is called an* **identity.**

The following identities are important in the study of algebraic expressions:

    I. $\underline{ab + ac = a(b + c)}$
   II. $a^2 + 2ab + b^2 = (a + b)^2$
  III. $a^2 - 2ab + b^2 = (a - b)^2$
  IV. $a^2 - b^2 = (a + b)(a - b)$
   V. $a^3 - b^3 = (a - b)(a^2 + ab + b^2)$
  VI. $a^3 + b^3 = (a + b)(a^2 - ab + b^2)$
 VII. $x^2 + (a + b)x + ab = (x + a)(x + b)$
VIII. $acx^2 + (ad + bc)x + bd = (ax + b)(cx + d)$

In these identities it should be observed that $a$, $b$, $c$, $d$, and $x$ may represent any numbers; for example, $(x + y)^2 - z^2$ is the same as IV with $a = x + y$ and $b = z$, hence

$$(x + y)^2 - z^2 = (x + y + z)(x + y - z).$$

## EXERCISES

*Classify the following as equations or identities:*

**1.** $x - 2 = 0$              **2.** $x^2 - 2xy + y^2 = (x - y)^2$
**3.** $ax + bx = x(a + b)$       **4.** $x^2 + 3x + 4 = 0$
**5.** $3x^2 - 7x + 5 = 2x^2 + 4x - 6$   **6.** $2x^2 - 4x + 8 = 2(x^2 - 2x + 4)$
**7.** $x^3 - 27y^3 = (x - 3y)(x^2 + 3xy + 9y^2)$
**8.** $(3x + 4)(2x - 7) = 2(x + 3)(2x - 5)$

* An algebraic expression may not be defined for certain values of the symbols; for example, in the equality $\dfrac{1}{1 - x} = 1 - \dfrac{x}{x - 1}$ neither member is defined for $x = 1$.

*Expand by inspection:*

**9.** $(a + 2b)(a - 2b)$　　　　**10.** $(3x + y)(3x - y)$

**11.** $(2a + b)^2$　　　　**12.** $(3y + 4x)(x - 3y)$

**13.** $(2a + b)(4a^2 - 2ab + b^2)$　　　**14.** $(a - 3b)^2$

**15.** $(-7x - 3y)^2$　**16.** $(x + 5)(x - 3)$　**17.** $3(x + 5)^2$　**18.** $(2x - 3y)^2$

*Expand:*

**19.** $(x + 2y - z)(x - 2y + z)$　　　**20.** $(ax + b + c)(ax - b + c)$

**21.** $(x^2 + y^2)(x^2 - y^2)$　　　　**22.** $(a^2 + b^2)(a^4 - a^2b^2 + b^4)$

**23.** $(a+2b-4c-d)(a+2b+4c+d)$　　**24.** $(5a - 3b)(9a - 4b)$

**25.** $(1 - 2a)(1 + 2a + 4a^2)$　　　**26.** $[(x + y)^2 - xy][x - y]$

**27.** $(a - b + c)(a - b - c)$　　　**28.** $(x + y - z)(z - y + x)$

**29.** $(2x^2 + y^3)(2x^2 - y^3)$　　　**30.** $(x^{\frac{1}{2}} - y^{\frac{1}{2}})(x^{\frac{1}{2}} + y^{\frac{1}{2}})$

**31.** $(x^{\frac{1}{3}} + y^{\frac{1}{3}})(x^{\frac{2}{3}} - x^{\frac{1}{3}}y^{\frac{1}{3}} + y^{\frac{2}{3}})$　　**32.** $(x^{-\frac{1}{2}} + 2y^{-\frac{1}{2}})(x^{-\frac{1}{2}} - 2y^{-\frac{1}{2}})$

**33.** $(a^{\frac{1}{4}} + 2b^{\frac{1}{4}})(a^{\frac{1}{2}} - 2a^{\frac{1}{4}}b^{\frac{1}{4}} + 4b^{\frac{1}{2}})$　**34.** $(x^0 + x^2)(y^0 - x^2)$

**35.** $(\sqrt{a} - \sqrt{b})(a^{\frac{1}{2}} + b^{\frac{1}{2}})$　　　**36.** $(\sqrt{-1} + \sqrt{1})(\sqrt{-1} - \sqrt{1})$

**37.** $(x^{\frac{1}{2}} + y^{\frac{1}{2}})^2$　　　　　**38.** $(x^3 + y^2)^2$

**39.** $(x^{-3} + x^3)^2$　　　　　**40.** $(2x^0y - 7y^0x)(7x - 2y)$

**17. Factoring.** *"Factoring" an expression consists in writing it as the product of two or more quantities called factors,* e.g.,

$$a^2 - b^2 = (a + b)(a - b).$$

Each of the expressions in the product is called a factor of the original expression. Factoring in algebra is in general limited to obtaining factors each term of which is a product of positive integral powers of the letters and a rational number. Such factors are called rational factors. *An expression which has no rational factors except itself and 1 is called a* **prime factor,** e.g., $a + b$ is a prime factor. *To factor a polynomial means to write it as the product of its prime rational factors.*

It should be observed that $a^n - b^n$ is divisible by $a - b$ if $n$ is any positive integer, and that $a^m + b^m$ is divisible by $a + b$ if $m$ is an odd integer.

EXAMPLES. Factor the following into prime rational factors:

I. $3x + 6y$.

**Solution.** $3x + 6y = 3(x + 2y)$　(Ans.)

II. $4x^2 + 4xy + y^2$.

**Solution.** $4x^2 + 4xy + y^2 = (2x + y)^2$　(Ans.)

III. $x^8 - y^8$.

**Solution.** $x^8 - y^8 = (x^4 + y^4)(x^4 - y^4)$
$$= (x^4 + y^4)(x^2 + y^2)(x^2 - y^2)$$
$$= (x^4 + y^4)(x^2 + y^2)(x + y)(x - y) \quad \text{(Ans.)}$$

IV. $1 + 8x^3$.

**Solution.** $1 + 8x^3 = (1 + 2x)(1 - 2x + 4x^2) \quad \text{(Ans.)}$

V. $2x^3 - 4x^2 + x - 2$.

**Solution.** $2x^3 - 4x^2 + x - 2 = 2x^2(x - 2) + (x - 2)$
$$= (x - 2)(2x^2 + 1) \quad \text{(Ans.)}$$

VI. $x^2 + y^2 - z^2 + 2xy$.

**Solution.** $x^2 + y^2 - z^2 + 2xy = x^2 + 2xy + y^2 - z^2$
$$= (x + y)^2 - z^2$$
$$= (x + y + z)(x + y - z) \quad \text{(Ans.)}$$

VII. $cx + dz - dx - cz$.

**Solution.** $cx + dz - dx - cz = cx - dx - (cz - dz)$
$$= x(c - d) - z(c - d)$$
$$= (c - d)(x - z) \quad \text{(Ans.)}$$

VIII. $a^4 + 64$.

**Solution.** $a^4 + 64 = a^4 + 16a^2 + 64 - 16a^2 = (a^2 + 8)^2 - (4a)^2$
$$= (a^2 + 8 + 4a)(a^2 + 8 - 4a) \quad \text{(Ans.)}$$

IX. $y^4 + 13y^2 + 49$.

**Solution.** $y^4 + 13y^2 + 49 = y^4 + 14y^2 + 49 - y^2$
$$= (y^2 + 7)^2 - (y)^2$$
$$= (y^2 + 7 + y)(y^2 + 7 - y) \quad \text{(Ans.)}$$

## EXERCISES

*Factor the following into prime rational factors:*

1. $4 - x^2$
2. $2x - 4y$
3. $x^3 + 27$
4. $x^2 - 4x + 4$
5. $8y + 16 + y^2$
6. $a^2 - x^2 - 18a + 81$
7. $a^2 - a + \frac{1}{4}$
8. $x^6 - 27y^6$
9. $2x^2 - 15x + 27$
10. $x^2 + 2xy + y^2 - 4z^2$
11. $12a^2 - 16ab^2$
12. $4y^2 - z^2 + 4xy + x^2$
13. $x^8 - 256$
14. $ax^2 - 2ax - 35a$
15. $x^4 + x^2y^2 + y^4$
16. $\frac{1}{25}a^4 - \frac{9}{49}c^2$
17. $8 + 27w^3$
18. $r^4 + 64t^4$
19. $y^2 - 9x^2 + 25 + 6xz - 10y - z^2$
20. $4r^2s^2 + 4rs^2 - 15s^2$
21. $16a^4 - 28a^2b^2 + 9b^4$
22. $40x^3 - 42 - 35x^2 + 48x$
23. $4a^2 - x^2 + 2xy - 12ab - y^2 + 9b^2$
24. $t^2 - r^2 - 2rs - s^2$
25. $10xy - 8xw + 15cy + 4bw - 12cw - 5by$

**26.** $w^6 - 7w^3 - 8$          **27.** $81z^2 + 20w - 4w^2 - 25$

**28.** $-6x^2 + ax + bx + a^2 + 2ab + b^2$    **29.** $4a^4 + 1$

**30.** $4m^4 + 19m^2n^2 + 49n^4$          **31.** $9a^4 + 2a^2b^2 + b^4$

**32.** $2rx + 2rz - sx + 3sy - 6ry - sz$    **33.** $25x^3 - 42 + 35x^2 - 30x$

**34.** $x^4 - y^4 + 2xy(x^2 - y^2)$     **35.** $2x^3 - x^2y + 2x^2 - xy + 2x - y$

**36.** $6abx^2 - b^2x^2 + 6aby^2 - b^2y^2$    **37.** $x^5 + x^4y + x^3y^2 + x^2y^3 + xy^4 + y^5$

**38.** $a^4 - a^2 + 12ab - 36b^2$        **39.** $4m^4 + 7m^2 - 36$

**40.** $2[2x^2 - (y - x) - 2x(2y - x)]$    **41.** $3p^5 - 54p^3 + 243p$

**42.** $x^4y^2 - 2x^2y^4 + x^3y - 2xy^3$

**43.** $9x^2 + 16y^2 - 49a^2 - 4b^2 + 28ab + 24xy$

**44.** $x^{a+b} + x^ay^a + x^by^b + y^{a+b}$    **45.** $9x^2(3x + 2)^2 + 6x(3x + 2) + 1$

**46.** $8u^6 - 27v^9$      **47.** $(a + b)^2 + (a + c)^2 - (c + d)^2 - (b + d)^2$

**48.** $m^6 + m^5n + m^4n^2 + m^3n^3 + m^2n^4 + mn^5$

**49.** $x^3y - 2x^2yz + xyz^2 - xy^3 - 2xy^2 - xy$

**50.** $45a^5 + 18a^4 + 60a^3 + 24a^2$

**18. Lowest common multiple.** *An expression which contains a second expression as a factor is called a* **multiple** *of that expression,* e.g., $a^2 - b^2$ is a multiple of $a - b$. *If an expression is a multiple of several expressions it is called a* **common multiple** *of them. The* **lowest common multiple** (L.C.M.) *of several expressions is that common multiple which contains the least number of prime factors.* To find the lowest common multiple of several expressions factor each expression into prime factors and form a product containing each of these prime factors raised to the highest power in which it occurs in any one of the expressions. Due to the fact that 1 and $-1$ are factors of every expression, the algebraic sign of the L.C.M. is arbitrary.

EXAMPLE I.    Find the L.C.M. of $3x^3 - 3y^3$, $2x^2 + 4xy - 6y^2$, $x^2 - y^2$.

**Solution.**          $3x^3 - 3y^3 = 3(x - y)(x^2 + xy + y^2)$
$$2x^2 + 4xy - 6y^2 = 2(x + 3y)(x - y)$$
$$x^2 - y^2 = (x + y)(x - y)$$

Thus, the L.C.M. is $3(x - y)(x^2 + xy + y^2)2(x + 3y)(x + y)$.  (Ans.)

EXAMPLE II.    Find the L.C.M. of
$$2a + 10b, 4a^2 + 2ab, a^2 + 10ab + 25b^2.$$

**Solution.**          $2a + 10b = 2(a + 5b)$
$$4a^2 + 2ab = 2a(2a + b)$$
$$a^2 + 10ab + 25b^2 = (a + 5b)^2$$

Thus, the L.C.M. is $2(a + 5b)^2a(2a + b)$.  (Ans.)

## EXERCISES

*Find the* L.C.M.:

**1.** 15, 6, 10          **2.** $9x^2y$, $6x^3y$          **3.** $18y^4$, $33y^2z$

**4.** $(y - x)^2$, $(y^2 - x^2)$          **5.** $(4x^2 - 16)$, $(x - 2)^2$          **6.** $(x - 2)^3$, $x^2 + x - 6$

**7.** $2a - 4$, $5a + 15$, $3a^2 + 3a - 18$

**8.** $y^2 - 5y + 6$, $y^2 + 2y - 8$, $y^2 + y - 12$

**9.** $x^2 + 2x - 24$, $x^2 - x - 42$, $x^2 - 49$

**10.** $x^2 - 1$, $2x^2 + x - 3$, $x^2 + x$

**11.** $8x^2 + 20x - 12$, $20x^2 - 22x + 6$

**12.** $6a^2 - a - 1$, $3a^2 + 7a + 2$, $2a^2 + 3a - 2$

**13.** $a^2 - a - 6$, $a^2 - 4a + 3$, $a^2 + a - 2$

**14.** $r^2 - 6ar + 9a^2$, $r^2 + 4ar - 21a^2$

**15.** $(x - 2)$, $(x - 2)^2$, $2x^2 - 7x + 5$          **16.** $x^2 - 25$, $x^2 + 6x + 5$

**17.** $14x^3(x + y)^3$, $35xy^2(x - y)$          **18.** $a^2(x + y)(x - y)$, $a^3b(x-y)^2$

**19.** $4a^3b - 8ab^3$, $6a^5 - 12a^2b^2$

**20.** $4x^2 - 25y^2$, $6x^2 + 9xy - 15y^2$, $10x^2 + 35xy + 25y^2$

**21.** $36x^2 - 49y^2$, $72x^3 - 36x^2y - 56xy^2$, $90x^2y + 165xy^2 + 70y^3$

**22.** $a^3 + b^3$, $a^2 - b^2$, $2a^2 + 2ab + 3a + 3b$

**23.** $x^3 - y^3$, $x^2 - y^2$, $3x^2 - 3xy + 5x - 5y$

**24.** $36x^6 + 9x^2$, $12x^3 + 6x - 24ax^2 + 24ax - 12x^2 - 12a$

**25.** $x^3 - 5x^2 + 6x$, $x^2 - 4$, $x^2 - 3x + 2$

**26.** $a^3 - 3a^2 + 4$, $a^3 - 2a^2 - 4a + 8$

**27.** $7x^4 + 56x^3 + 49x^2$, $12x^4 + 36x^3 - 12x^2 - 36x$, $21x^5 - 147x^4 + 126x^3$

**28.** $9x^3 + 3x^2y - 6xy^2$, $12x^3yz - 30x^3yw + 12x^2y^2z - 30x^2y^2w$, $12x^3y^2 - 12xy^4$

**29.** $10(xy^2)(a^2 - 2ax)$, $15x^3y(a^2 - ax - 2x^2)$, $25y^2(a^2 - x^2)^2$

**30.** $14x^3y^3(a^3 + a^2 - 2)$, $21x^4y^3(a^3 + 2a^2 - 3)$

**31.** $(x^3 + 1)(4x^2 + 2x - 12)$, $2(x^2 + 2x)(4x^2 - 8x + 3)$

**32.** $x^2 - (a + b)x + ab$, $2x^2 + ax - 3a^2$, $x^4 - a^4$

**19. Fractions.** *The quotient,* $a \div b$, *of two algebraic expressions is often written* $\frac{a}{b}$ *and, when thus written, is called an* **algebraic fraction;** *a is the* **numerator** *and b the* **denominator** *of the fraction.* Multiplying, or dividing, both numerator and denominator of a fraction by the same number, zero excluded, does not change the value of the fraction. As in arithmetic, the reduction of a fraction to lowest terms consists in dividing out the factors common to the numerator and denominator.

EXAMPLE I. Reduce $\dfrac{a^2 - 11ab + 28b^2}{a^2 - 14ab + 49b^2}$ to lowest terms.

**Solution.** $\dfrac{a^2 - 11ab + 28b^2}{a^2 - 14ab + 49b^2} = \dfrac{\overset{1}{\cancel{(a-7b)}}(a - 4b)}{\underset{1}{\cancel{(a-7b)}}(a - 7b)} = \dfrac{a - 4b}{a - 7b}$   (Ans.)

Here the numerator and denominator have been divided by $(a - 7b)$, the division being indicated by oblique lines called cancellation marks. It should be noted that in the answer $\dfrac{a - 4b}{a - 7b}$ the $a$'s cannot be cancelled since $a$ is not a factor of both the numerator and denominator.

EXAMPLE II.   Reduce $\dfrac{(2y^2 + 12yz - 80z^2)(y + 4z)}{(2y^2 - 32z^2)(y + 10z)}$ to lowest terms.

**Solution.** $\dfrac{(2y^2 + 12yz - 80z^2)(y + 4z)}{(2y^2 - 32z^2)(y + 10z)}$

$= \dfrac{2(y + 10z)(y - 4z)(y + 4z)}{2(y + 4z)(y - 4z)(y + 10z)} = 1$   (Ans.)

*Note.* The answer here is 1 because in each division we obtain 1.

## EXERCISES

*Reduce the following fractions to lowest terms:*

1. $\dfrac{15}{36}$

2. $\dfrac{39}{65}$

3. $\dfrac{x^2 - y^2}{x + y}$

4. $\dfrac{(3 + 4d)(x - y)}{(x - y)(4 + 5d)}$

5. $\dfrac{a - 2b}{a^2 - 4b^2}$

6. $\dfrac{12ab^3(x + y)}{4b^2(x + y)}$

7. $\dfrac{12x^3(a - b)}{15a^2x^4 - 15b^2x^4}$

8. $\dfrac{bd(x + y)}{bx + by}$

9. $\dfrac{(c + d)(x^2 - y^2)}{(x + y)(c + d)}$

10. $\dfrac{x^3 - 8}{x^3 - 2x^2 + 4x - 8}$

11. $\dfrac{a^2 + 11ab + 28b^2}{a^2 + 14ab + 49b^2}$

12. $\dfrac{3am^2 - 3an^2}{3m^2 + 6mn + 3n^2}$

13. $\dfrac{a^2b - 8ab + 12b}{ca^2 - 12ac + 36c}$

14. $\dfrac{9 - r^4}{12 + 2r^2 - 2r^4}$

15. $\dfrac{2x^5 + 3x^4 + 2x + 3}{4x^2 - 9}$

16. $\dfrac{a^2 + 7a - 30}{a^2 - 7a + 12}$

17. $\dfrac{a^2y^2 - 16a^2}{ay^2 + 9ay + 20a}$

18. $\dfrac{12x^2 - 2xy - 24y^2}{4x^2 - 2xy - 6y^2}$

19. $\dfrac{3x^2 - 7x - 20}{3ax + 5a - 6x - 10}$

**20.** $\dfrac{(m^2 + 2)2m - (m^2 - 2)2m}{(m^2 + 2)^2}$

**21.** $\dfrac{16x^3y - 32xy^5}{- 8xy}$

**22.** $\dfrac{x^2 - 9}{x^2 - 6x + 9}$

**23.** $\dfrac{a^2 + 6bc - 9b^2 - c^2}{a^2 - 9b^2 + c^2 - 2ac}$

**24.** $\dfrac{a^2 + a - 12}{a^3 + 4a^2 - 7a - 28}$

**25.** $\dfrac{y^3 - 5y^2 - y + 5}{y^3 - y^2 - 25y + 25}$

**26.** $\dfrac{2x^2 + 19x + 35}{3x^2 + 15x - 42}$

**27.** $\dfrac{m^3 + m^2 - 25m - 25}{3m^3 - 2m^2 - 75m + 50}$

**28.** $\dfrac{a^3 + a^2 - a + 2}{a^4 - a^3 - a^2 + 2a - 2}$

**29.** $\dfrac{(x^2 - 9)(x^2 - x - 6)}{(x^2 - 6x + 9)(x^2 + 5x + 6)}$

**30.** $\dfrac{(x^2 - 7x + 12)(x^2 - 6x + 8)}{(x^2 - 3x + 2)(x^2 - 8x + 16)}$

**31.** $\dfrac{(4x^2 - 5x + 1)(2x^2 - 3x + 1)(6x^2 - 5x + 1)(x + 1)}{(8x^2 - 2x - 1)(3x^2 - 4x + 1)(4x^2 + 3x - 1)(x - 1)}$

**32.** $\dfrac{(x^3 - 1)(2x^2 - x - 3)(x^2 - 2x)}{(x^2 - 1)(x^3 + x^2 + x)(2x^2 - 7x + 6)}$

**33.** $\dfrac{(x^3 + 8y^3)(x^2 - 4y^2)}{(x^2 - 2xy + 4y^2)(x^2 + 4xy + 4y^2)}$

**34.** $\dfrac{(8a^2 - 28a + 12)(a^2 - 8a + 16)(6a^2 - 5a - 6)}{(2a^3 - 11a^2 + 12a)(4a^2 + 6a - 4)(27a^3 - 12a)}$

**35.** $\dfrac{y^3 - 5y^2 + 7y - 3}{y^3 - y^2 - 5y - 3}$

**36.** $\dfrac{2m^3 + m^2 - 25m + 12}{3m^3 + 5m^2 - 34m - 24}$

**20. Changing the sign before a fraction.** *Changing the signs of an even number of factors of the numerator or denominator or both does not change the sign of the fraction; changing the sign of an odd number of factors does change the sign of the fraction.* For example:

$$\frac{ab}{cd} = \frac{(-a)b}{(-c)d} = \frac{(-a)(-b)}{(-c)(-d)} = \frac{a(-b)}{-c(d)} = \frac{(-a)(-b)}{cd}$$
$$= -\frac{(-a)b}{cd} = -\frac{(-a)(-b)}{(-c)d}$$

It should be observed that these sign changes refer to factors. In the fraction $\dfrac{a - b}{a + b}$ there is one factor in the numerator and one in the denominator; $a$ and $-b$ are terms of the factor $a - b$ and the signs of the individual terms of a factor can be changed only by changing the sign of the factor which contains them.

EXAMPLE I.  Remove the minus signs from the numerator and denominator of   (1) $\dfrac{2}{-3}$, (2) $-\dfrac{-b}{2c}$, (3) $\dfrac{-8y(-x^2)}{3z(-w)}$, (4) $-\dfrac{3x(-z)}{2b}$

**Solution.**   (1) $\dfrac{2}{-3} = -\dfrac{2}{3}$

(2) $-\dfrac{-b}{2c} = -\left(-\dfrac{b}{2c}\right) = \dfrac{b}{2c}$

(3) $\dfrac{-8y(-x^2)}{3z(-w)} = -\dfrac{8yx^2}{3zw}$

(4) $-\dfrac{3x(-z)}{2b} = \dfrac{3xz}{2b}$

EXAMPLE II.  Reduce $\dfrac{(x-y)x}{y^2 - x^2}$ to lowest terms.

**Solution.** $\dfrac{(x-y)x}{y^2 - x^2} = \dfrac{(x-y)(x)}{(y-x)(y+x)} = -\dfrac{(x-y)x}{[-(y-x)](y+x)}$

$= -\dfrac{(x-y)x}{(x-y)(x+y)} = -\dfrac{x}{(x+y)}$   (Ans.)

## EXERCISES

*Remove the minus signs from the numerator and denominator:*

1. $\dfrac{-5}{-3}$

2. $\dfrac{a(-x)}{c}$

3. $\dfrac{(-2x)5y}{(-3z)(-2c)}$

4. $\dfrac{(-2)(-x)5(-y)}{(-3z)(-4x)^2}$

5. $\dfrac{(-a)(-b)2c}{c(-2a)b}$

6. $-\dfrac{5cd(-e)^2}{(-2)ab}$

7. $\dfrac{8x(-2y)}{(-2z)^3}$

8. $\dfrac{(-3x)^3(2y)^2}{9(-y)^3(-z)^2}$

9. $\dfrac{(-x)(-3y)}{(-y)^3}$

*Reduce to lowest terms:*

10. $\dfrac{ay - 5a}{5 - y}$

11. $\dfrac{(c-d)^2}{cd - c^2}$

12. $\dfrac{6 + x - x^2}{x^2 + x - 12}$

13. $\dfrac{a^4 - 9}{-2a^4 + 2a^2 + 12}$

14. $\dfrac{4ax - 3ay}{3y^2 + 2xy - 8x^2}$

15. $\dfrac{x^2 - y^2}{y^2 + xy - 2x^2}$

16. $\dfrac{12y^2 - 2ay - 24a^2}{4y^2 - 2ay - 6a^2}$

17. $\dfrac{ax^4 - a^3x^2 + a^5}{x^6 + a^6}$

18. $\dfrac{ab^2 - ac^2}{ab^2 - abc}$

19. $\dfrac{2x^2 + 19x + 35}{3x^2 + 15x - 42}$

20. $\dfrac{a^2 + 7a - 30}{a^2 - 7a + 12}$

21. $\dfrac{x^2y^2 - x^2 - y^2 + 1}{xy - x - y + 1}$

22. $\dfrac{x^3 - 27y^3}{3y - x}$

23. $\dfrac{x^3 + 27}{-4x^2 - 24x - 36}$

24. $\dfrac{x^2y^2 - 16y^2}{20y + 9xy + yx^2}$

25. $\dfrac{32a^5 - 243y^5}{3y - 2a}$

26. $\dfrac{x^4 - y^4}{y^2 - x^2}$

27. $\dfrac{x^2 - 4xy + 3y^2}{y^2 - 3xy + 2x^2}$

**21. Product and quotient of two fractions.** *The product of two fractions is the fraction whose numerator is the product of the numerators of the given fractions and whose denominator is the product of the denominators.*

EXAMPLE I.   Multiply and reduce to lowest terms: $\frac{18}{25} \cdot \frac{15}{24}$.

**Solution.**   $\dfrac{18}{25} \cdot \dfrac{15}{24} = \dfrac{18 \cdot 15}{25 \cdot 24} = \dfrac{2 \cdot 3 \cdot 3 \cdot \not{5} \cdot \not{3}}{\not{5} \cdot 5 \cdot \not{2} \cdot 2 \cdot 2 \cdot \not{3}} = \dfrac{9}{20}$   (Ans.)

EXAMPLE II.   Multiply and reduce to lowest terms:

$$\frac{x - 3y}{x^2 - y^2} \cdot \frac{x + y}{x^2 - 9y^2}.$$

**Solution.**

$$\frac{x - 3y}{x^2 - y^2} \cdot \frac{x + y}{x^2 - 9y^2} = \frac{(x - 3y)(x + y)}{(x^2 - y^2)(x^2 - 9y^2)}$$

$$= \frac{\overset{1}{\cancel{(x - 3y)}\cancel{(x + y)}}}{\cancel{(x + y)}(x - y)(x + 3y)\cancel{(x - 3y)}}$$

$$= \frac{1}{(x - y)(x + 3y)}   \text{(Ans.)}$$

Of course, to find the product of three or more fractions we form a new fraction whose numerator is the product of the numerators of the fractions and whose denominator is the product of the denominators of the fractions.

To invert a fraction means to interchange the numerator and the denominator of the fraction; for example, if we invert $\frac{a}{b}$ we get $\frac{b}{a}$. *To divide one fraction by a second fraction invert the second fraction and multiply.*

EXAMPLE III.   Divide and reduce to lowest terms:

$$\frac{x^2 - 9}{x^2 - 5x + 6} \div \frac{x^2 + x - 6}{x^2 - 6x + 9}.$$

**Solution.**

$$\frac{x^2 - 9}{x^2 - 5x + 6} \div \frac{x^2 + x - 6}{x^2 - 6x + 9} = \frac{(x^2 - 9)}{(x^2 - 5x + 6)} \cdot \frac{(x^2 - 6x + 9)}{(x^2 + x - 6)}$$

$$= \frac{(x + 3)(x - 3)(x - 3)(x - 3)}{(x - 3)(x - 2)(x + 3)(x - 2)}$$

$$= \frac{(x - 3)^2}{(x - 2)^2}   \text{(Ans.)}$$

EXAMPLE IV.   Divide and reduce to lowest terms:
$$\frac{x^3 + 8y^3}{x^3 - 8y^3} \div \frac{x+2y}{x-2y}.$$

**Solution.**

$$\frac{x^3 + 8y^3}{x^3 - 8y^3} \div \frac{x + 2y}{x - 2y} = \frac{x^3 + 8y^3}{x^3 - 8y^3} \cdot \frac{x - 2y}{x + 2y}$$

$$= \frac{(x + 2y)(x^2 - 2xy + 4y^2)(x - 2y)}{(x - 2y)(x^2 + 2xy + 4y^2)(x + 2y)}$$

$$= \frac{x^2 - 2xy + 4y^2}{x^2 + 2xy + 4y^2}. \quad \text{(Ans.)}$$

The **reciprocal** of an algebraic expression is the fraction whose numerator is 1 and whose denominator is the expression; for example, the reciprocal of $x^2 - 7$ is $\dfrac{1}{x^2 - 7}$.

## EXERCISES

Write down the reciprocals of the following:

**1.** 7

**2.** 3

**3.** $-5$

**4.** $x + y$

**5.** $a + 3b$

**6.** $2x - 5y^2$

**7.** $x^2 - 3x + 4$

**8.** $(x + y)(x - 4y)$

**9.** $(a + b)(3a - 5b)$

Perform the indicated operations and reduce to lowest terms:

**10.** $\dfrac{x^2 + a^2}{x^2 - ax} \cdot \dfrac{ax - a^2}{x^4 - a^4}$

**11.** $\dfrac{a^3 - 1}{a^2 + a} \cdot \dfrac{a^2 - 1}{a^4 + a^2 + 1}$

**12.** $\dfrac{2a^2 - a - 1}{2a^2 + 5a + 2} \cdot \dfrac{4a^2 + a - 14}{16a^2 - 49}$

**13.** $\dfrac{xy^2 + y^3}{x^2 + xy + y^2} \cdot \dfrac{y^3 - x^3}{x^2y^2 - x^4}$

**14.** $\dfrac{a^3 - 6a^2 + 36a}{a^2 - 49} \cdot \dfrac{a^2 - a - 42}{a^4 + 216a}$

**15.** $\dfrac{x^2 - y^2}{x^2 + 2xy + y^2} \div \dfrac{2x + 2y}{3x}$

**16.** $\dfrac{3t}{y^2 - 6y + 8} \div \dfrac{2t^3}{y^2 - y - 12}$

**17.** $\dfrac{(r + 2s)^2}{r - s} \div \dfrac{rs + s^2}{r^2 - rs}$

**18.** $\dfrac{a^2 - ab - 2b^2}{a^3 - 9ab^2} \div \dfrac{a - 2b}{a - 3b}$

**19.** $\dfrac{8n^3 + 1}{2n^2 + 4n} \div \dfrac{4n^2 - 2n + 1}{n^2 + 4n + 4}$

**20.** $\dfrac{2a^2 - ab - 3b^2}{9a^2 - 25b^2} \div \dfrac{3a^2 + ab - 2b^2}{9a^2 - 30ab + 25b^2}$

**21.** $\dfrac{3w^2 - 5wz + 2z^2}{16w^2 - 8wz + z^2} \div \dfrac{27w^3 - 8z^3}{4w^3 - w^2z}$

**22.** $\dfrac{4y^2 - 1}{y^3 - 16y} \div \dfrac{1 - 2y}{y^2 + 4y}$

**23.** $\dfrac{16x - 4}{5x - 5} \div \dfrac{20x + 5}{6x - 6}$

**24.** $\dfrac{x^3 - xy^2}{x^3 + x^2y} \div \dfrac{x^2 - 2xy + y^2}{x^2 - xy - 2y^2}$

**25.** $\dfrac{x^2 - 7x + 12}{x^2 - 3x + 2} \cdot \dfrac{x^2 - 6x + 8}{x^2 - 8x + 16}$

**26.** $\dfrac{x^2 - 3x + 4}{x - 3} \div \dfrac{3x^2 - 39}{x^2 - 9}$

**27.** $\dfrac{p^2 + 3p + 9}{p^4 - 3p^2 + 9} \div \dfrac{p^3 - 27}{p^6 + 27}$

**28.** $\dfrac{a^2 - 10a + 21}{a^4 - a} \div \dfrac{a^2 - 9}{a^3 - a}$

**29.** $\dfrac{x^3 - 6x^2 + 36x}{x^2 - 49} \div \dfrac{x^4 + 216x}{x^2 - x - 42}$

**30.** $\dfrac{u^2 - 10u + 21}{u^2 - 49} \div \dfrac{u^2 - 9}{u^2 + 10u + 21}$

**31.** $\dfrac{a^2 + 3a - 4}{a^2 - a - 6} \div \dfrac{a^2 + a - 2}{a^2 + a - 12}$

**32.** $\dfrac{m^2 - 6m + 9}{m^4 - 3m^2 + 9} \div \dfrac{m^3 - 27}{m^6 + 27}$

**33.** $\dfrac{(a - 3)(a - 5)}{a - 7} \div \dfrac{a - 5}{(a - 3)(a - 7)}$

**34.** $\dfrac{a^3 - b^3}{a^2 + 2ab + b^2} \cdot \dfrac{5b}{3b - 3a} \cdot \dfrac{6a + 6b}{5a^2 + 5ab + 5b^2}$

**35.** $\dfrac{a^2 - b^2}{a^2 - 3ab + 2b^2} \cdot \dfrac{ab - 2b^2}{a^2 + ab} \cdot \dfrac{a^2 - ab}{(a - b)^2}$

**36.** $\dfrac{a^2 + a - 2}{a^2 - 7a} \cdot \dfrac{a^2 - 13a + 42}{a^2 + 2a}$

**37.** $\dfrac{1 - 2a}{1 - a^3} \div \dfrac{1 - 2a + a^2 - 2a^3}{1 + 2a + 2a^2 + a^3}$

**38.** $\dfrac{(2x^2 - x - 6)}{(6x^2 - 5x - 14)} \cdot \dfrac{(12x^2 - x - 20)}{(8x^2 + 22x + 15)} \div \dfrac{(15x^2 - 38x + 24)}{(30x^2 - x - 42)}$

**39.** $\dfrac{(x^3 - 1)(2x^2 - x - 3)}{(x^2 - 1)(x^3 + x^2 + x)} \cdot \dfrac{x^2 - 2x}{2x^2 - 7x + 6}$

**40.** $\dfrac{21a^2 - 58a + 21}{2a^2 - a - 15} \cdot \dfrac{12a^2 + 8a - 55}{27a^2 - 57a - 14} \div \dfrac{42a^2 - 95a + 33}{9a^2 - 25a - 6}$

**41.** $\dfrac{2a^2 - 18a + 40}{3a^2 - 75} \cdot \dfrac{a^2 + 5a}{(a + 3)^2} \div \dfrac{a^3 - 16a}{a^2 + a - 12}$

**42.** $\dfrac{3x^2 - 4xy - 4y^2}{2x^5 - 8x^3y^2} \cdot \dfrac{5x^3 + 8x^2y - 4xy^2}{10x^2 - 19xy + 6y^2} \div \dfrac{6x^2 + 13xy + 6y^2}{8x^4 - 18x^2y^2}$

**22. Sum and difference of two fractions.** *The algebraic sum of two fractions having the same denominator is the fraction whose numerator is the algebraic sum of the numerators and whose denominator is the common denominator.*

EXAMPLE I.   Add: $\dfrac{a}{b} + \dfrac{c}{b}$.

**Solution.**   $\dfrac{a}{b} + \dfrac{c}{b} = \dfrac{a + c}{b}$   (Ans.)

EXAMPLE II.   Subtract $\dfrac{c}{b}$ from $\dfrac{a}{b}$.

**Solution.**   $\dfrac{a}{b} - \dfrac{c}{b} = \dfrac{a - c}{b}$   (Ans.)

EXAMPLE III.   Add and simplify: $\dfrac{x^2 + 2xy + y^2}{x^2 - y^2} + \dfrac{x^2 - 2xy + y^2}{x^2 - y^2}$.

**Solution.**

$$\frac{x^2 + 2xy + y^2}{x^2 - y^2} + \frac{x^2 - 2xy + y^2}{x^2 - y^2} = \frac{x^2 + 2xy + y^2 + x^2 - 2xy + y^2}{x^2 - y^2}$$

$$= \frac{2x^2 + 2y^2}{x^2 - y^2} = \frac{2(x^2 + y^2)}{x^2 - y^2} \quad \text{(Ans.)}$$

In order to add two fractions whose denominators are different it is necessary to reduce each fraction to a common denominator. It should be recalled that the numerator and denominator of a fraction can be multiplied by the same expression (not zero) without changing the value of the fraction. *The* **lowest common denominator** (L.C.D.) *of several fractions is the L.C.M. of the denominators of the fractions.* In adding, the L.C.D. should always be used.

EXAMPLE I.    Add: $\dfrac{a}{b} + \dfrac{c}{d}$.

**Solution.**    The L.C.D. is $bd$

$$\frac{a}{b} = \frac{ad}{bd}, \quad \frac{c}{d} = \frac{bc}{bd}$$

Hence,        $\dfrac{a}{b} + \dfrac{c}{d} = \dfrac{ad}{bd} + \dfrac{bc}{bd} = \dfrac{ad + bc}{bd}$    (Ans.)

EXAMPLE II.    Combine into a single fraction and simplify:

$$\frac{5x}{x - 3} - \frac{4x^2 + 3x - 1}{x^2 + x - 12}.$$

**Solution.**    The denominators are $(x - 3)$, $(x + 4)(x - 3)$, hence the L.C.D. (or the L.C.M. of the denominators) is $(x + 4)(x - 3)$.

$$\frac{5x}{x - 3} = \frac{5x(x + 4)}{(x - 3)(x + 4)}$$

Thus,

$$\frac{5x}{x - 3} - \frac{4x^2 + 3x - 1}{x^2 + x - 12} = \frac{5x(x + 4)}{(x - 3)(x + 4)} - \frac{4x^2 + 3x - 1}{(x - 3)(x + 4)}$$

$$= \frac{5x(x + 4) - (4x^2 + 3x - 1)}{(x - 3)(x + 4)}$$

$$= \frac{5x^2 + 20x - 4x^2 - 3x + 1}{(x - 3)(x + 4)}$$

$$= \frac{x^2 + 17x + 1}{(x - 3)(x + 4)} \quad \text{(Ans.)}$$

EXAMPLE III.   Combine into a single fraction and simplify:

$$\frac{3a + 2}{6a^2 - a - 1} + \frac{a + 3}{3a^2 + 7a + 2} + \frac{a + 2}{2 - 3a - 2a^2}.$$

**Solution.**   The L.C.D. is $(3a + 1)(2a - 1)(a + 2)$

$$\frac{3a + 2}{(3a + 1)(2a - 1)} + \frac{a + 3}{(3a + 1)(a + 2)} + \frac{-(a + 2)}{(a + 2)(2a - 1)}$$

$$= \frac{(3a + 2)(a + 2) + (a + 3)(2a - 1) - (a + 2)(3a + 1)}{(3a + 1)(2a - 1)(a + 2)}$$

$$= \frac{3a^2 + 8a + 4 + 2a^2 + 5a - 3 - 3a^2 - 7a - 2}{(3a + 1)(2a - 1)(a + 2)}$$

$$= \frac{2a^2 + 6a - 1}{(3a + 1)(2a - 1)(a + 2)} \quad \text{(Ans.)}$$

It should be noted that in the third fraction of Example III we change the sign of the factor $(1 - 2a)$ making it $(2a - 1)$ in the denominator and the sign of the factor $(a + 2)$ in the numerator making it $-(a + 2)$; changing an even number of signs does not change the sign of the fraction.

*Any algebraic expression may be considered as a fraction with denominator* 1.

### EXERCISES

*Combine into a single fraction and simplify:*

1. $\dfrac{1}{2} + \dfrac{2}{3} + \dfrac{3}{4}$       2. $\dfrac{5}{2} + \dfrac{1}{3} - 7$       3. $\dfrac{x - 3}{2} + \dfrac{2x - 1}{4}$

4. $\dfrac{4y - 5}{12} - \dfrac{2a - 7}{16} + 4$   5. $\dfrac{5x + 3}{7} - \dfrac{3x - 1}{5} - 3$   6. $\dfrac{3x}{b} + \dfrac{y}{c} - 1$

7. $\dfrac{9a - 5b}{4ab} - \dfrac{5a - 6b}{3a^2 b}$   8. $\dfrac{3a}{4c} - 5a - \dfrac{6c}{a} + c$   9. $a - 4 - \dfrac{2 + 11a}{3a}$

10. $\dfrac{x - 1}{x + 1} - \dfrac{x + 1}{x - 1} + \dfrac{4x^2 + 1}{x^2 - 1}$       11. $\dfrac{1}{a + 3} - \dfrac{4a - 1}{a - 2}$

12. $\dfrac{2 + x^2}{2 + x} - \dfrac{2 - x^2}{x - 2}$       13. $\dfrac{9x - 5y}{4xy} - \dfrac{5x - 6y}{3x^2 y}$

14. $\dfrac{5a}{a - 3} - \dfrac{4a^2 + 3a - 1}{a^2 + a - 12}$       15. $\dfrac{a - 1}{2a^2 + 5a + 3} - \dfrac{a + 1}{2a + 3}$

16. $\dfrac{2x - y}{2x - 2y} - \dfrac{3x - 4y}{3x - 3y}$       17. $3x - \dfrac{3 - 7x}{2x - 3} + 1$

18. $\dfrac{5y + 7}{4x} - \dfrac{5y - 1}{4x + 1}$       19. $\dfrac{x}{4m - m^2} + \dfrac{2}{m^2 - 16}$

**20.** $\dfrac{3a}{a^2 - 9} + \dfrac{5}{3 - a}$

**21.** $\dfrac{1}{a^2 - ab} - \dfrac{1}{ab - b^2}$

**22.** $1 - \dfrac{6}{y} - \dfrac{1}{y^2 - 5y}$

**23.** $\dfrac{2x}{x^2 + 4x - 60} - \dfrac{2}{x + 10}$

**24.** $x + y - \dfrac{x^3 - y^3}{x^2 - xy + y^2}$

**25.** $\dfrac{x - 6}{x^2 + 3x - 4} - \dfrac{1}{1 - x}$

**26.** $\dfrac{1}{a + 3} + \dfrac{7}{a^2 - a - 12} + \dfrac{a - 3}{a + 4}$

**27.** $\dfrac{2}{a} - \dfrac{3}{2a + 1} + \dfrac{2a - 3}{1 - 4a^2}$

**28.** $\dfrac{3a}{a^2 + a - 2} - \left( \dfrac{2}{a + 2} + \dfrac{1}{a - 1} \right)$

**29.** $\dfrac{a + 2}{a^2 + 5a + 6} + \dfrac{a + 3}{a^2 + 7a + 12}$

**30.** $\dfrac{y - x}{y^2 - 6xy + 9x^2} - \dfrac{x}{y^2 + 4xy - 21x^2}$

**31.** $\dfrac{2}{2a - 1} - \dfrac{2a + 1}{4a^2 - 1} + \dfrac{a + 1}{a}$

**32.** $\dfrac{y}{y - x} - \dfrac{y}{y + 2x} + \dfrac{y^2 + 2}{(x - y)(y + 2x)}$

**33.** $\dfrac{a + b}{2a - 2b} + \dfrac{b - a}{4b + 4a} + \dfrac{a^2 + 14ab + b^2}{8b^2 - 8a^2}$

**34.** $\dfrac{a^2 - 2a + 5}{(a^3 - 1)(a + 1)} - \dfrac{10a - 1}{3(a^2 + a + 1)} + \dfrac{10a - 11}{3(a^2 - 1)}$

**35.** $\dfrac{x^3 + x^2y}{yx^2 - y^3} - \dfrac{x^2}{y(x + y)} + \dfrac{2x^2}{y^2 - x^2} + \dfrac{x}{y}$

**36.** $\dfrac{2 + a}{2 - a} + \dfrac{3 + a}{3 - a} + \dfrac{4 + a}{4 - a} + \dfrac{2(a^3 - a^2 - 19a + 36)}{(a - 2)(a - 3)(a - 4)}$

**37.** $\dfrac{9y^2 - (4w - 2x)^2}{(2x + 3y)^2 - 16w^2} + \dfrac{16w^2 - (2x - 3y)^2}{(3y + 4w)^2 - 4x^2} + \dfrac{4x^2 - (3y - 4w)^2}{(4w + 2x)^2 - 9y^2}$

**23. Complex fractions.** *A complex fraction is a fraction which contains a fraction in the numerator, denominator, or in both.* Thus, a complex fraction can be expressed as the quotient of two fractions and the rule for division of fractions applied.

EXAMPLE I.    Simplify: $\dfrac{\dfrac{a}{b}}{\dfrac{c}{d}}.$

Solution.    $\dfrac{\dfrac{a}{b}}{\dfrac{c}{d}} = \dfrac{a}{b} \div \dfrac{c}{d} = \dfrac{a}{b} \cdot \dfrac{d}{c} = \dfrac{ad}{bc}$    (Ans.)

EXAMPLE II. Simplify: $\dfrac{\dfrac{x+y}{x-y}+\dfrac{x-y}{x+y}}{\dfrac{1}{x-y}-\dfrac{1}{x+y}}$.

Solution. $\dfrac{\dfrac{x+y}{x-y}+\dfrac{x-y}{x+y}}{\dfrac{1}{x-y}-\dfrac{1}{x+y}}=\dfrac{\dfrac{x^2+2xy+y^2+x^2-2xy+y^2}{x^2-y^2}}{\dfrac{x+y-x+y}{x^2-y^2}}$

$=\dfrac{2(x^2+y^2)}{(x^2-y^2)}\div\dfrac{2y}{x^2-y^2}$

$=\dfrac{2(x^2+y^2)(x^2-y^2)}{(x^2-y^2)2y}=\dfrac{x^2+y^2}{y}$  (Ans.)

## EXERCISES

*Simplify:*

**1.** $\dfrac{\frac{3}{5}}{\frac{2}{6}}$

**2.** $\dfrac{\frac{2}{3}}{\frac{3}{2}}$

**3.** $\dfrac{\frac{7}{5}}{\frac{2}{3}}$

**4.** $\dfrac{\frac{x}{3y}}{\frac{2x}{5y}}$

**5.** $\dfrac{\frac{5a}{3b}}{\frac{8b^2}{3a^2}}$

**6.** $\dfrac{\frac{16a}{b}}{\frac{32a^2}{15b^2}}$

**7.** $\dfrac{\frac{a+b}{2}}{\frac{2}{a^2-b^2}}$

**8.** $\dfrac{\frac{a+x}{5y}}{\frac{a^2+2ax+x^2}{15xy}}$

**9.** $\dfrac{\frac{1}{3}+\frac{1}{6}}{\frac{2}{3}-\frac{1}{6}}$

**10.** $\dfrac{1+\frac{1}{5}}{1-\frac{1}{5}}$

**11.** $\dfrac{1-\frac{1}{2}+\frac{2}{8}}{1+\frac{1}{4}+\frac{1}{16}}$

**12.** $\dfrac{\frac{3}{7}+\frac{3}{14}-\frac{1}{21}+\frac{4}{2}}{\frac{1}{6}-\frac{4}{21}+\frac{2}{3}-6}$

**13.** $\dfrac{\frac{3x}{3x+y}+\frac{y}{3x-y}}{\frac{4x-y}{(3x-y)^2}}$

**14.** $\dfrac{\frac{x}{y^2}+\frac{y}{x^2}}{\frac{1}{x^2}-\frac{1}{xy}+\frac{1}{y^2}}$

**15.** $\dfrac{\frac{x}{1+x}+\frac{1-x}{x}}{\frac{x}{1+x}-\frac{1-x}{x}}$

**16.** $\dfrac{x-2+\frac{1}{x+2}}{x+2+\frac{1}{x-2}}$

**17.** $\dfrac{\frac{1+a}{a}+a}{a-\frac{1}{a^2}}$

**18.** $\dfrac{\frac{2x+y}{x+y}-1}{1-\frac{y}{x+y}}$

**19.** $\dfrac{\dfrac{y}{y-a}+1}{1-\dfrac{y}{y-a}}$

**20.** $\dfrac{x-1+\dfrac{a}{x-a}}{x-2+\dfrac{a}{x+a}}$

**21.** $\dfrac{\dfrac{x+y}{x-y}-\dfrac{x^2+y^2}{x^2-y^2}}{\dfrac{x^2+y^2}{x^2-y^2}-\dfrac{x^3+y^3}{x^3-y^3}}$

**22.** $\dfrac{\dfrac{1-a}{a}+\dfrac{4}{1-a}}{\dfrac{1+a^2}{a^2}-\dfrac{4}{1+a^2}}$

**23.** $\dfrac{\dfrac{(x+a)^2}{x^2-a^2}-\dfrac{x-a}{x+a}}{\dfrac{x}{x+a}+\dfrac{a}{x-a}}$

**24.** $\dfrac{\dfrac{x+a}{x^2+a^2}-\dfrac{x^2+a^2}{x^3+a^3}}{\dfrac{x^2+a^2}{x^3+a^3}-\dfrac{x^3+a^3}{x^4+a^4}}$

**25.** $\dfrac{\dfrac{1+a}{1+a^2}-\dfrac{1+a^2}{1+a^3}}{\dfrac{1+a^2}{1+a^3}-\dfrac{1+a^3}{1+a^4}}$

**26.** $\dfrac{\dfrac{2a}{x+2a}-\dfrac{x}{2a-x}+\dfrac{8a^2}{x^2-4a^2}}{\dfrac{4a-x}{(2a-x)^2}}$

**27.** $\dfrac{\dfrac{a+1}{a-1}-\dfrac{a^2+1}{a^2-1}}{\dfrac{a-1}{a+1}-\dfrac{a^2-1}{a^2+1}}$

**28.** $\dfrac{\dfrac{x+y}{x-y}-\dfrac{x-y}{x+y}}{1-\dfrac{x^2+y^2}{(x+y)^2}}$

**29.** $\dfrac{\dfrac{x}{x-3}-\dfrac{x}{x+3}}{\dfrac{x+2}{x-3}-\dfrac{x-2}{x+3}}$

**30.** $\dfrac{\dfrac{a^2-3a+2}{a^2-6a+9}}{\dfrac{a^2-a-2}{a^2-2a-3}}\cdot\dfrac{a-3}{a-1}$

**31.** $\dfrac{2x-3+\dfrac{1}{x}}{2-\dfrac{1}{x}}$

**32.** $\dfrac{\dfrac{x}{y}-\dfrac{y}{x}}{\dfrac{(x+y)^2}{xy}-4}$

**33.** $\dfrac{\dfrac{x^2}{y^2}+\dfrac{y}{x}}{\dfrac{x}{y^2}-\dfrac{1}{y}+\dfrac{1}{x}}$

**34.** $\dfrac{\dfrac{x^2+y^2}{y}-x}{\dfrac{1}{y}-\dfrac{1}{x}}\cdot\dfrac{x^2-y^2}{x^3+y^3}$

**35.** $\dfrac{x^2-\dfrac{1}{x}}{x+\dfrac{1}{x}+1}$

**36.** $\dfrac{y-x+\dfrac{x^2}{y}}{\dfrac{x}{y^2}+\dfrac{y}{x^2}}$

**37.** $\dfrac{\dfrac{x}{1+x}+\dfrac{1-x}{x}}{\dfrac{x}{1+x}-\dfrac{1-x}{x}}$

**38.** $\dfrac{x-y-\dfrac{2y(x-y)}{x+y}}{\left(\dfrac{x^2+y^2}{xy+y^2}-1\right)\left(1-\dfrac{y}{x}\right)}$

**39.** $\dfrac{\dfrac{1+x}{1-x} - \dfrac{1-x}{1+x}}{\dfrac{1+x}{1-x} + \dfrac{1-x}{1+x}}$

**40.** $\dfrac{\dfrac{6x - 11 - \dfrac{7}{x}}{2 + \dfrac{11}{x} + \dfrac{5}{x^2}}}{\dfrac{5-x}{3x} \Big/ (x^2 - 25)}$

**41.** $\dfrac{x}{x + 1 + \dfrac{x}{x + 1 - \dfrac{1}{x}}}$

**42.** $\dfrac{1 - \dfrac{1}{a}}{a - \dfrac{1}{2a - \dfrac{a+1}{a}}}$

**24. Radicals.** Algebraic expressions containing radicals may often be simplified by applying the rules stated in § 10. For purposes of reference we repeat these rules:

I. $(\sqrt[n]{a})^n = \sqrt[n]{a^n} = a$

II. $\sqrt[n]{a}\,\sqrt[n]{b} = \sqrt[n]{ab}$

III. $\dfrac{\sqrt[n]{a}}{\sqrt[n]{b}} = \sqrt[n]{\dfrac{a}{b}}$

IV. $\sqrt[m]{\sqrt[n]{a}} = \sqrt[mn]{a}$

The application of these rules in changing the radical form is accomplished in various ways.

A. Removing perfect powers from the radicand

Example I. Remove the perfect powers from the radicand in $\sqrt{700}$.

**Solution.** Factor 700 into as many "square powers" as possible.

$$\sqrt{700} = \sqrt{2^2 \cdot 5^2 \cdot 7} = \sqrt{2^2}\,\sqrt{5^2}\,\sqrt{7} = 2 \cdot 5\sqrt{7} = 10\sqrt{7} \quad \text{(Ans.)}$$

Example II. Remove the perfect powers from the radicand in

$$\sqrt[3]{\dfrac{81x^4y^6}{z^7}}.$$

**Solution.** $\sqrt[3]{\dfrac{81x^4y^6}{z^7}} = \sqrt[3]{\dfrac{3^3 3 x^3 x (y^2)^3}{(z^2)^3 z}} = \dfrac{3xy^2}{z^2}\sqrt[3]{\dfrac{3x}{z}} \quad \text{(Ans.)}$

B. Putting factors under the radical

Example III. Write $2\sqrt{3}$ as a radical with coefficient 1.

**Solution.** $2\sqrt{3} = \sqrt{2^2}\,\sqrt{3} = \sqrt{2^2 \cdot 3} = \sqrt{12} \quad \text{(Ans.)}$

EXAMPLE IV.  Write $(x + 2y)^2 \sqrt[3]{(x^2 + 2xy)}$ as a radical with coefficient 1.

**Solution.**  $(x + 2y)^2 \sqrt[3]{x^2 + 2xy} = \sqrt[3]{(x + 2y)^6} \sqrt[3]{x(x + 2y)}$
$$= \sqrt[3]{x(x + 2y)^7} \quad \text{(Ans.)}$$

### C. REDUCING THE ORDER OF A RADICAL

EXAMPLE V.  Reduce $\sqrt[4]{4}$ to a radical of lower order.

**Solution.**  $\sqrt[4]{4} = (4)^{\frac{1}{4}} = (2^2)^{\frac{1}{4}} = 2^{\frac{1}{2}} = \sqrt{2}$.  (Ans.)

EXAMPLE VI.  Reduce $\sqrt[6]{4x^2y^4}$ to a radical of lower order.

**Solution.**  $\sqrt[6]{4x^2y^4} = (2^2x^2y^4)^{\frac{1}{6}} = 2^{\frac{1}{3}}x^{\frac{1}{3}}(y^2)^{\frac{1}{3}} = \sqrt[3]{2xy^2}$  (Ans.)

### D. REPLACING A FRACTIONAL RADICAND BY AN INTEGER

EXAMPLE VII.  Write $\sqrt{\frac{2}{5}}$ with an integral radicand.

**Solution.**  $\sqrt{\frac{2}{5}} = \sqrt{\frac{2 \cdot 5}{5 \cdot 5}} = \frac{\sqrt{10}}{5}$  (Ans.)

EXAMPLE VIII.  Write $\sqrt[3]{\frac{5}{24}}$ with an integral radicand.

**Solution.**  $\sqrt[3]{\frac{5}{24}} = \sqrt[3]{\frac{5}{2^3 \cdot 3}} = \sqrt[3]{\frac{5 \cdot 3^2}{2^3 \cdot 3^3}} = \frac{\sqrt[3]{45}}{6}$  (Ans.)

### E. CHANGING TO RADICALS OF THE SAME ORDER

EXAMPLE IX.  Change $\sqrt{2}$, $\sqrt[3]{3}$, $\sqrt[4]{5}$ to radicals of the same order.

**Solution.**  $\sqrt{2} = 2^{\frac{1}{2}}$, $\sqrt[3]{3} = 3^{\frac{1}{3}}$, $\sqrt[4]{5} = 5^{\frac{1}{4}}$

The L.C.M. of the denominators in the exponents is 12, and

$$2^{\frac{1}{2}} = 2^{\frac{6}{12}} = (2^6)^{\frac{1}{12}}, \ 3^{\frac{1}{3}} = 3^{\frac{4}{12}} = (3^4)^{\frac{1}{12}}, \ 5^{\frac{1}{4}} = 5^{\frac{3}{12}} = (5^3)^{\frac{1}{12}}$$

Therefore,

$$\sqrt{2} = \sqrt[12]{2^6}, \ \sqrt[3]{3} = \sqrt[12]{3^4}, \ \sqrt[4]{5} = \sqrt[12]{5^3} \quad \text{(Ans.)}$$

The simplification of algebraic expressions containing radicals and fractional exponents is generally made easier by changing the radicals to exponential form.

EXAMPLE X.  Simplify: $\dfrac{\sqrt{a^2 - x^2}(2x) - x^2[\frac{1}{2}(a^2 - x^2)^{-\frac{1}{2}}(-2x)]}{a^2 - x^2}$

**Solution.**  $\dfrac{\sqrt{a^2 - x^2}\,2x - x^2\frac{1}{2}(a^2 - x^2)^{-\frac{1}{2}}(-2x)}{a^2 - x^2}$

$$= \frac{(a^2 - x^2)^{\frac{1}{2}}2x + x^3(a^2 - x^2)^{-\frac{1}{2}}}{a^2 - x^2}$$

Multiply numerator and denominator by $(a^2 - x^2)^{\frac{1}{2}}$

$$\frac{2x(a^2 - x^2) + x^3}{(a^2 - x^2)^{\frac{3}{2}}} = \frac{2a^2x - x^3}{(a^2 - x^2)^{\frac{3}{2}}} \quad \text{(Ans.)}$$

## EXERCISES

*Change to radical form* (see Chapter II):

**1.** $2^{\frac{1}{3}}$    $\sqrt[3]{2}$

**2.** $3^{\frac{2}{3}}y^{\frac{1}{2}}$    $\sqrt[3]{9}\,\sqrt{y}$

**3.** $2a^{\frac{1}{2}} + b^{\frac{1}{2}}$    $2\sqrt{a} + \sqrt{b}$

**4.** $(a^2 + b^2)^{\frac{1}{2}}$    $\sqrt{a^2 + b^2}$

**5.** $(x^2)^{\frac{2}{3}}y^{\frac{1}{3}}$    $\sqrt[3]{x^4y} = x\sqrt[3]{x\cdot y}$

**6.** $3x^{\frac{3}{2}}x^{\frac{1}{3}}$    $3\sqrt{x^3}\,\sqrt{x}$

**7.** $(\frac{1}{3})^{\frac{1}{5}}$

**8.** $(x^2 + 3y^2)^{\frac{2}{3}}$

**9.** $(ax^2)^{\frac{2}{3}} + (by)^{\frac{2}{3}}$

*Change to exponential form* (see Chapter II):

**10.** $\sqrt{2}$

**11.** $\sqrt{a^2 + b^2}$

**12.** $\sqrt[3]{(a + b)^3}$

**13.** $\sqrt[4]{x^2y^5}$

**14.** $\sqrt{x\sqrt[3]{5}}$

**15.** $\sqrt{4a^3}$

**16.** $\sqrt[3]{x^2}\sqrt[4]{y}$

**17.** $\sqrt[3]{\sqrt{3}\sqrt[4]{5x}}$   $\sqrt[?]{3}\,\sqrt[12]{5x}$   $3^{\frac{?}{?}}(5x)^{\frac{1}{2}}$

**18.** $\sqrt{x^{\frac{2}{3}}}$

*Remove the perfect powers from the radicand:*

**19.** $\sqrt{72}$

**20.** $\sqrt[3]{24}$

**21.** $\sqrt[4]{x^5y^4}$

**22.** $\sqrt{x^3 + 2x^2y + xy^2}$

**23.** $\sqrt{.36x^7}$   $.06\,x^3\sqrt{x}$

**24.** $\sqrt[3]{-128x^6}$

**25.** $\sqrt{a^2b - ca^2}$

**26.** $\sqrt[3]{16a^3 + 8a^2x^2}$

**27.** $\sqrt[3]{\dfrac{6x^5}{64z^9}}$

*Change to radicals with coefficients 1:*

**28.** $2\sqrt[3]{4}$

**29.** $(x + y)\sqrt[3]{x + y}$

**30.** $2\sqrt[3]{\frac{4}{9}}$

**31.** $\dfrac{a}{x}\sqrt{\dfrac{x}{a}}$

**32.** $\frac{1}{2}\sqrt[4]{16}$

**33.** $2\sqrt[3]{5}$

**34.** $\frac{1}{3}\sqrt{90}$

**35.** $2\sqrt{x} + 5\sqrt[3]{y}$

**36.** $3y\sqrt{\dfrac{x}{y}}$

*Reduce the order of the radicals:*

**37.** $\sqrt[4]{25x^2}$

**38.** $\sqrt[6]{a^2b^4}$

**39.** $\sqrt[8]{16y^2}$

**40.** $\sqrt[4]{.0144a^2}$

**41.** $\sqrt[6]{27a^3b^6}$

**42.** $\sqrt[4]{49a^2b^4}$

**43.** $\sqrt[12]{64x^6y^6}$

**44.** $\sqrt[12]{196x^8y^8} = \sqrt[6]{\sqrt{196\,x^8y^8}}$ $= \sqrt[6]{14\,x^4y^4}$

**45.** $\sqrt[4]{225a^4x^2y^2}$

*Write the following with radicands which do not contain fractions:*

**46.** $\sqrt[3]{\dfrac{9}{16}}$

**47.** $\sqrt[3]{-\dfrac{2}{9}}$   $\dfrac{\sqrt[3]{2}\cdot\sqrt[3]{3}}{\sqrt[3]{9}\cdot\sqrt[3]{3}} = \dfrac{\sqrt[3]{6}}{3}$

**48.** $\sqrt{\dfrac{9a}{8}}$

**49.** $\sqrt{\dfrac{1}{2}}$

**50.** $\sqrt{\dfrac{1}{3}}$

**51.** $\sqrt[3]{-\dfrac{81}{8a^5}}$

**52.** $\sqrt{\dfrac{5}{8x^2}}$

**53.** $\sqrt[3]{\dfrac{1}{4y^2}}$

**54.** $\sqrt{\dfrac{5y^3}{2x^5}}$

**55.** $\sqrt{\dfrac{5}{x+y}} = \dfrac{\sqrt{5}\cdot\sqrt{x+y}}{\sqrt{x+y}\cdot\sqrt{x+y}}$

**56.** $\sqrt[3]{-\dfrac{432}{250}}$

**57.** $\sqrt{\dfrac{x}{3y^2}}$

**58.** $\sqrt{\dfrac{8y^4}{27}}$

**59.** $\sqrt{\dfrac{x^2y^3}{x-y}}$

**60.** $\sqrt[5]{-\dfrac{1}{81z}}$

**61.** $\sqrt{\dfrac{3a+b}{x^2-y^2}}$

**62.** $\sqrt{\dfrac{4+8a}{(a+b)^3}}$

**63.** $\sqrt[3]{\dfrac{5y+7}{(x+y)(x-3y)}}$

**64.** $\sqrt[6]{\dfrac{a^2y^8}{16b^5}} \;\dfrac{\sqrt[4]{a^2y^2}\cdot\sqrt{4b}}{\sqrt[4]{16b^5}\cdot\sqrt{4b}} = \dfrac{\sqrt[4]{a^2b y^2}}{2b}$

**65.** $\sqrt{x^2+\dfrac{3}{x}}$

**66.** $\sqrt[3]{x-\dfrac{3}{y}+\dfrac{2}{27z^2}}$

*Change to radicals of the same order:*

**67.** $\sqrt{2},\ \sqrt[3]{3},\ \sqrt[4]{6}$

**68.** $\sqrt[4]{8},\ \sqrt{5},\ \sqrt[6]{6}$

**69.** $\sqrt[6]{7},\ \sqrt{4},\ \sqrt[3]{5}$

**70.** $\sqrt{x-1},\ \sqrt[3]{x+1},\ \sqrt[5]{x^3y^4}$

**71.** $\sqrt[5]{729},\ \sqrt[10]{9}$

**72.** $x^{\frac{1}{3}},\ x^{\frac{1}{4}},\ x^{\frac{1}{5}}$

**73.** $(xy^2)^{\frac{1}{2}},\ x^{\frac{2}{3}},\ y^{\frac{2}{4}}$

**74.** $\sqrt[4]{64},\ (256)^{\frac{1}{6}}$

**75.** $\sqrt{a^3b^3},\ \sqrt[3]{ab},\ \sqrt[6]{a^2b^2}$

*Simplify:*

**76.** $\dfrac{5}{\sqrt{5x-x^2}} - \sqrt{\dfrac{x}{5-x}}$

**77.** $\dfrac{\dfrac{a^2}{(x^2+a^2)^{\frac{3}{2}}}}{\sqrt{1-\dfrac{x^2}{x^2+a^2}}}$

**78.** $\dfrac{\sqrt{a^2-x^2}+\dfrac{x^2}{\sqrt{a^2-x^2}}}{(a^2-x^2)\left(1+\dfrac{x^2}{a^2-x^2}\right)}$

**79.** $\dfrac{\sqrt{x^2+a^2}-\dfrac{x^2}{\sqrt{x^2+a^2}}}{x\sqrt{\dfrac{x^2+a^2}{x^2}-1}}$

**80.** $\dfrac{1}{\sqrt{\dfrac{2y}{a}-\dfrac{y^2}{a^2}}} - \dfrac{(a-y)}{\sqrt{2ay-y^2}}$

**81.** $\dfrac{x^{\frac{1}{2}}+4x^{-\frac{1}{2}}y}{4y^{\frac{1}{2}}xy^{-\frac{1}{2}}}$

**82.** $\dfrac{1+x(x^2+1)^{-\frac{1}{2}}}{1+\sqrt{x^2+1}}$

**83.** $\dfrac{4x^{-\frac{1}{2}}+(4y)^{-\frac{1}{2}}}{16x^{-\frac{1}{2}}+2y^{-\frac{1}{2}}}$

**84.** $\dfrac{\left(\dfrac{x}{27}\div\dfrac{x^{-2}}{8}\right)^{-\frac{2}{3}}-a^2}{\dfrac{3x^{-1}+2a}{2}}$

**85.** $\dfrac{x(x^2+a^2)^{-\frac{1}{2}}}{\sqrt{x^2+a^2}}+\dfrac{\dfrac{1}{a}}{1+\dfrac{x^2}{a^2}}$

**86.** $\dfrac{a+3b^{-1}}{1-9a^{-2}b^{-2}}\div\dfrac{a^2b^3}{ab-3}$

**87.** $\dfrac{\sqrt{2x - x^2} - (x - 1)(2x - x^2)^{-\frac{1}{2}}(1 - x)}{2x - x^2}$

**88.** $- x^2(9 - x^2)^{-\frac{1}{2}} + \sqrt{9 - x^2} + \dfrac{3}{\sqrt{1 - \left(\dfrac{x}{3}\right)^2}}$

**89.** $\dfrac{(\sqrt{x^2 + 1} - 1)}{x^2} \cdot \dfrac{[(x^2 + 1)^{\frac{1}{2}} + 1]}{x^{-1}}$

**90.** $\dfrac{(a^3 - y^3)^{\frac{1}{2}}(3y^2) - y^3(a^3 - y^3)^{-\frac{1}{2}}(- 3y^2)}{(a^3 - y^3)^{\frac{2}{3}}}$

**91.** $\dfrac{x^2(4y^2 - x^2)^{-\frac{2}{3}}(- 2x) - (4y^2 - x^2)^{\frac{1}{3}}(2x)}{(4y^2 - x^2)^{\frac{3}{2}}}$

**92.** $x^{-\frac{1}{2}}\left[\frac{1}{3}(a^3 - x^3)^{-\frac{2}{3}}(- 3x^2)\right] + (a^3 - x^3)^{\frac{1}{3}}(- \frac{1}{2}x^{-\frac{3}{2}})$

**93.** $\dfrac{(a^5 + x^5)^{\frac{2}{5}}(\frac{1}{4}x^{-\frac{3}{4}}) - x^{\frac{1}{4}}\left[\frac{2}{5}(a^5 + x^5)^{-\frac{3}{5}}(5x^4)\right]}{(a^5 + x^5)^{\frac{4}{5}}}$

**94.** $\dfrac{1}{4}\left(\dfrac{1 - 2a^3}{1 + 2a^3}\right)^{-\frac{3}{4}}\left[\dfrac{(1 + 2a^3)(- 6a^2) - (1 - 2a^3)(6a^2)}{(1 + 2a^3)^2}\right]$

**95.** $\left[\dfrac{x^2(x^2 - 4a^2)^{-\frac{1}{2}} - \sqrt{x^2 - 4a^2}}{x^2\sqrt{\dfrac{x^2 + 4a^2}{x^2} - 1}}\right]\left[\dfrac{4ax}{x^2 + 4a^2}\right]$

**96.** $\dfrac{(x^2 + y^2)^{\frac{1}{2}} - (x^2 + y^2)^{-\frac{1}{2}}y^2}{x(x^2 + y^2)^{\frac{1}{2}}} \div \dfrac{y}{x^2 + y^2}$

**97.** $\dfrac{\sqrt{x^2 + 1} - x^2(x^2 + 1)^{-\frac{1}{2}}}{x\sqrt{\dfrac{x^2 + 1}{x^2} - 1}} \cdot \sqrt{x^3 + x}$

**98.** $\dfrac{\sqrt{a^2 + x^2} - x^2(a^2 + x^2)^{-\frac{1}{2}}}{\sqrt{1 - \left(\dfrac{x}{\sqrt{a^2 + x^2}}\right)^2}}$

**99.** $\dfrac{\left(\dfrac{y^{-1}}{81} \div \dfrac{y^2}{3}\right)^{-\frac{2}{3}} - \dfrac{1}{(2x)^{-2}}}{\dfrac{3x^{-1} - 2y^{-1}}{2}}$

**100.** $\dfrac{\sqrt{4 + x^2} - x^2(4 + x^2)^{-\frac{1}{2}}}{(4 + x^2)^{\frac{1}{2}}} \div \left(\dfrac{4}{4 + x^2}\right)^{-\frac{1}{2}}$

**25. Product of radicals.** The product of two or more radicals of the same order is found by applying Rule III of § 24.

EXAMPLE I. Find the product: $\sqrt{5}\,\sqrt{2}$.

**Solution.** $\sqrt{5}\,\sqrt{2} = \sqrt{5 \cdot 2} = \sqrt{10}$  (Ans.)

EXAMPLE II.   Find the product: $\sqrt[3]{x+y}\ \sqrt[3]{x-y}\ \sqrt[3]{xy}$.

**Solution.**   $\sqrt[3]{x+y}\ \sqrt[3]{x-y}\ \sqrt[3]{xy} = \sqrt[3]{(x+y)(x-y)(xy)}$
$$= \sqrt[3]{x^3y - xy^3} \quad \text{(Ans.)}$$

To find the product of radicals of different orders they must first be changed to radicals of the same order and then the method above may be applied.

EXAMPLE III.   Find the product: $\sqrt{2}\ \sqrt[3]{3}$.

**Solution.**   $\sqrt{2} = 2^{\frac{1}{2}} = 2^{\frac{3}{6}} = \sqrt[6]{2^3} = \sqrt[6]{8}$.
$$\sqrt[3]{3} = 3^{\frac{1}{3}} = 3^{\frac{2}{6}} = \sqrt[6]{3^2} = \sqrt[6]{9}.$$

Therefore,   $\sqrt{2}\ \sqrt[3]{3} = \sqrt[6]{8}\ \sqrt[6]{9} = \sqrt[6]{72}$   (Ans.)

EXAMPLE IV.   Find the product: $\sqrt[6]{\frac{1}{2}}\ \sqrt[4]{4}$.

**Solution.**   $\sqrt[4]{4} = 4^{\frac{1}{4}} = (2^2)^{\frac{1}{4}} = 2^{\frac{1}{2}} = 2^{\frac{3}{6}} = \sqrt[6]{8}$.

Therefore,   $\sqrt[6]{\frac{1}{2}}\ \sqrt[4]{4} = \sqrt[6]{\frac{1}{2}}\ \sqrt[6]{8} = \sqrt[6]{\frac{1}{2}\cdot 8} = \sqrt[6]{4} = \sqrt[3]{2}$   (Ans.)

The following example illustrates the method of finding the product of two polynomials containing radicals.

EXAMPLE V.   Find the product: $(\sqrt{2}+\sqrt{5})(3\sqrt{2}-\sqrt{5})$.

**Solution.**
$$\sqrt{2}+\sqrt{5}$$
$$\underline{3\sqrt{2}-\sqrt{5}}$$
$$3\cdot 2 + 3\sqrt{10}$$
$$\underline{\quad -\ \sqrt{10}-5}$$
$$6 + 2\sqrt{10} - 5 = 1 + 2\sqrt{10} \quad \text{(Ans.)}$$

## EXERCISES

*Perform the indicated operations:*

**1.** $\sqrt{2}\ \sqrt{x+y}$

**2.** $\sqrt[3]{3}\ \sqrt{2}$

**3.** $15^{\frac{1}{2}}\cdot 70^{\frac{1}{2}}$

**4.** $\sqrt{a}\ \sqrt[3]{2b}$

**5.** $\sqrt[4]{\frac{4}{27}}\ \sqrt[6]{\frac{27}{8}}$

**6.** $2^{\frac{1}{3}}\ \sqrt[3]{4}$

**7.** $\frac{2}{5}\sqrt{3}\cdot\frac{4}{9}\sqrt{5}$

**8.** $\sqrt{\frac{2}{3}}\ \sqrt[3]{\frac{3}{4}}$

**9.** $\sqrt[3]{-6}\ \sqrt{18}$

**10.** $\sqrt{\frac{1}{2}}\ \sqrt[3]{\frac{3}{4}}\ \sqrt[6]{\frac{8}{9}}$

**11.** $\sqrt{16a^{-4}b^{-6}}\ \sqrt[3]{8a^3b^{-6}}$

**12.** $\sqrt{8x}\ \sqrt[3]{5x^2y}\ \sqrt[6]{4x^3y^2}$

**13.** $\sqrt[3]{27x^3y^6}\ \sqrt[5]{243y^5 2^5}\ \sqrt{16x^4 2^2}$

**14.** $\sqrt[4]{\frac{2a^3}{3}}\ \sqrt[3]{\frac{3}{a^2}}$

**15.** $\sqrt[3]{9}\ \sqrt[4]{27}\ (3)^{\frac{1}{3}}\ (3)^{\frac{1}{4}}$

**16.** $\sqrt{2}\,(1+\sqrt{3})$

**17.** $(1+\sqrt{2})(1-\sqrt{2})$

**18.** $(\sqrt{3} + 2\sqrt{2})(\sqrt{2} + 2\sqrt{3})$

**19.** $(\sqrt{5} + 3)(5^{\frac{1}{2}} + 2)$

**20.** $(3 - 2\sqrt{2})^2$

**21.** $(\sqrt{3} + 2x)^2$

**22.** $(2\sqrt{3} - \sqrt{ay})(2\sqrt{3} + \sqrt{ay})$

**23.** $\sqrt[3]{a}\,(3\sqrt[3]{a} - 5)$

**24.** $\sqrt{12 + \sqrt{23}}\ \sqrt{12 - \sqrt{23}}$

**25.** $(2\sqrt{a} - 3\sqrt{a-1})(\sqrt{a} + 2\sqrt{a-1})$

**26.** $(\sqrt{5y} - 2)(\sqrt{5y} + 2)$

**27.** $\left(\dfrac{-2 + 3\sqrt{2}}{4}\right)^2$

**28.** $\sqrt{7 - 3\sqrt{5}}\ \sqrt{7 + 3\sqrt{5}}$

**29.** $(x^{-\frac{1}{2}} - \sqrt{y})(y^{-\frac{1}{2}} - \sqrt{x})$

**30.** $\left(\sqrt{x} - \sqrt{y}\right)\left(\sqrt{x} + \sqrt{y}\right)$

**31.** $(1 - \sqrt{3} + \sqrt{5})(3^{\frac{1}{2}} - \sqrt{5})$

**32.** $\left(\sqrt{\dfrac{a}{b}} - \sqrt{\dfrac{b}{a}}\right)\sqrt{ab}$

**33.** $(2\sqrt{x} + 5\sqrt{x-y})(\sqrt{x} - \sqrt{x-y})$

**34.** $(4\sqrt{a + 1} - 5\sqrt{a - 1})(3\sqrt{a + 1} - 2\sqrt{a - 1})$

**35.** $\left(5\sqrt[4]{a^7} - \dfrac{6ab}{\sqrt[4]{a}}\right)\left(a^{\frac{1}{3}} - \dfrac{7b}{\sqrt[3]{a^2}}\right)$

**36.** $(-2 + 3\sqrt{2})^2\,(11 + 6\sqrt{2})$

**37.** $\sqrt{6}\,(2\sqrt{3} - 3\sqrt{2})(3\sqrt{2} + \sqrt{3})$

**38.** $\left(\dfrac{3 - \sqrt{13}}{2}\right)^2 - 3\left(\dfrac{3 - \sqrt{13}}{2}\right) - 1$

**39.** $\left(x + \dfrac{y}{2} + \sqrt{\dfrac{y^2}{4} - b^2}\right)\left(x + \dfrac{y}{2} - \sqrt{\dfrac{y^2}{4} - b^2}\right)$

**40.** $2 - 3\left(\dfrac{-1 - \sqrt{3}}{2}\right) - 2\left(\dfrac{-1 - \sqrt{3}}{2}\right)^2$

**41.** $3 + 2\left(\dfrac{2 + \sqrt{5}}{3}\right) + \left(\dfrac{2 + \sqrt{5}}{3}\right)^2$

**42.** Find the value of $x^2 - 3x + 1$ if $x = \dfrac{3 + \sqrt{5}}{2}$.

**43.** Find the value of $3x^2 - 7x - 12$ if $x = \dfrac{7 - \sqrt{193}}{6}$.

**44.** Find the value of $x^2 + x - 1$ if $x = \dfrac{-1 + \sqrt{5}}{2}$.

**26. Sum and difference of radicals.** *Radicals having the same order and the same radicand are called* **like radicals**. *Like radicals can be added and subtracted algebraically.*

EXAMPLE I. Find the algebraic sum of $\sqrt{2} + 3\sqrt{3} - \sqrt{12} + \sqrt{8}$.

**Solution.** $\sqrt{12} = \sqrt{2^2 3} = 2\sqrt{3}$, $\sqrt{8} = \sqrt{2^2 2} = 2\sqrt{2}$

Thus, $\sqrt{2} + 3\sqrt{3} - \sqrt{12} + \sqrt{8} = \sqrt{2} + 3\sqrt{3} - 2\sqrt{3} + 2\sqrt{2}$
$= 3\sqrt{2} + \sqrt{3}$   (Ans.)

The sum or difference of unlike radicals can only be indicated; e.g., $\sqrt{2} + \sqrt{3}$ is in its simplest form. However, it is sometimes possible to change unlike radicals into like radicals with coefficients as in the above example.

## EXERCISES

*Find the algebraic sum:*

**1.** $\sqrt{2} + \sqrt{8} + \sqrt{32}$

**2.** $\sqrt{8} - 6\sqrt{\frac{1}{2}} - 4\sqrt{\frac{3}{8}}$

**3.** $12\sqrt{\frac{7}{3}} - \sqrt{189} + \sqrt{84}$

**4.** $\sqrt[3]{24} + 2\sqrt[3]{81} - 5\sqrt[3]{3}$

**5.** $5\sqrt{2} + 2\sqrt{2} - \sqrt{98}$

**6.** $\sqrt{18} + \sqrt[3]{8} - \sqrt[6]{8}$

**7.** $\sqrt{147} + \sqrt{\frac{1}{3}}$

**8.** $10\sqrt{\frac{2}{5}} - \sqrt{10} + 3\sqrt{8}$

**9.** $x\sqrt{2} + y\sqrt{2} + 3\sqrt{2}$

**10.** $\sqrt[3]{ab} - 3\sqrt[3]{27x^3y^3ab}$

**11.** $\sqrt[4]{81a^5} + \sqrt[8]{a^{10}b^8}$

**12.** $3x\sqrt{16x} - \sqrt{144x^3}$

**13.** $2\sqrt[3]{24} + 3\sqrt[3]{128} - \sqrt[3]{1024}$

**14.** $\sqrt{28} - \sqrt{63} + \sqrt{700}$

**15.** $\sqrt{5\frac{11}{80}} + \sqrt{45} - \sqrt{125} + \sqrt{20}$

**16.** $\frac{1}{2}\sqrt{\frac{1}{2}} + \frac{4}{\sqrt{2}} - 7\sqrt{98} + \sqrt{8^3} + \frac{\sqrt{2}}{3^{-2}} - \frac{1}{2^0}$

**17.** $\frac{1}{3}\sqrt{\frac{9x}{2}} + \sqrt[3]{\frac{27x}{4}} - 6\sqrt{\frac{x}{18}} + 2\sqrt[3]{-\frac{x}{32}}$

**18.** $\sqrt{75x^3y} + \sqrt{\frac{16x}{3y}} - 8\sqrt{\frac{x^3y^3}{3}} + \sqrt[3]{\frac{24xy}{-27z^3}}$

**19.** $2\sqrt[3]{x^6y} - 3x^3\sqrt[3]{\frac{y}{64}} + 3\sqrt[3]{\frac{125}{y^2}}$

**20.** $2b\sqrt{\frac{a}{b}} + ab\sqrt{\frac{a^2 + b^2 + 2ab}{ab}} - 3a\sqrt{\frac{b}{a}}$

**21.** $2a^2\sqrt{9a^2 + 81} + 27\sqrt{4a^2 + 36}$

**22.** $\sqrt{9x + 27} + 3\sqrt{4x + 12}$

**23.** $\frac{\sqrt{x^2y}}{3} + x\sqrt{12y} - \sqrt{3y^3}$

**24.** $a^2\sqrt{150a} + \sqrt{96a^3} - \sqrt{54a^5} - a\sqrt{24a^3}$

**25.** $\sqrt{33\frac{1}{3}x^3} - \sqrt{\frac{216}{x^{-3}}} + \sqrt[3]{\frac{16x^3}{x^5}} + \sqrt[3]{\frac{343x^4z^{-3}}{8}}$

**26.** $\sqrt{\frac{a-1}{a+1}} - \sqrt{\frac{a+1}{a-1}} - \frac{1}{a^2-1}\sqrt{4a^2 - 4}$

**27.** $\sqrt{\frac{2}{3}} + 4\sqrt{\frac{3}{2}} - 5x\sqrt{24} + 3y\sqrt[4]{36}$

**28.** $2c\sqrt{m^2x - m^2z} + 4m\sqrt{c^2x - c^2z} + 3\sqrt{c^2m^2x - c^2m^2z}$

**29.** $\sqrt{2ab^2} - b\sqrt{8a} + 2a\sqrt{72b^2}$

**30.** $\sqrt[3]{(a-c)^4} + 6c\sqrt[6]{a^2 - 2ac + c^2} + (a+c)\sqrt[3]{a-c}$

**31.** $\left(\dfrac{3^3a^2}{2^2b^2}\right)^{\frac{1}{2}} + \left(\dfrac{2^2a^3}{3b^2}\right)^{\frac{1}{2}} - \sqrt{\dfrac{a}{3b^2}}$     **32.** $\sqrt[4]{64} - \sqrt[3]{-\dfrac{16}{54}} + \sqrt[6]{256}$

**33.** $\dfrac{a}{\sqrt{1\frac{1}{3}}} - \dfrac{y}{\sqrt{5\frac{1}{3}}} + \dfrac{z}{\sqrt{8\frac{1}{3}}}$     **34.** $x\sqrt{1 + \left(\dfrac{y}{x}\right)^{\frac{1}{2}}} - y\sqrt{1 + \left(\dfrac{x}{y}\right)^{\frac{1}{2}}}$

**35.** $5a\sqrt[3]{\frac{1}{4}a} + 3x\sqrt{49x^3y} + 5\sqrt[3]{2a^4} - 2y\sqrt{64y^3x}$

**36.** $3^{-\frac{1}{2}} + \sqrt{12} + \dfrac{\sqrt{8}}{\sqrt{6}} + (\sqrt{3}+1)(2 + 3^{\frac{1}{2}})$

**27. Quotient of radicals; rationalizing the denominator.** The quotient of two radicals with the same index (order) follows from the rule $\dfrac{\sqrt[n]{a}}{\sqrt[n]{b}} = \sqrt[n]{\dfrac{a}{b}}$.

EXAMPLE I.   Divide $\sqrt{3}$ by $2\sqrt{2}$.

**Solution.**  $\dfrac{\sqrt{3}}{2\sqrt{2}} = \dfrac{1}{2}\dfrac{\sqrt{3}}{\sqrt{2}} = \dfrac{1}{2}\sqrt{\dfrac{3}{2}}$   (Ans.)

It is frequently necessary to evaluate a fraction (quotient) which contains radicals in the denominator; to simplify such an evaluation we *remove the radicals from the denominator* or *rationalize the denominator*.

EXAMPLE II.   Divide $2\sqrt{5}$ by $3\sqrt{2}$, rationalizing the denominator.

**Solution.**  $\dfrac{2\sqrt{5}}{3\sqrt{2}} = \dfrac{2\sqrt{5}\sqrt{2}}{3\sqrt{2}\sqrt{2}} = \dfrac{2\sqrt{10}}{6} = \dfrac{\sqrt{10}}{3}$   (Ans.)

EXAMPLE III.   Rationalize the denominator of $\dfrac{\sqrt{7} - \sqrt{5}}{3\sqrt{5} + 4\sqrt{6}}$.

**Solution.**  $\dfrac{\sqrt{7} - \sqrt{5}}{3\sqrt{5} + 4\sqrt{6}} = \dfrac{(\sqrt{7} - \sqrt{5})(3\sqrt{5} - 4\sqrt{6})}{(3\sqrt{5} + 4\sqrt{6})(3\sqrt{5} - 4\sqrt{6})}$

$$= \dfrac{3\sqrt{35} - 4\sqrt{42} - 15 + 4\sqrt{30}}{45 - 96}$$

$$= \dfrac{3\sqrt{35} - 4\sqrt{42} - 15 + 4\sqrt{30}}{-51}$$

$$= \dfrac{4\sqrt{42} + 15 - 3\sqrt{35} - 4\sqrt{30}}{51} \quad \text{(Ans.)}$$

Whenever the denominator contains a sum (difference) of two square roots with coefficients, the denominator can be rationalized by multiplying numerator and denominator by the corresponding difference (sum).

### EXERCISES

*Rationalize the denominator:*

**1.** $\dfrac{3}{2\sqrt{2}}$     **2.** $\sqrt{\dfrac{1}{2}}$     **3.** $2\sqrt{\dfrac{1}{3}}$     **4.** $\sqrt{\dfrac{1}{7}}$

**5.** $8\sqrt[3]{\dfrac{1}{4}}$     **6.** $\dfrac{3\sqrt{5}}{\sqrt{11}}$     **7.** $\sqrt{\dfrac{5}{7a}}$     **8.** $\sqrt[3]{-\dfrac{5}{4x}}$

**9.** $\sqrt{\dfrac{ab^2}{20}}$     **10.** $x\sqrt[3]{\dfrac{2}{3xy}}$     **11.** $\sqrt{\dfrac{5y^3}{2x^5}}$     **12.** $\sqrt{\dfrac{5x}{6y}}$

**13.** $\sqrt{a^2 + \dfrac{3}{a}}$     **14.** $\sqrt[6]{\dfrac{x^2y^8}{16z^5}}$     **15.** $\sqrt{\dfrac{1}{5a^2b}}$     **16.** $\sqrt[5]{\dfrac{-1}{81x}}$

**17.** $\sqrt[3]{\dfrac{8x^3}{3y^4}}$     **18.** $\sqrt{\dfrac{3xy}{z-w}}$     **19.** $\dfrac{\sqrt{3}-1}{\sqrt{3}+1}$     **20.** $\dfrac{3-\sqrt{2}}{2+\sqrt{3}}$

**21.** $\dfrac{\sqrt{2}+\sqrt{3}}{\sqrt{3}-\sqrt{2}}$     **22.** $\dfrac{\sqrt{2}+\sqrt{3}}{\sqrt{8}-\sqrt{12}}$     **23.** $\dfrac{\sqrt{\frac{2}{3}}+(\frac{3}{2})^{\frac{1}{2}}}{\sqrt{\frac{2}{3}}-\sqrt{\frac{3}{2}}}$     **24.** $\dfrac{\sqrt{7}-\sqrt{5}}{\sqrt{7}+(5)^{\frac{1}{2}}}$

**25.** $\dfrac{\sqrt{5}-1}{2\sqrt{2}-3}$     **26.** $\dfrac{\sqrt{3}-\sqrt{2}}{2\sqrt{3}+2x^0}$     **27.** $\dfrac{1}{\sqrt{3}-(2)^{\frac{1}{2}}}$     **28.** $\dfrac{4\sqrt{3}+5\sqrt{2}}{5\sqrt{3}-3(2)^{\frac{1}{2}}}$

**29.** $\dfrac{2\sqrt{5}-3\sqrt{2}}{3\sqrt{5}-4\sqrt{2}}$     **30.** $\dfrac{7-3\sqrt{5}}{4+2\sqrt{5}}$

**31.** $\dfrac{2\sqrt{3}-3\sqrt{2}+\sqrt{5}}{3\sqrt{2}+2\sqrt{3}}$     **32.** $\dfrac{\sqrt{3}-\sqrt{\frac{1}{2}}}{\sqrt{2}+\sqrt{\frac{1}{3}}}$

**33.** $\dfrac{a\sqrt{x}-2b\sqrt{z}}{a\sqrt{x}+b\sqrt{z}}$     **34.** $\dfrac{\sqrt{x+y}-\sqrt{x-y}}{\sqrt{x+y}+\sqrt{x-y}}$

**35.** $\dfrac{\sqrt{a}-4\sqrt{a-2}}{2\sqrt{a}+3\sqrt{a-2}}$     **36.** $\dfrac{\sqrt{a^2+b^2}+a-b}{a+b-\sqrt{a^2+b^2}}$

**37.** $\dfrac{b^2}{a+\sqrt{a^2-b^2}}$     **38.** $\dfrac{2\sqrt{a-2}+5}{\sqrt{a-2}+\sqrt{a-4}}$

**39.** $\dfrac{a^{-2}-b^{-2}}{a^{-\frac{1}{2}}+b^{-\frac{1}{2}}}$     **40.** $\dfrac{x-\sqrt{x^2-1}}{x+\sqrt{x^2-1}}$

**41.** $\dfrac{\sqrt{\dfrac{1+q}{1-q}} + 1}{1 - \sqrt{\dfrac{1+q}{1-q}}}$

**42.** $\dfrac{1 - \dfrac{\sqrt{1-x^2}}{\sqrt{1+x^2}}}{1 + \dfrac{\sqrt{1-x^2}}{\sqrt{1+x^2}}}$

**43.** $\dfrac{2\sqrt{x^2+y^2} + 3\sqrt{x^2-y^2}}{3\sqrt{x^2+y^2} - 2\sqrt{x^2-y^2}}$

**44.** $\dfrac{\sqrt{1-4a^2} + 3}{2 - 3\sqrt{1-4a^2}}$

**45.** $\dfrac{\sqrt{3b} + 2\sqrt{a-b}}{\sqrt{5b} + 2\sqrt{a-b}}$

**46.** $\dfrac{3}{\sqrt[3]{x} + \sqrt[3]{y}}$

**47.** $\dfrac{2\sqrt[3]{2} + 3\sqrt[3]{3}}{2\sqrt[3]{2} - 3\sqrt[3]{3}}$

**48.** $\dfrac{5 - 4\sqrt[3]{2}}{\sqrt[3]{16} + \sqrt[3]{81}}$

**49.** $\dfrac{8\sqrt{a} + \sqrt{b}}{\sqrt[4]{a^2} - \sqrt[4]{b^2}}$

**50.** $\dfrac{\left(a^{\frac{1}{2}} + \dfrac{1}{b^{-\frac{1}{2}}}\right)^2 - \left(\dfrac{1}{a^{-\frac{1}{2}}} - b^{\frac{1}{2}}\right)^2}{b + \sqrt{a^2+b^2}}$

**51.** Evaluate to three decimals exercises 19 through 32.

**28. Complex numbers.** As explained in § 11 the $\sqrt{-1}$ or $i$ is an imaginary number. *A number of the form $a + bi$, where a and b are real numbers, is called a* **complex number;** if $a = 0, a + bi = bi$ is an imaginary number, if $b = 0$, $a + bi = a$ is a real number. *In the complex number $a + bi$, a is called the* **real part** *and bi the* **imaginary part.** *The number $a - bi$ is called the* **conjugate** *of $a + bi$;* these numbers differ only in the signs of their imaginary parts. We note that the product and sum of two conjugate complex numbers are real numbers.

The sum, difference, product, or quotient of two complex numbers is a complex number and can be written in the form $a + bi$.

EXAMPLE I.   Write $\dfrac{3 - i}{3 + i}$ in the form $a + bi$.

**Solution.**   $\dfrac{3 - i}{3 + i} = \dfrac{(3 - i)(3 - i)}{(3 + i)(3 - i)} = \dfrac{9 - 6i + i^2}{9 - i^2} = \dfrac{8 - 6i}{10}$

$\qquad\qquad = \dfrac{8}{10} - \dfrac{6}{10}i = \dfrac{4}{5} - \dfrac{3}{5}i$   (Ans.)

EXAMPLE II.   Write $(2 - 5i)(3 + 4i)$ in the form $a + bi$.

**Solution.**   $(2 - 5i)(3 + 4i) = 6 - 15i + 8i - 20i^2$

$\qquad\qquad\qquad\qquad = 6 - 7i + 20$

$\qquad\qquad\qquad\qquad = 26 - 7i$   (Ans.)

The usual rules of operations apply to algebraic expressions containing complex numbers. From the definition of $i$ we have

$$i^2 = -1, \ i^3 = i^2 i = -i, \ i^4 = i^2 i^2 = (-1)(-1) = 1, \text{ etc.}$$

In working problems containing square roots of negative numbers $i$ should be substituted for $\sqrt{-1}$ to avoid the following common error

$$\sqrt{-5} \ \sqrt{-20} = \sqrt{(-5)(-20)} = \sqrt{100} = 10 \quad \textbf{(wrong)};$$

the correct procedure is

$$\sqrt{-5} \ \sqrt{-20} = \sqrt{5} \ i \ \sqrt{20} \ i = \sqrt{100} \ i^2 = 10(-1) = -10 \quad \text{(Ans.)}$$

EXAMPLE III. Simplify: $\sqrt{-5} + \sqrt{-20}$.

**Solution.** $\sqrt{-5} + \sqrt{-20} = i\sqrt{5} + i\sqrt{20} = i\sqrt{5} + i2\sqrt{5} = 3\sqrt{5}i$
(Ans.)

## EXERCISES

*Simplify:*

**1.** $(2\sqrt{-5})^2$     **2.** $\sqrt{-12}\sqrt{-3}$     **3.** $(2i - 3)(-4 - 5i)$

**4.** $(2i^3 - i^2 - i^4 + 3)^2$     **5.** $\left(\dfrac{2 - 3\sqrt{-3}}{5}\right)^2$     **6.** $\dfrac{3i - 4}{3 + 2i}$

**7.** $\dfrac{5 + 3i}{2 + 4i}$     **8.** $5i(-4i)$     **9.** $\dfrac{-5}{7i - 2}$

**10.** $\dfrac{3 + \sqrt{-2}}{3 - 5\sqrt{-2}}$     **11.** $\dfrac{1}{3 + 7i}$     **12.** $(i + 2)^{-2}$

**13.** $\dfrac{5\sqrt{3}}{3 + i\sqrt{3}}$     **14.** $-\dfrac{1}{i}$     **15.** $\dfrac{3}{2i}$

**16.** $(2i + 5)^{-1}$     **17.** $(3 - 2i) + (4 - 7i)$

**18.** $(2 - 3\sqrt{-5})(\sqrt{5} + \sqrt{-3})$     **19.** $2 - \sqrt{-4} - (3 - 5\sqrt{-4})$

**20.** $(5 + 3\sqrt{-2})(6 - \sqrt{-18})$     **21.** $(4 + 3\sqrt{-2})(4 - 3\sqrt{-2})$

**22.** $(1 - \sqrt{-3}) \cdot (2\sqrt{3} - \sqrt{-4}) + 2\sqrt{-1}(2 + \sqrt{-12}) + \sqrt{-5}$

**23.** $\left[\dfrac{4 + 3i}{2}\right]^2 + \left[\dfrac{4 - 3i}{2}\right]^2$

**24.** $2\left[\dfrac{1 - i\sqrt{5}}{2}\right]^2 - 2\left[\dfrac{1 - i\sqrt{5}}{2}\right] + 3$

**25.** $2 - 4\left[\dfrac{2 - \sqrt{-2}}{3}\right] + 3\left[\dfrac{2 - \sqrt{-2}}{3}\right]^2$

**26.** $1 - \dfrac{1 - i\sqrt{7}}{4} + 2\left[\dfrac{1 - i\sqrt{7}}{4}\right]^2$

**27.** $\left[\dfrac{-1 - \sqrt{-3}}{2}\right]^2 + 3\left[\dfrac{-1 - \sqrt{-3}}{2}\right] + 5$

**28.** $2\left[\dfrac{1 + 2i\sqrt{2}}{3}\right] + 3 - 3\left[\dfrac{1 + 2i\sqrt{2}}{3}\right]^2$

**29.** Find the value of $x^2 + 2x + 3$ if $x = -1 + i\sqrt{2}$.

**30.** Find the value of $2x^2 + 3x + 2$ if $x = \dfrac{-3 - \sqrt{-7}}{4}$.

**31.** Find the value of $x^2 + 1$ if $x = i$; if $x = -i$.

# CHAPTER IV

## LINEAR EQUATIONS

**29. Algebraic equations.** As explained in § 16, an equality which is not valid for all values of the symbols involved is called an equation. For example, $x - 2 = 1$ is not valid for $x = 2$, because substituting 2 for $x$ in the equation we have $2 - 2 = 0 \neq 1$. Thus, $x - 2 = 1$ is an equation and not an identity.

*A symbol which, throughout a discussion, represents a fixed number incapable of change is called a* **constant.** *A symbol which, throughout a discussion, may assume more than one value is called a* **variable.** For example, the formula $A = \pi r^2$ gives the area $A$ of a circle in terms of the radius $r$. The value of $A$ changes as $r$ varies. Thus, $A$ and $r$ are variables, while $\pi$ is a constant. If $r$ is given $A$ is determined, and we say that $A$ *is a function of* $r$, or $A = f(r)$, read *"A equals f of r."*

*An expression of the form*

$$(1) \qquad a_n x^n + a_{n-1} x^{n-1} + a_{n-2} x^{n-2} + \cdots + a_1 x + a_0,$$

*where n is a positive integer and* $a_n$, $a_{n-1}$, $\cdots$, $a_0$ *are constants, is called a* **polynomial in x.** *If* $a_n \neq 0$ *the polynomial is said to be of* **degree n** *(the highest power of x).* For example, $3x^3 - 4x^2 + 7x - 8$ is a polynomial of degree 3, or of the 3d degree, in $x$. In (1) $x$ is called the **variable** or the **unknown.** *The value of the polynomial for* $x = k$ *is the number obtained by substituting k for x in the polynomial.* Thus the polynomial is a function of $x$, and we write

$$f(x) = 3x^3 - 4x^2 + 7x - 8.$$

Consequently,

$$f(2) = 3(2)^3 - 4(2)^2 + 7(2) - 8 = 24 - 16 + 14 - 8 = 14$$
$$f(0) = 3(0)^3 - 4(0)^2 + 7(0) - 8 = -8$$
$$f(k) = 3k^3 - 4k^2 + 7k - 8.$$

*The values of x which make* $f(x) = 0$ *are called* **roots of the polynomial.** *A polynomial in x of degree n has n roots.* For example, $f(x) = x^2 + 5x - 6$ is a polynomial of degree 2 and

52

$$f(-6) = (-6)^2 + 5(-6) - 6 = 36 - 30 - 6 = 0$$
$$f(1) = 1^2 + 5(1) - 6 = 1 + 5 - 6 = 0.$$

Hence $-6$ and $1$ are roots of the polynomial $x^2 + 5x - 6$. *If k is a root of a polynomial, then $x - k$ is a factor*, thus $(x + 6)$ and $(x - 1)$ are factors of $x^2 + 5x - 6$. *If we set the polynomial equal to zero, the resulting equation is called a* **rational integral equation in x,** *or a* **polynomial equation in x.**

*For any equation in x the values of x which, when substituted for x in the equation, make the two sides (or members) of the equality equal are called* **solutions of the equation.** For example, $x = 2$ is a solution of $x^2 - 3 = x - 1$ because $(2)^2 - 3 = 2 - 1$, or $1 = 1$. *Such values of x are said to* **satisfy the equation.** *To solve an equation means to find all the values of x which satisfy the equation, or all the solutions of the equation.*

When we set a polynomial in $x$ equal to zero we have an equation whose solutions are the roots of the polynomial; *these roots are often called the* **roots of the equation.**

*An equation obtained from another by applying algebraic operations to its members is called a* **derived equation.** *A derived equation is said to be* **equivalent** *to its original equation if it contains all the roots of the original equation and no others.*

The following operations always lead to **equivalent equations:**

*Adding the same number or expression to, or subtracting the same number or expression from, both members or sides of the equation.*

*Multiplying or dividing both members by the same number or expression, provided this expression is not zero and does not contain the unknown.*

For example, $x^2 + 5x - 5 = 1$ and $x^2 + 5x - 6 = 0$ are equivalent since the second can be obtained from the first by adding $-1$ to both members. As a matter of fact, *any term of an equation can be moved from one member to the other by changing the sign — this is called* **transposition.** Thus, $x^2 + 5x - 5 = 1$ is equivalent to $x^2 + 5x - 6 = 0$, or $x^2 - 5 = 1 - 5x$. *Like terms appearing on both sides of an equation may be cancelled by subtracting this same term from both members,* e.g., $x^2 + 5 = x + 5$; since cancellation here amounts to subtracting a number from itself each cancelled term is replaced by 0; thus, $x + \overset{0}{5} = \overset{0}{5}$ becomes $x = 0$.

Also, $2(x^2 + 5x - 6) = 2x^3$, and $x^2 + 5x - 6 = x^3$ are equivalent since the second is obtained from the first by dividing each member by 2. *When the two members of an equation are written as products of factors, like factors different from zero appearing in both members may be cancelled,* e.g., $\overset{1}{\cancel{2}}(x^2 + 3x) = \overset{1}{\cancel{2}}(x^2 - 5)$; since cancellation here amounts to the division of a number by itself each cancelled factor is replaced by 1. Zeros cannot be cancelled in this way since division by zero is meaningless, $0 \cdot 9 = 0 \cdot 11$, but $9 \neq 11$.

*If both members of an equation are multiplied by an expression containing the unknown or are raised to the same power, the resulting equation may have more roots than the original equation.* These roots are called **extraneous roots** and the derived equation is said to be **redundant** with respect to the original equation. For example, $x + 2 = 0$ has only one root, $x = -2$. But, if we multiply both members by $x - 1$ we have $x^2 + x - 2 = 0$, which has two roots, $x = -2$ and $x = -1$. Also, $x = -2$ has only one root, $x = -2$, but if we square both sides, we have $x^2 = 4$ and this has two roots, $x = 2$ and $x = -2$.

*If both members of an equation are divided by an expression containing the unknown, the derived equation may have fewer roots than the original equation.* Such an equation is said to be **defective** with respect to the original equation. For example, $x^2 - 4 = 0$ has two roots, $x = 2$ and $x = -2$, but if we divide both members by $x + 2$ we have $x - 2 = 0$ which has only the one root, $x = 2$.

### EXERCISES

*By substitution answer the following questions:*

1. Is 3 a root of $x + 5 = 0$?    2. Is 5 a root of $x^2 - 6x + 5 = 0$?
3. Is 2 a root of $x^2 - 4 = 0$?    4. Is $-2$ a root of $x^3 - x - 6 = 0$?
5. Is $2i$ a root of $x^3 - 2x^2 + 4x + 8 = 0$?
6. Is $(2 - 3i)$ a root of $x^2 - 4x + 13 = 0$?
7. Is $(2\sqrt{2} - 3)$ a root of $x^2 + 6x - 1 = 0$?
8. If both members of the equation $x - 5 = 4$ are multiplied by (a) 2, (b) $-5$, (c) $2x$, (d) $x - 1$, and (e) $x^2 - 4$, are the derived equations equivalent, redundant, or defective? Why?
9. Given $2(2 - x) = (2 - x)(x + 4)$. What must be assumed before you can write $2 = x + 4$?

**30. Linear equations.** *An equation of which each member is a polynomial of the first degree is called a* **linear equation.** For example, $3x - 5 = 2x - 4$ is a linear equation in $x$. To solve such an equation multiply both members by L.C.D. of the denominators in the equation, remove all parentheses, and transpose all terms involving the unknown to the left member and all other terms to the right member. Write the left member as the product of the unknown and a coefficient and then divide both sides by this coefficient. Check solution by substitution in original equation.

EXAMPLE I.  Solve: $3x - 5 = 2x - 4$.

**Solution.**
$$3x - 2x = 5 - 4$$
$$x = 1 \quad \text{(Ans.)}$$

*Check.*
$$3(1) - 5 \stackrel{?}{=} 2(1) - 4$$
$$3 - 5 \stackrel{?}{=} 2 - 4$$
$$-2 = -2 \checkmark$$

EXAMPLE II.  Solve: $\dfrac{x}{3} - \dfrac{1}{4} = \dfrac{1}{2}x - \dfrac{5}{4}$.

**Solution.**
$$\frac{x}{3} - \frac{1}{4} = \frac{1}{2}x - \frac{5}{4}$$

Multiply by 12 (L.C.D.)
$$4x - 3 = 6x - 15$$
$$4x - 6x = -15 + 3$$
$$-2x = -12$$
$$x = \frac{-12}{-2} = 6 \quad \text{(Ans.)}$$

*Check.*
$$\tfrac{6}{3} - \tfrac{1}{4} \stackrel{?}{=} \tfrac{6}{2} - \tfrac{5}{4}$$
$$2 - \tfrac{1}{4} \stackrel{?}{=} 3 - \tfrac{5}{4}$$
$$\tfrac{7}{4} = \tfrac{7}{4} \checkmark$$

EXAMPLE III.  Solve: $\dfrac{3(2x - 7)}{5} - \dfrac{2(x - 8)}{3} = \dfrac{4x + 1}{15} + 4$.

**Solution.** The L.C.D. of the denominators is 15, and multiplying through by 15 we have

$$\frac{\overset{3}{\cancel{15}} \cdot 3(2x - 7)}{\cancel{5}} - \frac{\overset{5}{\cancel{15}} \cdot 2(x - 8)}{\cancel{3}} = \frac{\cancel{15}(4x + 1)}{\cancel{15}} + 15 \cdot 4.$$
$$9(2x - 7) - 10(x - 8) = (4x + 1) + 60$$
$$18x - 63 - 10x + 80 = 4x + 1 + 60$$
$$18x - 10x - 4x = 61 + 63 - 80$$
$$4x = 44$$
$$x = 11 \quad \text{(Ans.)}$$

*Check.*  $$\frac{3(2 \cdot 11 - 7)}{5} - \frac{2(11 - 8)}{3} \overset{?}{=} \frac{4 \cdot 11 + 1}{15} + 4$$

$$\frac{3(22 - 7)}{5} - \frac{2 \cdot 3}{3} \overset{?}{=} \frac{44 + 1}{15} + 4$$

$$\frac{3 \cdot \overset{3}{\cancel{15}}}{\cancel{5}} - 2 \overset{?}{=} \frac{\overset{3}{\cancel{45}}}{\cancel{15}} + 4$$

$$9 - 2 \overset{?}{=} 3 + 4$$
$$7 = 7 \checkmark$$

### EXERCISES

*Solve the following equations:*

**1.** $5x - 3 = x + 5$     **2.** $2x + 4 = x - 5$

**3.** $6x + 4 = 3x - 8$     **4.** $2t - 5 = 3 - 4t$

**5.** $z + \dfrac{2}{3} = 3z + 5$     **6.** $5x - 4(x - 3) = \dfrac{x - 1}{2}$

**7.** $\dfrac{2y - 9}{27} + \dfrac{y}{18} - \dfrac{y - 3}{4} = \dfrac{25}{3} - y$   **8.** $\dfrac{z + 1}{3} - \dfrac{5z + 4}{9} = \dfrac{13 - 2z}{7}$

**9.** $\frac{1}{4}(3x - 5) - [x - \frac{1}{3}(7 - 3x)] = \frac{1}{6}$

**10.** $\frac{1}{9}(5y - 4) - \frac{1}{7}(2y - 13) = \frac{1}{3}(1 + y)$

**11.** $\dfrac{5u + 2}{3} - \left(3 - \dfrac{3u - 1}{2}\right) = \dfrac{3u + 19}{2} - \left(\dfrac{u + 1}{6} + 3\right)$

**12.** $0.5(x - 1) + \frac{7}{12} - \frac{1}{6}x = .25$    **13.** $3y - .53 = .03y + .361$

**14.** $.96x - .46 = .79 + .21x$

*In the following the first letters of the alphabet represent constants, the last letters represent variables.*

**15.** $\dfrac{a(a - y)}{b} - \dfrac{b(b + y)}{a} = y$

**16.** $(x - a)(a - b + c) = (x + a)(b - a + c)$

**17.** $\dfrac{by + b}{a} - y + 1 = \dfrac{4b}{a + b}$    **18.** $y + \dfrac{c}{a + b} = \dfrac{cy}{a^2 - b^2} + a - b$

**19.** $\dfrac{x}{c} - b = \dfrac{x}{b} - c$     **20.** $\dfrac{aw - b}{c} - \dfrac{bw + c}{a} = abc$

**31. Equations reducible to linear equations.** The equation

$$2(x - 3)(x + 1) = (2x + 5)(x - 2) + 14$$

is not a linear equation, but performing the indicated multiplications we have

$$2x^2 - 4x - 6 = 2x^2 + x - 10 + 14$$

or       $$- 4x - 6 = x + 4,$$

which is a linear equation and can be solved by the method explained in § 30. Likewise, the equation

(1) $$\frac{2 - x}{3 - x} - \frac{x + 2}{x + 3} = \frac{5}{x^2 - 9}$$

is not linear. The L.C.D. of the denominators of this equation is $x^2 - 9$ and *the derived equation obtained by multiplying an equation by the L.C.D. is equivalent to the original equation, even though this L.C.D. involves the unknown.* Thus, multiplying both members of (1) by $x^2 - 9$, we have

(2) $$(x - 2)(x + 3) - (x + 2)(x - 3) = 5$$
$$x^2 + x - 6 - x^2 + x + 6 = 5$$
$$2x = 5$$

which is a linear equation. Equations (1) and (2) are **reducible to linear equations.** *When each term in such an equation is multiplied by the L.C.D. and the indicated operations performed, the equivalent derived equation is linear.*

EXAMPLE I. Solve: $\dfrac{4x}{5 - x} - \dfrac{20 - 3x}{3} = x$.

**Solution.** The L.C.D. is $3(5 - x)$ and multiplying each term by $3(5 - x)$ we have

$$3(4x) - (20 - 3x)(5 - x) = 3(5 - x)x$$
$$12x - 100 + 35x - 3x^2 = 15x - 3x^2$$

Cancellation here is equivalent to adding $3x^2$ to both sides.

$$12x + 35x - 15x = 100$$
$$32x = 100$$
$$x = \tfrac{100}{32} = \tfrac{25}{8} \quad \text{(Ans.)}$$

*Check.*
$$\frac{4(\tfrac{25}{8})}{5 - \tfrac{25}{8}} - \frac{20 - 3(\tfrac{25}{8})}{3} \overset{?}{=} \frac{25}{8}$$

$$\frac{\dfrac{100}{8}}{\dfrac{40 - 25}{8}} - \frac{85}{8 \cdot 3} \overset{?}{=} \frac{25}{8}$$

$$\tfrac{100}{15} - \tfrac{85}{24} \overset{?}{=} \tfrac{25}{8}$$
$$\tfrac{800}{120} - \tfrac{425}{120} \overset{?}{=} \tfrac{375}{120}$$
$$\tfrac{375}{120} = \tfrac{375}{120} \checkmark$$

## EXERCISES

*Solve the following equations:*

**1.** $x^2 - (1 - 2x)^2 = 6 - 3x(x + 2)$    **2.** $(y - 1)(y + 1) = (y + 2)(y - 3)$

**3.** $5(x^2 - 2) = (5x - 1)(x + 3)$    **4.** $\dfrac{9}{5x} - \dfrac{8}{10x - 5} = \dfrac{4x - 1}{4x^2 - 1}$

**5.** $\dfrac{6u - 3}{2u + 7} = \dfrac{3u - 2}{u + 5}$    **6.** $2 + \dfrac{2y}{y + 3} = \dfrac{4y}{y + 7}$

**7.** $\dfrac{3v - 1}{v - 5} = \dfrac{5v + 4}{v + 8} - 2$    **8.** $\dfrac{x + 2}{x - 2} - \dfrac{2x + 4}{1 - 2x} = 2$

**9.** $\dfrac{x + 2}{x - 2} = \dfrac{19}{21}$    **10.** $\dfrac{x}{3} + \dfrac{5x - x^2}{3x - 7} = \dfrac{2}{3}$

**11.** $5z - \dfrac{3z - 3}{z - 3} = 2z - \dfrac{3 - 6z}{2}$

**12.** $\dfrac{6}{v + 2} - \dfrac{v + 2}{v - 2} - \dfrac{v^2}{4 - v^2} = 0$

**13.** $\dfrac{15y - 7}{3 + 3y} - \dfrac{3y^2 - 51y - 71}{6(y^2 - 1)} = \dfrac{9y + 5}{2y - 2}$

**14.** $\dfrac{2t}{3t - 4} = \dfrac{4t + 5}{6t - 1} - \dfrac{3}{3t - 4}$

**15.** $\dfrac{1}{1 + w} + \dfrac{1}{2 + w} + \dfrac{1}{3 + w} = \dfrac{3(w + 1)(w + 2)}{(w + 1)(w + 2)(w + 3)}$

**16.** $\dfrac{2v + 7}{4} - \dfrac{3v + 8}{5v + 3} = \dfrac{4v + 3}{8}$

**17.** $\dfrac{5x^2 + 6}{x^2 - 4} - \dfrac{3}{x - 2} = 5 - \dfrac{7}{x + 2}$

**18.** $\dfrac{2y - 1}{2y - 2} - \dfrac{23}{10y - 10} = \dfrac{3}{5}\left(\dfrac{1}{y - 1} - \dfrac{1}{3}\right)$

**19.** $\dfrac{u^2 - u + 1}{u - 1} + \dfrac{u^2 + u + 1}{u + 1} = 2u$

**20.** $\dfrac{1}{x - 5} + 5 + x = \dfrac{18 + 3x}{3}$

**21.** $\dfrac{x - \dfrac{3(x - 5)}{4}}{8} - \dfrac{x - 3}{4} = x + 1 - \dfrac{8x - \dfrac{2(x + 16)}{17}}{6}$

**22.** $\dfrac{2y}{2y + 3} - \dfrac{y}{2y - 3} = \dfrac{2y^2 - 18}{4y^2 - 9}$

**23.** $(2m + 3)(3m - 5) - 6(m - 4)(m - 3) + 5 = 0$

**24.** $\dfrac{\frac{1}{4} - y}{\frac{1}{4} + y} + \dfrac{1}{4} = \dfrac{y}{\frac{1}{4} + y} - \dfrac{1}{4}$

**25.** $\dfrac{x + 4}{.3} + \dfrac{2 - 2x}{.6} = \dfrac{x + 1}{.2} - \dfrac{10}{.3}$ $9$

**26.** $\dfrac{3}{m} + \dfrac{6}{m - 1} + \dfrac{m + 13}{m(1 - m)} = 0$ $2$

**27.** $\dfrac{.3}{n} + \dfrac{1}{4n} - .1 = \dfrac{1}{5}$ $\dfrac{11}{6}$    **28.** $\dfrac{y}{3} - \dfrac{y^2 - 5y}{3y - 7} + .4 = \dfrac{16}{15}$ $-7$

**29.** $\dfrac{13v - 10}{36} + \dfrac{4v + 9}{18} - \dfrac{7(v - 2)}{12} = \dfrac{13v - 28}{17v - 66}$

**30.** $(m + 1)(m + 2)(m + 6) = m^3 + 9m^2 + 4(7m - 1)$

**31.** $\dfrac{1}{\frac{3y + 1}{3}} = 3 - \dfrac{1}{3}$    **32.** $3 - \dfrac{1}{\frac{1}{3} + \frac{1}{y}} = \dfrac{1}{3}$

**33.** $7\left(m - \dfrac{9}{2}\right) - \left[(2m - 3) - 5\left(\dfrac{m}{11} + \dfrac{4m + 5}{54}\right)\right] = 4$ $\dfrac{11}{2}$

**34.** $\dfrac{3y - 4}{y + 5} - \dfrac{4y - 1}{y + 4} + \dfrac{y^2 + 44}{y^2 + 9y + 20} = 0$ $3$

**35.** $\dfrac{1}{5}\left(3x - \dfrac{1}{4}\right) + \dfrac{x}{3} + 6\left(x - \dfrac{1}{4}\right) = 1$ $\dfrac{153}{416}$

**36.** $\dfrac{4}{x + 2} + \dfrac{7}{x + 3} - \dfrac{37}{x^2 + 5x + 6} = 0$ $1$

**37.** $\dfrac{3}{u^2 - 9} - \dfrac{5}{u^2 + 7u + 12} = \dfrac{2}{u^2 - 16} - \dfrac{4}{u^2 - 7u + 12}$ $\dfrac{2}{3}$

**38.** $\dfrac{3}{5}(2x - 7) + \dfrac{2}{3}(8 - x) = \dfrac{4x + 1}{15} + 4$ $11$

**39.** $\dfrac{1}{x - a + b} + \dfrac{1}{x + a - b} = \dfrac{2}{x - a - b}$ $\dfrac{(a-b)^2}{a+b}$

**40.** $\dfrac{ay - b}{ay + b} - \dfrac{by - a}{by + a} = \dfrac{a - b}{(ay + b)(by + a)}$ $\dfrac{1}{2(a+b)}$

**41.** $\dfrac{a + \dfrac{y}{a - b}}{a - \dfrac{y}{a + b}} - 1 = \dfrac{2a}{b}$ $a^2 - b^2$    **42.** $\dfrac{b}{\dfrac{a}{m + 1}} - m + 1 = \dfrac{4b}{a + b}$ $\dfrac{a - b}{a + b}$

**43.** If $x = \dfrac{a + 2t}{b - at}$, find the value of $t$ in terms of the other letters. $\dfrac{bx - a}{ax + 2}$

**44.** Find the value of $y$ if $\dfrac{m}{ay} + \dfrac{n}{by} = c$. $\dfrac{bm + an}{abc}$

**45.** Solve for $b$:

$$\frac{\dfrac{bc+d}{a}}{\dfrac{bc}{d}} = \frac{2d}{a} \qquad \frac{d}{c}$$

**46.** Solve for $x$ in terms of $a$, $b$, and $c$:

$$\frac{2c}{a} + \frac{b}{x} = \frac{c}{2-x} - \frac{2cx}{a(2-x)}. \qquad \frac{2ab}{ab+ac-4c}$$

**47.** Solve for $x$:

$$\frac{x-a}{x-b} = \frac{(2x-a)^2}{(2x-b)^2}. \qquad \frac{ab}{a+b}$$

**32. Applications.** Practical problems involving unknown quantities can frequently be translated into linear equations in one unknown and hence solved by the method described above. *In solving such problems read the problem carefully to determine what is required, denote by a letter the unknown, and translate the conditions on the unknown into an algebraic equation.*

EXAMPLE I. A rectangular field is twice as long as it is wide. By increasing its length 20 feet and its width 30 feet, the area will be increased 2200 square feet. What are its dimensions?

**Solution.** We want to find the width and length of the field, hence let $x$ represent the width. Then, since the field is twice as long as it is wide, $2x$ is its length. Its area is $2x \cdot x = 2x^2$. Increasing its width 30 feet and its length 20 feet, $x + 30$ is the new width and $2x + 20$ is the new length; the new area is $(2x+20)(x+30) = 2x^2 + 80x + 600$. But we are given that the new area is 2200 square feet more than the original area, hence

$$2x^2 + 80x + 600 = 2x^2 + 2200$$
$$80x = 1600$$
$$x = 20 \text{ feet (width)}$$
$$2x = 40 \text{ feet (length)}.$$

*Check.*     $2x^2 = 40 \cdot 20 = 800$ square feet (area).
New length $= 40 + 20 = 60$
New width $= 20 + 30 = 50$
New area $= 60 \cdot 50 = 3000$
$3000 - 800 = 2200$ ✓

EXAMPLE II. A man has 6 hours at his disposal. How far can he ride in a trolley car at 9 miles per hour so as to return in time, walking back at the rate of 3 miles per hour?

**Solution.** Let $x$ be the distance in miles he can ride in the trolley. Then $\frac{x}{9}$ is the number of hours spent on the trolley and $\frac{x}{3}$ the number of hours spent walking back. Hence

$$\frac{x}{9} + \frac{x}{3} = 6$$
$$1x + 3x = 54$$
$$4x = 54$$
$$x = \frac{54}{4} = 13\tfrac{1}{2} \text{ miles} \quad \text{(Ans.)}$$

*Check.* At 9 miles per hour he travels $13\tfrac{1}{2}$ miles in $1\tfrac{1}{2}$ hours. At 3 miles per hour he walks $13\tfrac{1}{2}$ miles in $4\tfrac{1}{2}$ hours. But $4\tfrac{1}{2} + 1\tfrac{1}{2} = 6.$ ✓

### EXERCISES

**1.** The altitude of a triangle is 2 feet more than twice its base, and its area is 2 square feet more than the area of a square having a side equal to the base of the triangle. Find the area of the triangle.

**2.** A rectangle whose length is 2 feet more than its breadth would have its area increased by 11 square feet if its length and breadth were each made a foot longer. Find its dimensions.

**3.** Express in square yards the area of a rectangle that is 60 feet long and 9 feet wide.

**4.** $A$ is now three times as old as $B$. In 5 years $A$ will be twice as old as $B$ will be then. How old is each now?

**5.** Find three consecutive integers whose sum is 21.

**6.** The length of a room exceeds its width by 2 feet. If 2 feet were added to the length and 3 feet to the width, the area would be increased by 37 square feet. Find the dimensions.

**7.** If the length of a rectangle is doubled and 7 inches added to the width, the area of the resulting rectangle is 70 square inches greater than twice the original area. If the length and width differ by 3 inches, what are the dimensions of the rectangle?

**8.** An athletic field is surrounded by a circular track. The outer edge is 154 feet longer than the inner edge. Find the width of the track. (Use $3\tfrac{1}{7}$ for $\pi$.)

**9.** The height of a pole is 12 feet more than 8 times its diameter. If the height is 24 feet, what is the diameter of the pole?

**10.** An automobile travels over a certain distance in 3 hours. If it had run 15 miles an hour faster, the trip would have been completed in 1 hour less time. Find the distance and rate.

**11.** Two men travel toward each other from points which are 150 miles apart at the rate of 10 and 15 miles an hour, respectively. In how many hours will they meet?

**12.** A man drives to a certain place at the rate of 25 miles an hour. He returns by a road that is 12 miles longer at the rate of 30 miles an hour and takes 4 minutes longer than in going. How long is each road?

*Hint.* The rate being in miles per hour, the 4 minutes should be expressed in hours.

**13.** A grocer offered for sale 20 bushels of apples at such a rate as to give him a 25 per cent gain on the cost. However, he sold only 15 bushels and had to throw away the others. If he lost $1.25 on the transaction, find the price per bushel which he paid.

**14.** Separate 35 into two parts such that the larger part divided by the smaller gives 3 as a quotient and 3 as a remainder.

**15.** The difference of the squares of two consecutive integers is 37; find the numbers.

**16.** What number when added to both numerator and denominator of $\frac{2}{5}$ will cause the fraction to be $\frac{3}{4}$?

**17.** State what value of $y$ will make the expression $3(y + 2) - 4(y - 3)$ equal to twice the value of $y$.

**18.** Divide 72 into two such parts that one fourth of the first part will be equal to one fifth of the second.

**19.** The sum of two numbers is five times the lesser, and the difference of the numbers is 51; find the numbers.

**20.** Divide 105 into two parts such that one part will be less than the other by 39.

**21.** The sum of two numbers is 285. One tenth of the greater equals one ninth of the lesser. Find the numbers.

**22.** If 2 be subtracted from a certain number and the remainder be multiplied by 4, the same result is obtained as if twice the number and one half less half the number be added together. What is the number?

**23.** *A* can do a piece of work in 30 days and *B* in 50 days; after they have worked together 6 days, how many days will be required for *B* to finish the work?

*Hint.* *A* does $\frac{1}{30}$ of the work in one day; for completion of the work the fractional contributions must total 1.

**24.** A farmer can mow a field in 25 hours, his eldest son can mow it in 30 hours, and his second son in 36 hours. In how many hours can the three working together mow it?

**25.** A man invests $1000, part of it at 4 per cent and the rest at 5 per cent, and the total income is $44. How was the money divided?

**26.** The profits on a business this year are 20 per cent more than they were last year. This year they are $10,000. What were they last year?

**27.** A clerk earned $600 in a certain number of months. His salary was increased 25 per cent and he then earned $500 in two months less time than that in which he earned $600. What was his original monthly salary?

**28.** A train runs from $A$ to $B$ in 3 hours; another train running 2 miles per hour less than the former, runs from $A$ to $C$, a point 18 miles beyond $B$ in $3\frac{1}{2}$ hours. Find the distance from $A$ to $B$.

**29.** A messenger on a motorcycle follows a truck which has a start of an hour and overtakes it in 2 hours. If the messenger travels at the rate of 60 miles an hour, what was the rate of the truck?

**30.** A man walking 2 miles per hour leaves a town $A$. He is followed by a second man who leaves $A$ 4 hours later, walking 4 miles per hour. How long must the second man walk to overtake the first?

**31.** The square of an integer is 7 less than the product of this integer and the next larger one. Find the integer.

**32.** Of a group of girls every girl but two is blonde, every girl but two is brunette, and every girl but two is redheaded. How many girls are there?

**33.** A basket contains a certain number of eggs. $A$ removes half the eggs plus half an egg. Then $B$ removes half the remaining eggs plus half an egg. Finally, $C$ empties the basket by removing half the remaining eggs plus half an egg. How many eggs did the basket originally contain?

**34.** A tank can be filled by two pipes in 24 minutes and 30 minutes respectively, and emptied by a third pipe in 20 minutes. What time will be required to fill the tank if all three are running?

**35.** One pipe can fill a tank in 24 hours; another can empty it in 19 hours. If the tank is empty and the first pipe is opened at 8 A.M. and the second 3 hours later, at what time will the tank be empty again?

**36.** A merchant has tea worth 50 cents per pound and also tea worth 65 cents per pound. How many pounds of each must be used to make a mixture of 18 pounds worth 55 cents per pound?

**37.** To 100 cubic centimeters of a 6 per cent acid solution, how much water should be added to make it a $2\frac{1}{2}$ per cent solution?

**38.** Of 30 pounds of salt water, 12 per cent is salt; of another mixture, 4 per cent is salt. How many pounds of the second should be added to the first in order to get a mixture containing 10 per cent salt?

*Hint.* Let $x$ be the number of pounds in the second mixture, but form the equation from the number of pounds of salt in each mixture.

**39.** A woman buys a certain number of eggs for $1.44; she finds that 3 eggs cost as much more than 5 cents as 8 eggs cost less than 19 cents. How many eggs did she buy?  *16 eggs*

**40.** The Panama Canal is 46 miles long. Of this distance the lower land parts on the Atlantic and Pacific sides are together 9 times the length of the Culebra Cut, or the hill part. How many miles long is the Culebra Cut?  *4.6 mi*

**41.** A certain merchant sells his best grade of silk at $x$ dollars per yard. He finds that he lacks 3 yards of having enough to fill an order for $100 worth of this material. How many yards does he have on hand?  *$\frac{100}{x} - 3$*

**42.** Beef dealers in a certain town used to sell 10,500 pounds of beef per week. After raising the price 5 per cent they find they lost, by so doing, 16 per cent of their receipts. How many pounds per week do they now sell?  *8400 lb*

# CHAPTER V

## LINEAR SYSTEMS

**33. Solution by addition and subtraction, and by substitution.**
We shall consider here equations involving more than one unknown, e.g.,

$$3x^2y^2 - 4xy^2 + 7x - 2y + 5 = 0$$

is an equation with $x$ and $y$ as the unknowns. *The* **degree of a term** *is the sum of the exponents of the unknowns in the term,* e.g., the degree of $3x^2y^2$ is $2 + 2 = 4$; the degree of $- 4xy^2$ is $1 + 2 = 3$; the degree of 5 is 0; etc. *A* **solution of such an equation** *is a pair of values $x$ and $y$ which when substituted in the equation make it an identity.*

*An equation in several unknowns is linear if at least one of the unknowns appears in the equation and the degree of each term is at most 1.* Of course, the linear equation

$$x - y = 3$$

has any number of solutions because for each value of $y$ we have a corresponding value of $x$,

$$x = y + 3,$$

hence if $y = 1$, $x = 4$, if $y = 2$, $x = 5$, etc. But, if we are given the two equations

$$(1) \quad x - y = 3,$$
$$(2) \quad 2x + y = 3,$$

and require the solution to satisfy both equations simultaneously, there may be only one pair of values for $x$ and $y$ which is a solution. Equations (1) and (2) form a **linear system** and we shall consider here systems in which the number of unknowns is the same as the number of equations.

There are several methods of solving such a system. The following examples illustrate the method of addition and subtraction.

EXAMPLE I.   Solve:          $x - y = 3$          (1)

$2x + y = 3$          (2)

**Solution.**   Adding (1) and (2) we have

$3x = 6$          (3)

Solving (3) for $x$          $x = 2$          (4)

Substituting $x = 2$ in (1)   $2 - y = 3$

$y = -1$          (5)

Thus the solution is   $x = 2, y = -1$.   (Ans.)

*Check.*          $2 - (-1) = 2 + 1 = 3 \checkmark$

$2(2) + (-1) = 4 - 1 = 3 \checkmark$

EXAMPLE II.   Solve:   $5x + 3y = -9$          (6)

$3x - 4y = -17$          (7)

**Solution.**

Multiply (6) by 4          $20x + 12y = -36$          (8)

Multiply (7) by 3          $9x - 12y = -51$          (9)

Add (8) and (9)          $29x = -87$          (10)

Thus we obtain one linear equation in one unknown.

Solve (10) for $x$          $x = -3$          (11)

Substitute $x = -3$ in either (6) or (7) and find $y$

$5(-3) + 3y = -9$

$-15 + 3y = -9$

$3y = 6$

$y = 2$

Thus the solution is   $x = -3, y = 2$.   (Ans.)

*Check.*          $5(-3) + 3(2) = -15 + 6 = -9 \checkmark$

$3(-3) - 4(2) = -9 - 8 = -17 \checkmark$

In the above examples we multiply each equation through by suitably chosen constants so that addition or subtraction of the new equations results in eliminating one of the variables. The equation thus obtained is a linear equation in one unknown and can be solved by the method of Chapter IV. By substituting this solution in either of the original equations we obtain the corresponding value of the other unknown.

The method of substitution consists in solving one of the equations for one of the unknowns in terms of the other and substituting this value in the second equation. Thus a linear equation in one unknown is obtained. This equation is solved for the unknown and the other unknown obtained as above.

**EXAMPLE III.** Solve:
$$\frac{2y + 6}{y} - \frac{2x + 4}{x} = \frac{5}{y} \qquad (12)$$
$$\tfrac{1}{3}(x + 4) = 6 - \tfrac{1}{5}(x + y) \qquad (13)$$

**Solution.** First clear of fractions by multiplying by the L.C.D. in each equation.

$$x(2y + 6) - y(2x + 4) = 5x$$
$$2xy + 6x - 2xy - 4y = 5x$$
$$x - 4y = 0$$
$$5(x + 4) = 90 - 3(x + y)$$
$$5x + 20 = 90 - 3x - 3y$$
$$8x + 3y = 70$$

Thus the system reduces to
$$x - 4y = 0 \qquad (14)$$
$$8x + 3y = 70 \qquad (15)$$

From (14) we have $x = 4y$

Substituting $4y$ for $x$ in (15)

$$8(4y) + 3y = 70$$
$$32y + 3y = 70$$
$$35y = 70$$
$$y = 2$$

Since $x = 4y$, $x = 4(2) = 8$, and the solution is $x = 8$, $y = 2$. (Ans.)

*Check.*
$$\frac{2(2) + 6}{2} - \frac{2(8) + 4}{8} \overset{?}{=} \frac{5}{2}$$
$$\tfrac{10}{2} - \tfrac{20}{8} \overset{?}{=} \tfrac{5}{2}$$
$$5 - \tfrac{5}{2} = \tfrac{5}{2} \checkmark$$
$$\tfrac{1}{3}(8 + 4) \overset{?}{=} 6 - \tfrac{1}{5}(8 + 2)$$
$$\tfrac{12}{3} \overset{?}{=} 6 - \tfrac{10}{5}$$
$$4 \overset{?}{=} 6 - 2$$
$$4 = 4 \checkmark$$

**EXAMPLE IV.** Solve:
$$ax + by = 2 \qquad (16)$$
$$cx + dy = 3 \qquad (17)$$
where $a$, $b$, $c$, and $d$ are constants.

**Solution.** Multiply (16) by $d$ and (17) by $-b$ and add.

$$adx + bdy = 2d$$
$$\underline{-\,bcx - bdy = -\,3b}$$

Adding
$$adx - bcx = 2d - 3b$$
$$(ad - bc)x = 2d - 3b$$
$$x = \frac{2d - 3b}{ad - bc}$$

Substituting this value of $x$ in (16) we have

$$a\left(\frac{2d - 3b}{ad - bc}\right) + by = 2$$

$$by = 2 - \frac{a(2d - 3b)}{ad - bc}$$

$$by = \frac{2ad - 2bc - 2ad + 3ab}{ad - bc}$$

$$y = \frac{3ab - 2bc}{b(ad - bc)} = \frac{b(3a - 2c)}{b(ad - bc)}$$

Thus the solution is $\quad x = \dfrac{2d - 3b}{ad - bc}, \quad y = \dfrac{3a - 2c}{ad - bc}$.   (Ans.)

Check.        $a\left(\dfrac{2d - 3b}{ad - bc}\right) + b\left(\dfrac{3a - 2c}{ad - bc}\right) \overset{?}{=} 2$

$$\frac{2ad - 3ab + 3ab - 2bc}{ad - bc} \overset{?}{=} 2$$

$$\frac{2(ad - bc)}{ad - bc} = 2 \checkmark$$

$$c\left(\frac{2d - 3b}{ad - bc}\right) + d\left(\frac{3a - 2c}{ad - bc}\right) \overset{?}{=} 3$$

$$\frac{2cd - 3bc + 3ad - 2cd}{ad - bc} \overset{?}{=} 3$$

$$\frac{3(ad - bc)}{ad - bc} = 3 \checkmark$$

Of course, in this example we assume that $ad - bc \neq 0$.

A variation of the method of substitution is to solve both equations for the same variable and equate the two expressions.

### EXERCISES

*Solve the following systems:*

**1.** $2x - 3y + 4 = 0$
$\quad 3x + y + 6 = 0$

**2.** $5u + 6v = 8$
$\quad 5u - v = 22$

**3.** $\dfrac{w}{3} + \dfrac{y}{4} = 6$

$\quad \dfrac{w}{4} + \dfrac{y}{2} = 7$

**4.** $\dfrac{5m}{3} + n + 3 = 0$

$\quad m - \dfrac{4n}{3} - \dfrac{2}{3} = 5$

**5.** $2x + 3y = 13$
$\quad 4y = 5x + 6$

**6.** $\dfrac{7u - 15}{3} = y$

$\quad 2u - y = 3$

**7.** $2a - b = 10$
$3b + 17a = 177$

**8.** $u - v = 2$
$2u + v = 6$

**9.** $\dfrac{u+v}{8} - \dfrac{u-v}{6} = 5$
$\dfrac{u+v}{4} - \dfrac{u-v}{2} = 10$

**10.** $\dfrac{7+z}{5} - \dfrac{2z-y}{4} = 3y - 5$
$\dfrac{5y-7}{2} + \dfrac{4z-3}{6} = 18 - 5z$

**11.** $\dfrac{u}{5} + 5v = 51$
$5u + \dfrac{v}{5} = 27$

**12.** $\dfrac{3m+1}{3} - \dfrac{4n+1}{2} + \dfrac{1}{2} = 0$
$\dfrac{2m-1}{2} - \dfrac{4n-1}{3} - \dfrac{1}{2} = 0$

**13.** $\dfrac{1}{a} + \dfrac{b}{b+1} = 1$
$\dfrac{1}{b} + \dfrac{2a}{a+1} = 2$

**14.** $\dfrac{3}{u-1} + \dfrac{4}{v-1} = 0$
$\dfrac{5}{2u-3} - \dfrac{7}{2v+13} = 0$

**15.** $\dfrac{x+y}{3} - \dfrac{x-y}{2} = 5$
$\dfrac{x}{2} + \dfrac{x+y}{9} = 7$

**16.** $z + \dfrac{w\sqrt{2}}{\sqrt{3}} = 3$
$\dfrac{w\sqrt{3}}{\sqrt{2}} - z = 2$

**17.** $\dfrac{u + \dfrac{v}{2} - 3}{u - 5} + 7 = 0$
$\dfrac{3v - 10(u-1)}{6} + \dfrac{u-v}{4} + 1 = 0$

**18.** $\dfrac{m-3}{m-1} = \dfrac{n-8}{n-5}$
$\dfrac{2m-3}{2(n-1)} = \dfrac{5m-6}{5n-7}$

**19.** $\dfrac{u}{a} = \dfrac{v}{b}$
$u + v = c$

**20.** $\dfrac{x}{a} - \dfrac{y}{b} - 1 = 0$
$ax + by = b^2$

**21.** $\dfrac{a}{b}w + \dfrac{b}{a}z = \left(\dfrac{1}{a} + \dfrac{1}{b}\right)(a^2 + b^2)$
$(w + z)(a^2 + b^2) = ab(w + z) + 2(a^3 + b^3)$

**22.** $\dfrac{mx + ax}{m - b} = y$
$x - y = a + b$

**23.** $\dfrac{u+v-1}{u-v+1} = a$
$\dfrac{v-u+1}{u-v+1} = b$

**24.** $\dfrac{u}{a} + \dfrac{2y}{b} = 1$
$\dfrac{2u}{a} - \dfrac{y}{b} = \dfrac{1}{3}$

**25.** $\dfrac{5}{x} - \dfrac{3}{y} + 2 = 0$
$\dfrac{25}{x} + \dfrac{1}{y} = 6$

*Hint.* Solve first for $\dfrac{1}{x}$ and $\dfrac{1}{y}$.

**26.** $\dfrac{3}{x} - 3 = -\dfrac{8}{y}$

$\dfrac{15}{x} - 4 = \dfrac{4}{y}$

**27.** $\dfrac{5}{x} + \dfrac{6}{y} = 20$

$\dfrac{6}{x} + \dfrac{5}{y} = 10$

**28.** $\dfrac{1}{u} - \dfrac{4}{v} = \dfrac{3}{2}$

$\dfrac{3}{u} + \dfrac{1}{v} = \dfrac{1}{6}$

**29.** $\dfrac{7}{x-1} - \dfrac{2}{y-2} = \dfrac{13}{2}$

$\dfrac{3}{x-1} + \dfrac{4}{y-2} - 4 = 0$

**30.** $\dfrac{5}{3u} - \dfrac{7}{v} = -\dfrac{29}{9}$

$\dfrac{3}{u} + \dfrac{5}{4v} = \dfrac{9}{8}$

**31.** $\dfrac{a}{w} + \dfrac{b}{z} = m$

$\dfrac{c}{w} + \dfrac{d}{z} = n$

*Hint.* Solve first for $\dfrac{1}{x-1}$ and $\dfrac{1}{y-2}$.

**32.** $\dfrac{a}{u} + \dfrac{b}{v} = \dfrac{a-b}{a}$

$\dfrac{b}{u} + \dfrac{a}{v} = \dfrac{b-a}{a}$

**33.** $\dfrac{a}{u} + \dfrac{b}{v} = \dfrac{1}{c}$

$\dfrac{c}{u} - \dfrac{a}{v} = \dfrac{1}{b}$

**34.** $\dfrac{a}{bx} + \dfrac{b}{ay} - a = b$

$\dfrac{b}{x} + \dfrac{a}{y} = a^2 + b^2$

**34. Systems of three linear equations in three unknowns.** By substitution, or addition and subtraction, we can eliminate the same unknown from any two pairs of equations. Then we have two linear equations in two unknowns which can be solved by the method of § 33. By substituting these solutions in one of the given equations we obtain the third unknown. The solution should always be checked by substitution in each one of the original equations.

EXAMPLE I. Solve:

$$2x - 3y + z = 6 \qquad (1)$$
$$x + 4y - 3z = -17 \qquad (2)$$
$$3x + y + 4z = -5 \qquad (3)$$

**Solution.**

Multiply (1) by 3     $6x - 9y + 3z = 18 \qquad (4)$
Add (4) and (2)        $7x - 5y = 1 \qquad (5)$
Multiply (1) by $-4$   $-8x + 12y - 4z = -24 \qquad (6)$
Add (6) and (3)        $-5x + 13y = -29 \qquad (7)$

Solving the system (5) and (7) we obtain $x = -2$, $y = -3$, and substituting these values in (1) we have

$$2(-2) - 3(-3) + z = 6$$
$$-4 + 9 + z = 6$$
$$z = 1.$$

Thus the solution is $x = -2$, $y = -3$, $z = 1$. (Ans.)

*Check.*

$$-4 + 9 + 1 \overset{?}{=} 6$$
$$6 = 6 \checkmark$$
$$-2 - 12 - 3 \overset{?}{=} -17$$
$$-17 = -17 \checkmark$$
$$-6 - 3 + 4 \overset{?}{=} -5$$
$$-5 = -5 \checkmark$$

## EXERCISES

*Solve the following systems:*

**1.** $x - 2y + 3z = 6$
$2x + 3y - 4z = 20$
$3x - 2y + 5z = 26$

**2.** $2r - 3s - t = -7$
$3r + 7s + t = 30$
$11r - 11s - 2t = -3$

**3.** $2u + 2v - 5w = 3$
$u - 2v + w = 0$
$3u + v + 3w = 7$

**4.** $a + b + 2c = 1$
$2a + 3b + 2c = 4$
$4a + 9b + 2c = 16$

**5.** $3x + y - 37 = 0$
$x + 3z = 25$
$3y + z = 22$

**6.** $\dfrac{2u}{3} + v = w$
$w - 2v = 2$
$u + w = 4$

**7.** $x - z = 1$
$3y + 4z = 7$
$2x - 5y = -19$

**8.** $3m + 4n + 5p = -68$
$2m + n + 2 = 0$
$4n - p = -14$

**9.** $u - \dfrac{3v}{2} + 2w = \dfrac{11}{2}$

$w - \dfrac{v + 3u}{2} + 3.5 = 0$

$w - \dfrac{5u}{6} + 2 = 0$

**10.** $\dfrac{x}{2} + \dfrac{y}{3} + z = 1$

$x - \dfrac{y}{3} - \dfrac{z}{2} - 1 = 0$

$-\dfrac{x}{3} - y + \dfrac{z}{2} = 1$

**11.** $\dfrac{1}{6}a - \dfrac{1}{5}b + \dfrac{1}{4}c = 3$

$\dfrac{1}{5}a - \dfrac{1}{4}b + \dfrac{1}{5}c = 1$

$\dfrac{1}{4}a - \dfrac{1}{3}b + \dfrac{1}{2}c = 5$

**12.** $\dfrac{u}{3 + w} = \dfrac{3}{7}$

$\dfrac{v}{4 + w} = \dfrac{4}{9}$

$\dfrac{w}{u + 5} = \dfrac{5}{8}$

**13.** $\dfrac{1}{3}(m + n) - \dfrac{1}{5}p = \dfrac{2}{3}$

$\dfrac{1}{4}(n + p) - \dfrac{1}{2}m = \dfrac{5}{12}$

$3m + 2n = 12 - 3p$

**14.** $\dfrac{1}{x} + \dfrac{1}{y} + \dfrac{1}{z} = 20$

$\dfrac{1}{2x} + \dfrac{1}{6y} + \dfrac{1}{12z} - 3 = 0$

$\dfrac{1}{x} + \dfrac{1}{3y} + \dfrac{1}{4z} = 7$

**15.** $\dfrac{1}{a} + \dfrac{1}{b} + \dfrac{1}{c} = 36$

$\dfrac{1}{a} + \dfrac{3}{b} - \dfrac{1}{c} = 28$

$\dfrac{1}{a} + \dfrac{1}{3b} + \dfrac{1}{2c} = 20$

**16.** $\dfrac{1}{u} + \dfrac{1}{v} = 2$

$\dfrac{1}{u} + \dfrac{1}{w} = 3$

$\dfrac{1}{v} + \dfrac{1}{w} = 4$

**17.** $\dfrac{2}{r} + \dfrac{3}{s} + \dfrac{1}{t} = \dfrac{41}{40}$

$\dfrac{3}{r} - \dfrac{2}{s} + \dfrac{3}{t} = \dfrac{77}{120}$

$\dfrac{1}{r} + \dfrac{1}{s} + \dfrac{1}{t} = \dfrac{59}{120}$

**18.** $x - \dfrac{by}{a} = \dfrac{a^2 + b^2}{a}$

$y - \dfrac{az}{b} = \dfrac{a^2 - b^2}{b}$

$\dfrac{x}{a} + \dfrac{z}{b} = \dfrac{2ab + b^2 - a^2}{ab}$

**19.** $\dfrac{a}{x} + \dfrac{b}{y} + \dfrac{a + b}{z} = 3$

$\dfrac{a + b}{x} - \dfrac{a + b}{y} = \dfrac{b^2 - a^2}{ab}$

$\dfrac{a}{z} - \dfrac{a - b}{x} = \dfrac{b^2}{a(a + b)}$

**20.** $w + x + y + z = -\dfrac{73}{60}$

$y = 1 - \dfrac{12}{5}x$

$z = 1 - \dfrac{15}{4}y$

$w = 1 - 12z$

**21.** $p + q + r + s = 0$
$p + 2q + 3r + 4s = 2$
$p + 3q + 6r + 10s = 6$
$p + 4q + 10r + 20s = 13$

**35. Solution by determinants.** *A determinant is a number written in the form of a square array of numbers.* For example,

$$\begin{vmatrix} a_1 & b_1 \\ a_2 & b_2 \end{vmatrix}, \qquad \begin{vmatrix} a_1 & b_1 & c_1 \\ a_2 & b_2 & c_2 \\ a_3 & b_3 & c_3 \end{vmatrix},$$

are two determinants, where $a_1$, $b_1$, $c_1$, $a_2$, $b_2$, etc., are any numbers. The first determinant has two rows and two columns of numbers and is said to be of the second order; the other determinant is of the third order. The rows are numbered from the top to the bottom in order, and the columns from left to right; thus in the second determinant the first row is $a_1$, $b_1$, $c_1$, the third column is $c_1$, $c_2$, $c_3$. Each number in a determinant is called an element, e.g., $a_1$, $b_2$, $c_2$, are elements.

*To evaluate a determinant of the second order:*

(1) Multiply the upper left element by the lower right element.

(2) Subtract from this product the product of the lower left and upper right elements.

Thus,   $= + (a_1b_2) - (a_2b_1)$

The product of the elements in the diagonal down to the right is preceded by a plus sign; the product of the elements in diagonal down to the left is preceded by a minus sign. The value of the determinant is the algebraic sum of these products.

*To evaluate a determinant of the third order:*

(1) Rewrite the first column to the right of the third column, thus forming a fourth column.

(2) Rewrite the second column to the right of this fourth column.

(3) Draw the diagonals as shown below:

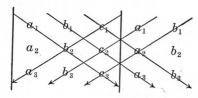

(4) The products of the elements in the diagonals running down to the right are preceded by plus signs, and the products of the elements in the diagonals running down to the left are preceded by minus signs.

(5) The value of the determinant is the algebraic sum of these products.

EXAMPLE I. Evaluate:   $\begin{vmatrix} 2 & 3 \\ -3 & -4 \end{vmatrix}$

Solution.   $= 2(-4) - (3)(-3) = -8 + 9 = 1$ (Ans.)

EXAMPLE II. Evaluate:
$$\begin{vmatrix} 2 & -3 & 1 \\ 1 & 4 & -3 \\ 3 & 1 & 4 \end{vmatrix}$$

Solution.

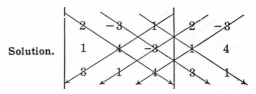

$$= (2)(4)(4) + (-3)(-3)(3) + (1)(1)(1) - (3)(4)(1) - (1)(-3)(2)$$
$$- (4)(1)(-3)$$
$$= 32 + 27 + 1 - 12 + 6 + 12 = 66 \quad \text{(Ans.)}$$

By means of determinants we can write down immediately the solution of a system of linear equations. The solution of the system

$$\begin{aligned} a_1x + b_1y &= d_1 \\ a_2x + b_2y &= d_2 \end{aligned} \qquad \text{(A)}$$

is

$$x = \frac{\begin{vmatrix} d_1 & b_1 \\ d_2 & b_2 \end{vmatrix}}{\begin{vmatrix} a_1 & b_1 \\ a_2 & b_2 \end{vmatrix}}, \qquad y = \frac{\begin{vmatrix} a_1 & d_1 \\ a_2 & d_2 \end{vmatrix}}{\begin{vmatrix} a_1 & b_1 \\ a_2 & b_2 \end{vmatrix}}$$

The solution of the system

$$\begin{aligned} a_1x + b_1y + c_1z &= d_1 \\ a_2x + b_2y + c_2z &= d_2 \\ a_3x + b_3y + c_3z &= d_3 \end{aligned} \qquad \text{(B)}$$

is

$$x = \frac{\begin{vmatrix} d_1 & b_1 & c_1 \\ d_2 & b_2 & c_2 \\ d_3 & b_3 & c_3 \end{vmatrix}}{\begin{vmatrix} a_1 & b_1 & c_1 \\ a_2 & b_2 & c_2 \\ a_3 & b_3 & c_3 \end{vmatrix}}, \qquad y = \frac{\begin{vmatrix} a_1 & d_1 & c_1 \\ a_2 & d_2 & c_2 \\ a_3 & d_3 & c_3 \end{vmatrix}}{\begin{vmatrix} a_1 & b_1 & c_1 \\ a_2 & b_2 & c_2 \\ a_3 & b_3 & c_3 \end{vmatrix}}, \qquad z = \frac{\begin{vmatrix} a_1 & b_1 & d_1 \\ a_2 & b_2 & d_2 \\ a_3 & b_3 & d_3 \end{vmatrix}}{\begin{vmatrix} a_1 & b_1 & c_1 \\ a_2 & b_2 & c_2 \\ a_3 & b_3 & c_3 \end{vmatrix}}$$

That these are solutions can be easily verified by substitution. Of course, we assume here that the determinants in the denominators are not zero.

To solve a system by determinants the first step is to write the system as in (A) or (B) with the corresponding unknowns in columns on the left and the constants on the right. *The determinant formed from the coefficients of the unknowns is called the* **determinant of the system.** The value of each unknown is given in the form of a fraction and the denominator of this fraction is the determinant of the system. The numerator of this fraction is the determinant formed from the determinant of the system by replacing the coefficients of this unknown by the corresponding constants.

**EXAMPLE III.**   Solve by determinants:
$$\tfrac{1}{5}(2x + 3y) - \tfrac{1}{2}(2x - 3) = 0$$
$$\tfrac{1}{2}(8x + 5y) - \tfrac{1}{7}(10x - y) = -4$$

**Solution.**   (1) Clear of fractions by multiplying by the L.C.D.'s.
$$2(2x + 3y) - 5(2x - 3) = 0$$
$$7(8x + 5y) - 2(10x - y) = -56$$

(2) Perform the indicated operations, remove parentheses, and write in the form (A).
$$2x - 2y = 5$$
$$36x + 37y = -56$$

(3) Form the determinant of the system using the coefficients of the unknowns (with their signs) as the elements, so that the upper left coefficient is the upper left element, etc.  Evaluate the determinant.

$$\begin{vmatrix} 2 & -2 \\ 36 & 37 \end{vmatrix} = 2(37) - (-2)(36) = 74 + 72 = 146$$

(4) If the value of the determinant is not zero, each unknown is given by the fraction whose denominator is the determinant of the system and whose numerator is the determinant formed from the determinant of the system by replacing the coefficients of the unknown sought by the constants in the corresponding equations.

$$x = \frac{\begin{vmatrix} 5 & -2 \\ -56 & 37 \end{vmatrix}}{146} = \frac{5(37) - (-2)(-56)}{146} = \frac{185 - 112}{146} = \frac{73}{146} = \frac{1}{2}$$

$$y = \frac{\begin{vmatrix} 2 & 5 \\ 36 & -56 \end{vmatrix}}{146} = \frac{2(-56) - 5(36)}{146} = \frac{-112 - 180}{146} = -2$$

Thus the solution is $x = \tfrac{1}{2}$, $y = -2$.   (Ans.)

*Check.* $\quad \frac{1}{5}[2(\frac{1}{2}) + 3(-2)] + \frac{1}{2}[2(\frac{1}{2}) - 3] \overset{?}{=} 0$

$$\frac{1}{5}(1 - 6) - \frac{1}{2}(1 - 3) \overset{?}{=} 0$$

$$-1 + 1 = 0 \checkmark$$

$$\frac{1}{2}[8(\frac{1}{2}) + 5(-2)] - \frac{1}{7}[10(\frac{1}{2}) - (-2)] \overset{?}{=} -4$$

$$\frac{1}{2}(4 - 10) - \frac{1}{7}(5 + 2) \overset{?}{=} -4$$

$$-3 - 1 = -4 \checkmark$$

EXAMPLE IV.   Solve: $2x + 3y + 6z = 6$

$$z + 4x - 3 = -y$$

$$3z - \tfrac{1}{2} + x = 6y$$

**Solution.** (1) Clear of fractions by multiplying by the L.C.D.'s.

(2) Perform the indicated operations, remove parentheses, and write in the form (B).

$$2x + 3y + 6z = 6$$

$$4x + y + z = 3$$

$$2x - 12y + 6z = 1$$

(3) Form the determinant of the system using the coefficients of the unknowns (with their signs) as the elements, so that the upper left coefficient is the upper left element, etc. Evaluate this determinant.

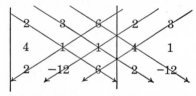

$$= 2(1)(6) + 3(1)(2) + 6(4)(-12) - 2(1)(6) - (-12)(1)(2) - 6(4)(3)$$

$$= 12 + 6 - 288 - 12 + 24 - 72 = -330$$

(4) If the value of the determinant is not zero, each unknown is given by the fraction whose denominator is the determinant of the system and whose numerator is the determinant formed from the determinant of the system by replacing the coefficients of the unknown sought by the constants in the corresponding equations.

$$x = \frac{\begin{vmatrix} 6 & 3 & 6 \\ 3 & 1 & 1 \\ 1 & -12 & 6 \end{vmatrix} \begin{matrix} 6 & 3 \\ 3 & 1 \\ 1 & -12 \end{matrix}}{-330}$$

$$= \frac{6(1)(6) + 3(1)(1) + 6(3)(-12) - (1)(1)(6) - (-12)(1)(6) - 6(3)(3)}{-330}$$

$$= \frac{-165}{-330} = \frac{1}{2}$$

$$y = \frac{\begin{vmatrix} 2 & 6 & 6 \\ 4 & 3 & 1 \\ 2 & 1 & 6 \end{vmatrix} \begin{matrix} 2 & 6 \\ 4 & 3 \\ 2 & 1 \end{matrix}}{-330}$$

$$= \frac{2(3)(6) + 6(1)(2) + 6(4)(1) - 2(3)(6) - 1(1)(2) - 6(4)(6)}{-330}$$

$$= \frac{-110}{-330} = \frac{1}{3}$$

$$z = \frac{\begin{vmatrix} 2 & 3 & 6 \\ 4 & 1 & 3 \\ 2 & -12 & 1 \end{vmatrix} \begin{matrix} 2 & 3 \\ 4 & 1 \\ 2 & -12 \end{matrix}}{-330}$$

$$= \frac{2(1)(1) + 3(3)(2) + 6(4)(-12) - (2)(1)(6) - (-12)(3)(2) - (1)(4)(3)}{-330}$$

$$= \frac{-220}{-330} = \frac{2}{3}$$

Thus the solution is $x = \frac{1}{2}$, $y = \frac{1}{3}$, $z = \frac{2}{3}$.   (Ans.)

*Check.*
$$2(\tfrac{1}{2}) + 3(\tfrac{1}{3}) + 6(\tfrac{2}{3}) \overset{?}{=} 6$$
$$1 + 1 + 4 = 6 \checkmark$$
$$\tfrac{2}{3} + 4(\tfrac{1}{2}) - 3 \overset{?}{=} -\tfrac{1}{3}$$
$$\tfrac{2}{3} + 2 - 3 \overset{?}{=} -\tfrac{1}{3}$$
$$\tfrac{2}{3} - 1 = -\tfrac{1}{3} \checkmark$$
$$3(\tfrac{2}{3}) - \tfrac{1}{2} + \tfrac{1}{2} \overset{?}{=} 6(\tfrac{1}{3})$$
$$2 = 2 \checkmark$$

*In (A) or (B) if the determinant of the system is zero and the constants are not all zero there is no solution. If the constants are all zero,* of course, *a solution is zero for each unknown.*

### EXERCISES

*Solve the exercises of §§ 33 and 34 by determinants.*

**36. Applications.** The method used in solving practical problems reducible to linear systems is the same as that of § 32.

EXAMPLE I.   The sum of two numbers is 137 and the difference of these same numbers is 13.   Find the numbers.

**Solution.**   Let $x$ represent one number and $y$ the other.
Then,
$$x + y = 137$$
$$x - y = 13$$

Adding

$$2x = 150$$
$$x = 75 \text{ (one number)}$$

Subtracting

$$2y = 124$$
$$y = 62 \text{ (the other number)}$$

Check.

$$75 + 62 = 137 \checkmark$$
$$75 - 62 = 13 \checkmark$$

EXAMPLE II. Find the area of a rectangle from the following data: If 6 inches be added to its length and 6 inches to its breadth, the one becomes $\frac{3}{2}$ the other, and the area is increased by 84.

**Solution.** Let $x$ be the length and $y$ the breadth.

Then

$$x + 6 = \tfrac{3}{2}(y + 6) \tag{1}$$

Also,

$$(x + 6)(y + 6) = xy + 84 \tag{2}$$

From (1)

$$2x + 12 = 3y + 18$$
$$2x - 3y = 6 \tag{3}$$

From (2)

$$\cancel{xy} + 6x + 6y + 36 = \cancel{xy} + 84$$
$$6x + 6y = 48$$
$$x + y = 8$$
$$x = 8 - y \tag{4}$$

Substituting in (3)

$$2(8 - y) - 3y = 6$$
$$16 - 2y - 3y = 6$$
$$-5y = -10$$
$$y = 2 \text{ (width)}$$
$$x = 8 - 2 = 6 \text{ (length)}$$

Check.

$$6 + 6 \overset{?}{=} \tfrac{3}{2}(2 + 6)$$
$$12 = 12 \checkmark$$

Original area $= 6 \times 2 = 12$

New area $= 12 \times 8 = 96.\ \ 96 - 12 = 84 \checkmark$

## EXERCISES

**1.** Find two numbers such that 4 times the greater exceeds 5 times the lesser by 7, and twice the greater exceeds 3 times the lesser by 1.

**2.** Find two numbers such that twice the first minus the second equals 16, and twice the second plus the first equals 3.

**3.** A fraction which is equal to $\frac{3}{4}$ is increased to $\frac{9}{11}$ when 3 is added to each of its terms. Find the fraction.

**4.** One rectangle has the same area as another which is 4 feet longer and 2 feet narrower; it has also the same area as a third which is 12 feet longer and 4 feet narrower. What is the area of the rectangles?

**5.** A rectangular field is surrounded by a walk 10 feet wide. The area of the walk is 1800 square feet. If the width of the field were doubled, the area of the 10-foot walk would be 2200 square feet. Find the dimensions of the field.

**6.** A service station sold on the average 5000 gallons of gasoline a day. The owner reduced the price 10 per cent, and found that his daily cash receipts were increased 8 per cent. How many gallons did he sell daily at the reduced price?

**7.** A certain sum of money invested at simple interest amounted to $896 in two years, and to $1040 in five years. What was the sum invested, and what was the rate of interest?

**8.** A and B together can do a piece of work in 15 days. After A has worked alone for 6 days, B finishes the work in 42 days. In what time can each alone do the work?

**9.** Two pipes A and B running together can empty a tank containing 840 gallons in 12 minutes. But after they have run together for 9 minutes A is closed and B finishes emptying the tank in 7 minutes more. How many gallons a minute does each pipe carry?

**10.** A, B, and C can together do a piece of work in 8 days. B and C can together do it in 9 days, and C does twice as much as A and B together. In what time can each do the work?

**11.** A grocer sold two baskets of peaches and four of strawberries to a customer for $2.68, and three baskets of peaches and two of strawberries to another for $1.98. Find the price of each per basket.

**12.** A merchant mixed good wheat, costing $1.00 a bushel, with poor wheat, costing 75 cents a bushel, in such proportions as to gain 10 per cent by selling it at 88 cents a bushel. What were the percentages of good wheat and poor wheat in the mixture?

**13.** A man wishes to buy two grades of chickens at a total cost of $12. If he buys 5 of the first grade and 10 of the second, he finds that he lacks 25 cents of the amount necessary to buy them. If he buys 8 of the first grade and 6 of the second, he still lacks 60 cents of the necessary amount. What is the cost per chicken of each grade?

**14.** A motorist made a trip of 270 miles. At the end of 90 miles he was forced to reduce his speed. He finished the entire trip in 7 hours. If he had been able to keep his original speed for 180 miles before slowing down to the reduced speed, he would have finished the trip in 6 hours. Find his original speed and his reduced speed.

**15.** A man can row 4 miles downstream in 1 hour; it takes him 2 hours to row the same distance upstream. Find rate of current and rate of rowing.

*Hint.* In going upstream progress is at the rate of rowing minus the rate of current, while downstream progress is at the sum of these rates.

**16.** In a certain mill some of the workmen receive $4.50 a day and others more. The total paid in wages each day is $1880. An assessment made by a labor union to raise $1000 required $3.00 from each man receiving $4.50 a day and half of one day's pay from each man receiving more. How many men receive $4.50 a day?

**17.** A child's bank contains $2.00 in dimes and nickels. If 6 nickels and 7 dimes are withdrawn, 5 more of one kind of coin than of the other remain in the bank. Show that the question, "How many coins of each kind were there in the bank originally?" can have only one solution.

**18.** The sides of a triangle are $a$, $b$, $c$. If perpendiculars are drawn from the center of the inscribed circle, prove that the segments of the sides are $s - a$, $s - b$, $s - c$, where $2s = a + b + c$.

**19.** If $h$ is the height in meters above sea level and $b$ the reading of a barometer in millimeters, it is known that $b = k + hm$ where $k$ and $m$ are constants. At 120 meters above sea level the barometer reads 748, and at 650 meters it reads 695. Find the formula showing the relation between $b$ and $h$.

**20.** The boiling point $w$ of water in degrees Fahrenheit and the height $h$ in feet above sea level is given by the equation $x - wy = h$, where $x$ and $y$ are constants. At a height of 2200 feet the boiling point is 208°, and at sea level, the boiling point is 212°. Find the formula for $h$ in terms of $w$.

# CHAPTER VI

## QUADRATIC EQUATIONS

**37. Solution by factoring.** Any equation of the second degree (quadratic equation) in one unknown can be written in the form $ax^2 + bx + c = 0$, where $a$, $b$, $c$ are constants, $a \neq 0$, and $x$ is the variable. The left member of this equation is a polynomial of the second degree and it has two roots which are the solutions of the equation. If the polynomial is readily factored, the solutions are found by setting each linear factor equal to zero.

EXAMPLE I. Solve: $x^2 - 5x - 6 = 0$.

**Solution.** $\qquad\qquad\qquad x^2 - 5x - 6 = 0 \qquad\qquad\qquad (1)$

Factoring (1) $\qquad\qquad (x - 6)(x + 1) = 0 \qquad\qquad\qquad (2)$

Putting $\qquad\qquad x - 6 = 0$, we have $x = 6$,

and $\qquad\qquad\qquad x + 1 = 0$, we have $x = -1$.

Thus the solutions are $x = 6$, $x = -1$, because a value of $x$ which makes either factor of (2) zero, makes the product zero and hence satisfies the equation.

*Check.* $\quad (6)^2 - 5(6) - 6 = 36 - 30 - 6 = 36 - 36 = 0 \checkmark$

$\qquad\qquad (-1)^2 - 5(-1) - 6 = 1 + 5 - 6 = 6 - 6 = 0 \checkmark$

EXAMPLE II. Solve: $(1 - 2x)^2 = \frac{2}{3}[5 - x(3 - 4x)] + x^2$.

**Solution.** By multiplying by the L.C.D., removing parentheses, and transposing we write the equation in standard form.

$$(1 - 2x)^2 = \tfrac{2}{3}[5 - x(3 - 4x)] + x^2$$
$$3(1 - 4x + 4x^2) = 2[5 - 3x + 4x^2] + 3x^2$$
$$3 - 12x + 12x^2 = 10 - 6x + 8x^2 + 3x^2$$
$$x^2 - 6x - 7 = 0 \qquad\qquad\qquad (1)$$

Factoring (1) $\qquad (x - 7)(x + 1) = 0$

Putting $\qquad\qquad x - 7 = 0$, we have $x = 7$,

and $\qquad\qquad\qquad x + 1 = 0$, we have $x = -1$.

Thus the solutions are $x = 7$, $x = -1$.  (Ans.)

81

*Check.*   $[1 - 2(-1)]^2 \overset{?}{=} \frac{2}{3}[5 - (-1)(3 - 4(-1))] + (-1)^2$

$\qquad\qquad (1 + 2)^2 \overset{?}{=} \frac{2}{3}[5 + 3 + 4] + 1$

$\qquad\qquad\qquad 9 \overset{?}{=} \frac{2}{3}(12) + 1$

$\qquad\qquad\qquad 9 = 9 \checkmark$

$\qquad [1 - 2(7)]^2 \overset{?}{=} \frac{2}{3}[5 - 7(3 - 4(7))] + 7^2$

$\qquad\qquad (1 - 14)^2 \overset{?}{=} \frac{2}{3}[5 - 21 + 196] + 49$

$\qquad\qquad\qquad 169 \overset{?}{=} \frac{2}{3}(180) + 49$

$\qquad\qquad\qquad 169 = 169 \checkmark$

**EXAMPLE III.**  Solve: $x^3 + 5x^2 - 7x - 2 = x(3x - 4 + x^2)$

**Solution.**  $\qquad\qquad x^3 + 5x^2 - 7x - 2 = 3x^2 - 4x + x^3$

$\qquad\qquad\qquad 2x^2 - 3x - 2 = 0$

$\qquad\qquad\qquad (2x + 1)(x - 2) = 0$

$\qquad\qquad 2x + 1 = 0,\ x = -\frac{1}{2}$

$\qquad\qquad x - 2 = 0,\ x = 2.$

Thus the solutions are $x = -\frac{1}{2},\ x = 2.$  (Ans.)

*Check.*   $(-\frac{1}{2})^3 + 5(-\frac{1}{2})^2 - 7(-\frac{1}{2}) - 2 \overset{?}{=} -\frac{1}{2}[3(-\frac{1}{2}) - 4 + (-\frac{1}{2})^2]$

$\qquad\qquad -\frac{1}{8} + \frac{5}{4} + \frac{7}{2} - 2 \overset{?}{=} \frac{3}{4} + 2 - \frac{1}{8}$

$\qquad\qquad -\frac{1}{8} + \frac{10}{8} + \frac{28}{8} - \frac{16}{8} \overset{?}{=} \frac{6}{8} + \frac{16}{8} - \frac{1}{8}$

$\qquad\qquad\qquad \frac{21}{8} = \frac{21}{8} \checkmark$

$\qquad 2^3 + 5(2)^2 - 7(2) - 2 \overset{?}{=} 2[3(2) - 4 + (2)^2]$

$\qquad\qquad 8 + 20 - 14 - 2 \overset{?}{=} 2[6 - 4 + 4]$

$\qquad\qquad\qquad 12 = 12 \checkmark$

In factoring a quadratic we have

$$ax^2 + bx + c = (Ax + B)(Cx + D)$$
$$= ACx^2 + (AD + BC)x + BD.$$

Thus $ACBD = ac$ and hence the first step is to factor $ac$ into two factors whose algebraic sum is $b$; these two factors are $AD$ and $BC$. Now factor $AD$ and $BC$ into two factors each so that the algebraic product of one factor from each is $c$; these two numbers are $D$ and $B$ respectively.

**EXAMPLE IV.**  Solve: $6x^2 + x - 12 = 0.$

**Solution.**  $6(-12) = -72$, which factors into $9(-8)$ whose sum, $9 - 8 = 1$, is $b = 1$. Now $9 = 3 \cdot 3$ and $-8 = (-2)(2)(2)$.

Since $\qquad\qquad\qquad 3(-4) = -12,$

we have $\qquad\qquad (3x - 4)(2x + 3) = 0.$

$\qquad\qquad\qquad x = \frac{4}{3},\ x = -\frac{3}{2}$  (Ans.)

## EXERCISES

*Solve the following:*

**1.** $x^2 - 4x - 21 = 0$

**2.** $y^2 - 9y + 14 = 0$

**3.** $6v^2 + 5v - 21 = 0$

**4.** $2x^2 - 24x = 56$

**5.** $6y^2 - 5y = 4$

**6.** $3z^2 + 8z + 4 = 0$

**7.** $3a^2 + 4a + 1 = 0$

**8.** $w^2 + 7w + 12 = 0$

**9.** $x^2 + 9x = 0$

**10.** $3u^2 - 25u + 28 = 0$

**11.** $s^2 + 12s = 24 + 2s$

**12.** $25x^2 + 20x + 4 = 0$

**13.** $\dfrac{8}{y - 3} = \dfrac{y - 2}{y - 4} + 1$

**14.** $u^2 - 5u = 16u - 2u^2$

**15.** $z^2 - 144 = 0$

**16.** $3x^2 = 5x$

**17.** $\dfrac{2 - m}{3 + m} = \dfrac{6 - 3m}{m - 1}$

**18.** $\dfrac{3}{4r^2} + \dfrac{7}{8r} - \dfrac{5}{2} = 0$

**19.** $\dfrac{s + 2}{s + 3} + 1 = \dfrac{36}{(s + 3)^2}$

**20.** $\dfrac{3}{2w^2} + \dfrac{5}{2w} - 1 = 0$

**38. The quadratic formula.** Oftentimes a quadratic polynomial is difficult to factor. In this case we can find the roots by means of the quadratic formula. *The derivation of this formula makes use of the method of completing the square and any quadratic equation can be solved by* **completing the square.**

Let
$$ax^2 + bx + c = 0, \ a \neq 0. \tag{1}$$

Since $a \neq 0$, we can divide by $a$ and we have

$$x^2 + \frac{b}{a}x + \frac{c}{a} = 0,$$

or

$$x^2 + \frac{b}{a}x = -\frac{c}{a}.$$

The left member is the sum of the first two terms of a binomial square. To get the third term we take half the coefficient of $x$ and square it; this is

$$\left[\frac{1}{2}\left(\frac{b}{a}\right)\right]^2 = \frac{b^2}{4a^2}$$

Adding this to both members we have

$$x^2 + \frac{b}{a}x + \frac{b^2}{4a^2} = \frac{b^2}{4a^2} - \frac{c}{a}$$

$$\left(x + \frac{b}{2a}\right)^2 = \frac{b^2 - 4ac}{4a^2}.$$

Taking the square root of both members we have

$$x + \frac{b}{2a} = \frac{+ \sqrt{b^2 - 4ac}}{2a}$$

$$x + \frac{b}{2a} = \frac{- \sqrt{b^2 - 4ac}}{2a}.$$

Since every number has two square roots and since we have agreed that $\sqrt{a}$, where $a$ is positive, shall be taken as positive it is necessary to indicate these two roots by the two signs $+$ and $-$.

Thus,
$$x = \frac{- b + \sqrt{b^2 - 4ac}}{2a} \qquad (2)$$

and
$$x = \frac{- b - \sqrt{b^2 - 4ac}}{2a} \qquad (3)$$

are the two roots of $ax^2 + bx + c = 0$. This is the quadratic formula and is written

$$x = \frac{- b \pm \sqrt{b^2 - 4ac}}{2a} \qquad (4)$$

where $\pm$, read "**plus or minus**," *indicates that two different numbers are represented*. In fact, (4) is simply a short way of writing (2) and (3) in one equation.

EXAMPLE I.   Solve: $2x^2 - 2x - 1 = 0$ by the formula.

**Solution.**   Putting $a = 2$, $b = -2$, and $c = -1$, we see that

$$ax^2 + bx + c = 0 \text{ becomes } 2x^2 - 2x - 1 = 0.$$

Thus, by the formula

$$x = \frac{-(-2) \pm \sqrt{4 - 4(2)(-1)}}{2(2)} = \frac{2 \pm \sqrt{12}}{4}$$

$$x = \frac{2 \pm 2\sqrt{3}}{4} = \frac{1 \pm \sqrt{3}}{2}$$

The two solutions are $x = \dfrac{1 + \sqrt{3}}{2}$, $x = \dfrac{1 - \sqrt{3}}{2}$.   (Ans.)

*Check.*
$$2\left(\frac{1+\sqrt{3}}{2}\right)^2 - 2\left(\frac{1+\sqrt{3}}{2}\right) - 1 \overset{?}{=} 0$$

$$\frac{2(1+2\sqrt{3}+3)}{4} - 1 - \sqrt{3} - 1 \overset{?}{=} 0$$

$$\frac{8+4\sqrt{3}}{4} - 2 - \sqrt{3} \overset{?}{=} 0$$

$$2 + \sqrt{3} - 2 - \sqrt{3} = 0 \;\checkmark$$

$$2\left(\frac{1-\sqrt{3}}{2}\right)^2 - 2\left(\frac{1-\sqrt{3}}{2}\right) - 1 \overset{?}{=} 0$$

$$\frac{2(1-2\sqrt{3}+3)}{4} - 1 + \sqrt{3} - 1 \overset{?}{=} 0$$

$$\frac{8-4\sqrt{3}}{4} - 2 + \sqrt{3} \overset{?}{=} 0$$

$$2 - \sqrt{3} - 2 + \sqrt{3} = 0 \;\checkmark$$

**EXAMPLE II.** Solve $3x^2 - 6x + 4 = 0$ by completing the square.

**Solution.**
$$3x^2 - 6x + 4 = 0 \tag{5}$$

Divide (5) by 3,
$$x^2 - 2x + \tfrac{4}{3} = 0 \tag{6}$$

$$x^2 - 2x = -\tfrac{4}{3}$$

$$x^2 - 2x + 1 = -\tfrac{4}{3} + 1$$

$$(x-1)^2 = -\tfrac{1}{3}$$

$$x - 1 = \pm\frac{\sqrt{3}}{3}i$$

$$x = 1 \pm \frac{\sqrt{3}}{3}i \quad \text{(Ans.)}$$

*The solution should be checked by substitution in the original equation.*

## EXERCISES

*Solve the following by the formula and by completing the square:*

1. $5x^2 - x - 1 = 0$

2. $x^2 - 3x - 1 = 0$

3. $z^2 - 3z - 2z^2 = 0$

4. $2z = 3z^2 - 2$

5. $2x^2 + 1 = x^2$

6. $3z^2 - 8z + 2 = 0$

7. $6x^2 = 7x + 3$

8. $y^2 + 6y - 4 = 0$

9. $6y^2 + 13y + 6 = 0$

10. $x^2 - 37x + 322 = 0$

11. $28z^2 + 13z - 6 = 0$

12. $55y^2 - 73y - 24 = 0$

13. $x^2 - 19x + 91 = 0$

14. $y^2 - y - 1 = 0$

15. $z^2 + 5z - 10 = 0$

16. $3y^2 - 5y + 12 = 0$

17. $14z^2 - 11z - 15 = 0$

18. $5x^2 - 9x - 5 = 0$

19. $u^2 + au - b = 0$

20. $bx^2 + b = (b^2 + 1)x$

**21.** $u^2 + au + ac + cu = 0$

**22.** $\dfrac{x}{b} = 2 + \dfrac{b}{x - 2b}$

**23.** $\dfrac{a + v}{a - v} = \dfrac{v - 2a}{v + 2a}$

**24.** $\dfrac{1}{6w - 5a} - \dfrac{2}{a} = \dfrac{5}{a - 6w}$

**25.** $5u - \dfrac{3u - 3}{u - 3} = 2u - \dfrac{6 - 3u}{2}$

**26.** $(x + 2)^3 - (x - 3)^3 - 65 = 0$

**27.** $\dfrac{y + 2}{y - 1} - \dfrac{7 - 2y}{2y} = \dfrac{7}{3}$

**28.** $\dfrac{w^2}{4} - (3w + 2)^2 = 1$

**29.** $\dfrac{3}{y - 1} = \dfrac{4}{3} - \dfrac{y - 4}{2y}$

**30.** $\dfrac{1}{z^2 + 3z + 2} - \dfrac{1}{1 - z} = \dfrac{2}{z^2 - 1}$

**31.** $\dfrac{y - 2}{y - 1} - \dfrac{y - 3}{y + 3} = -\left(\dfrac{7}{4} + \dfrac{y + 4}{1 - y}\right)$

**32.** $\dfrac{7x + 3}{x^2 - 4x + 3} + \dfrac{5}{x - 1} + \dfrac{x + 6}{3 - x} = 0$

*Solve for x in terms of y:*

**33.** $x^2 - yx - 2y^2 = 0$

**34.** $2x^2 + 5yx - 3y^2 = 0$

**35.** $2x^2 + (5y - 3)x + (2y^2 - 6y) = 0$

**36.** $y^2 + 4xy + 4x^2 - y + 2 = 0$

**37.** $4y^2 - 2xy + 3x^2 - y + x - 1 = 0$

**38.** $7xy - 3y^2 + 2x - 3y - 1 = 0$

*Find the roots correct to two decimals:*

**39.** $3y^2 - 7y + 3 = 0$

**40.** $2u^2 - 7u + 4 = 0$

**41.** $2x^2 + 4x - 3 = 0$

**42.** $2y^2 - 39y + 45 = 0$

**43.** $8y^2 + 11y + 2 = 0$

**44.** $z^2 + 1.3z + 0.2 = 0$

**45.** $x^2 = 1.8x - 0.5$

**46.** $3x^2 + 3x = 5$

**47.** $y^2 - 2y = 2$

**48.** $(y + 2)(y - 2) = -2$

**39. Equations involving radicals.** *An equation in which the unknown appears under radicals is called an* **irrational equation.** By properly arranging the terms of such an equation and raising both members to suitably chosen powers certain radicals can be removed. A repetition of this process leads to an equation free from radicals. If this final equation is linear or quadratic, it can be solved by the methods already described. *It is absolutely necessary to check all solutions because raising to powers often leads to redundant equations and extraneous roots.*

EXAMPLE I. Solve: $\sqrt[4]{x - 1} - 2 = 0$.

**Solution.** If both members of this equation are raised to the fourth power, the resulting equation will contain three radicals. However, by transposing, we have

$$\sqrt[4]{x - 1} = 2,$$

and raising both sides to the fourth power yields

$$x - 1 = 16. \quad x = 17 \quad \text{(Ans.)}$$

*Check.*  $\sqrt[4]{17 - 1} - 2 = \sqrt[4]{16} - 2 = 2 - 2 = 0 \checkmark$

*Note. It should be recalled that by the indicated root of a positive number we mean the positive root, e.g.* $\sqrt{4} = 2$ *and not* $-2$.

EXAMPLE II.  $\sqrt{x + 1} + 4 = 0$

**Solution.** Transposing $\sqrt{x + 1} = -4$
Squaring $x + 1 = 16$
$x = 15$ (extraneous)

*Check.*  $\sqrt{15 + 1} + 4 = \sqrt{16} + 4 = 8 \neq 0$

Thus the equation has no solution.

As a matter of fact, since $\sqrt{x + 1}$ is either positive or zero, it is obvious from the original equation that there are no solutions.

EXAMPLE III. Solve: $\sqrt{2 - 3x} + \sqrt{3 + x} - \sqrt{1 + 4x} = 0$.

**Solution.** Transposing $\sqrt{2 - 3x} + \sqrt{3 + x} = \sqrt{1 + 4x}$

There is no way to avoid irrational expressions in squaring both members of this equation, but the above transposition reduces the number of radicals in the resulting equation to a minimum.

Squaring $2 - 3x + 2\sqrt{(2 - 3x)(3 + x)} + 3 + x = 1 + 4x$
$$2\sqrt{6 - 7x - 3x^2} = 6x - 4$$
$$\sqrt{6 - 7x - 3x^2} = 3x - 2$$

We have transposed here so that the radical is isolated on one side of the equation, hence on squaring there will be no middle term involving a radical.

Squaring
$$6 - 7x - 3x^2 = (3x - 2)^2$$
$$6 - 7x - 3x^2 = 9x^2 - 12x + 4$$
$$-12x^2 + 5x + 2 = 0$$
$$12x^2 - 5x - 2 = 0$$
$$(4x + 1)(3x - 2) = 0$$
$$4x = -1$$
$$x = -\tfrac{1}{4}$$
$$3x = 2$$
$$x = \tfrac{2}{3}$$

*Check.*  $\sqrt{2 - 3(-\tfrac{1}{4})} + \sqrt{3 - \tfrac{1}{4}} - \sqrt{1 + 4(-\tfrac{1}{4})} \overset{?}{=} 0$
$$\sqrt{\frac{11}{4}} + \sqrt{\frac{11}{4}} = \sqrt{11} \neq 0$$

Thus $x = -\frac{1}{4}$ is extraneous.

$$\sqrt{2 - 3(\tfrac{2}{3})} + \sqrt{3 + \tfrac{2}{3}} - \sqrt{1 + 4(\tfrac{2}{3})} \overset{?}{=} 0$$
$$\sqrt{1\tfrac{1}{3}} - \sqrt{1\tfrac{1}{3}} = 0 \checkmark$$

Thus $x = \frac{2}{3}$ is the root of the equation.    (Ans.)

## EXERCISES

*Solve the following equations:*

**1.** $\sqrt{x - 1} = 3$

**2.** $\sqrt{x + 2} = \sqrt{2x - 5}$

**3.** $\sqrt{z^2 + z} = -3\sqrt{z + 1}$

**4.** $\sqrt[4]{x + 1} = 2$

**5.** $2x = \sqrt{3}$

**6.** $\sqrt{3z + 2} = -3$

**7.** $\sqrt{\dfrac{z - 3}{z + 3}} = 2$

**8.** $\sqrt{z + 4} = \sqrt{z} + 1$

**9.** $x^{\frac{2}{3}} = 4$

**10.** $\sqrt[3]{z^2 - 2z} - 2 = 0$

**11.** $y + 5\sqrt{y} = -6$

**12.** $1 - \sqrt{z} + \sqrt{2z + 1} = 0$

**13.** $x + 4 = 6 + \sqrt{2x - 1}$

**14.** $9 - \sqrt{z} - \sqrt{3z + 4} = 3$

**15.** $\sqrt{y^2 - 8} + y = 8$

**16.** $\dfrac{z - \sqrt{z + 1}}{z + \sqrt{z + 1}} = \dfrac{5}{11}$

**17.** $\sqrt[4]{\dfrac{36}{x}} - \sqrt{6} = 0$

**18.** $\sqrt{2y + 7} = \sqrt{y} + 2$

**19.** $3\sqrt{x} - \dfrac{3}{\sqrt{x}} = 8$

**20.** $\sqrt{12 - x} = 6 - \sqrt{x}$

**21.** $\sqrt{x + 5} - \sqrt{2x - 7} - \sqrt{x} = 0$

**22.** $\sqrt{5z - 1} - \sqrt{3z - 2} - \sqrt{z + 8} = 0$    $-\frac{113}{11}$

**23.** $\sqrt{7x + 14} - \sqrt{2x + 6} = \sqrt{x + 4}$

**24.** $\sqrt{x + 6} + \sqrt{2x + 10} - \sqrt{7x + 28} = 0$

**25.** $\sqrt{5z} - \sqrt{3z + 1} = \dfrac{4}{\sqrt{3z + 1}}$

**26.** $\sqrt{x + 7} + \sqrt{3x - 2} - \dfrac{4x + 9}{\sqrt{3x - 2}} = 0$

**27.** $\sqrt{x + 3} + \dfrac{2}{\sqrt{x - 3}} - 3\sqrt{x - 3} = 0$

**28.** $\sqrt{5y + 3} + \sqrt{4y + 1} = \sqrt{y + 2}$

**29.** $\sqrt{3z + 10} - \sqrt{10z + 16} = \sqrt{z + 2}$

**30.** $\sqrt{2x + 1} + \sqrt{x - 3} = 2\sqrt{x}$

**31.** $\sqrt{9 - x} + \sqrt{6 + 2x} - \sqrt{6x + 6} = 0$

**32.** $\sqrt{4y - 5 + \sqrt{2y - 9}} = 4$

**33.** $\sqrt{z^2 + 2z + 18} - \sqrt{z^2 - 2z - 10} = 4$

**34.** $\sqrt{17 + 2\sqrt{3 + y + \sqrt{y + 7}}} - 5 = 0$

**35.** $a(x^2 + 4)^{\frac{3}{2}} - ax[\frac{3}{2}(x^2 + 4)^{\frac{1}{2}}(2x)] = 0$

**36.** $6 + x[\frac{1}{2}(36 - x^2)^{-\frac{1}{2}}(2x)] + (36 - x^2)^{\frac{1}{2}} = 0$

**40. Equations in quadratic form.** *An equation which by a change of variable becomes a quadratic in the new variable is said to be in* quadratic form. For example, $x^4 - 5x^2 - 6 = 0$ is not a quadratic equation in $x$, but if we put $x^2 = u$, the equation becomes $u^2 - 5u - 6 = 0$ which is a quadratic equation in $u$. Hence $x^4 - 5x^2 - 6 = 0$ is a quadratic equation in $x^2$. The following examples illustrate the method of solution. *As in the case of equations involving radicals all solutions must be checked.*

EXAMPLE I. Solve: $\sqrt{x} + \dfrac{6}{\sqrt{x}} - 7 = 0.$ (1)

**Solution.** Since $x = 0$ cannot be a solution, we can multiply by $\sqrt{x}$ and we have

$$(\sqrt{x})^2 + 6 - 7\sqrt{x} = 0$$

or $(\sqrt{x})^2 - 7\sqrt{x} + 6 = 0$ (2)

Let $\sqrt{x} = u$, then (2) becomes

$$u^2 - 7u + 6 = 0 \tag{3}$$

Solving (3) $\qquad (u - 6)(u - 1) = 0$

| | $u = 6$ | $u = 1$ |
|---|---|---|
| Since $\sqrt{x} = u$ | $\sqrt{x} = 6$ | $\sqrt{x} = 1$ |
| | $x = 36$ | $x = 1$ |

Check. $\sqrt{36} + \dfrac{6}{\sqrt{36}} - 7 \overset{?}{=} 0$ $\qquad \sqrt{1} + \dfrac{6}{\sqrt{1}} - 7 \overset{?}{=} 0$

$\qquad\qquad 6 + \frac{6}{6} - 7 \overset{?}{=} 0 \qquad\qquad 1 + 6 - 7 = 0\ \checkmark$

$\qquad\qquad\quad 7 - 7 = 0\ \checkmark$

Thus the solutions are $x = 36$, $x = 1$. (Ans.)

EXAMPLE II.  Solve: $\sqrt{\dfrac{3x+5}{3x-5}} + 8\sqrt{\dfrac{3x-5}{3x+5}} - 6 = 0$ $\qquad$ (4)

**Solution.**  Let $\sqrt{\dfrac{3x+5}{3x-5}} = u$, then $\sqrt{\dfrac{3x-5}{3x+5}} = \dfrac{1}{\sqrt{\dfrac{3x+5}{3x-5}}} = \dfrac{1}{u}$

and (4) becomes

$$u + \frac{8}{u} - 6 = 0$$
$$u^2 + 8 - 6u = 0$$
$$(u-4)(u-2) = 0$$

| | |
|---|---|
| $u = 4$ | $u = 2$ |
| $\sqrt{\dfrac{3x+5}{3x-5}} = 4$ | $\sqrt{\dfrac{3x+5}{3x-5}} = 2$ |
| $\dfrac{3x+5}{3x-5} = 16$ | $\dfrac{3x+5}{3x-5} = 4$ |
| $3x + 5 = 48x - 80$ | $3x + 5 = 12x - 20$ |
| $-45x = -85$ | $-9x = -25$ |
| $x = \tfrac{17}{9}$ | $x = \tfrac{25}{9}$ |

*Check.*

| | |
|---|---|
| $\sqrt{\dfrac{\frac{17}{3}+5}{\frac{17}{3}-5}} + 8\sqrt{\dfrac{\frac{17}{3}-5}{\frac{17}{3}+5}} - 6 \overset{?}{=} 0$ | $\sqrt{\dfrac{\frac{25}{3}+5}{\frac{25}{3}-5}} + 8\sqrt{\dfrac{\frac{25}{3}-5}{\frac{25}{3}+5}} - 6 = 0$ |
| $\sqrt{\frac{32}{2}} + 8\sqrt{\frac{2}{32}} - 6 \overset{?}{=} 0$ | $\sqrt{\frac{40}{10}} + 8\sqrt{\frac{10}{40}} - 6 = 0$ |
| $4 + \frac{8}{4} - 6 \overset{?}{=} 0$ | $2 + 4 - 6 = 0\ \checkmark$ |
| $6 - 6 = 0\ \checkmark$ | |

Thus $x = \tfrac{17}{9}$, $x = \tfrac{25}{9}$ are the solutions.  (Ans.)

EXAMPLE III.  Solve: $2x^2 - \sqrt{x^2 + 8x + 37} = -64 - 16x$.

**Solution.**  Transposing we have

$$2x^2 + 16x - \sqrt{x^2 + 8x + 37} + 64 = 0$$

If we add 74 to $2x^2 + 16x$, the first three terms give an expression which is precisely twice the expression under the radical.  Of course, 74 must be added to both members and we have

$$2x^2 + 16x + 74 - \sqrt{x^2 + 8x + 37} + 64 = 74$$

or $\qquad 2(x^2 + 8x + 37) - \sqrt{x^2 + 8x + 37} - 10 = 0$ $\qquad$ (5)

Putting $u = \sqrt{x^2 + 8x + 37}$, equation (5) becomes

$$2u^2 - u - 10 = 0$$
$$(2u - 5)(u + 2) = 0$$

$$u = \tfrac{5}{2}$$

$$\sqrt{x^2 + 8x + 37} = \tfrac{5}{2}$$
$$x^2 + 8x + 37 = \tfrac{25}{4}$$
$$4x^2 + 32x + 148 = 25$$
$$4x^2 + 32x + 123 = 0$$

$$x = \frac{-32 \pm \sqrt{1024 - 4(4)(123)}}{8}$$

$$x = \frac{-32 \pm \sqrt{-944}}{8}$$

$$x = \frac{-32 \pm 4i\sqrt{59}}{8}$$

$$x = \frac{-8 \pm i\sqrt{59}}{2}$$

$$u = -2$$

$$\sqrt{x^2 + 8x + 37} = -2$$

This leads to extraneous roots since $\sqrt{x^2 + 8x + 37}$ cannot represent a negative number.

*Check.*

$$2\left(\frac{-8 + i\sqrt{59}}{2}\right)^2 - \sqrt{\left(\frac{-8 + i\sqrt{59}}{2}\right)^2 + 8\left(\frac{-8 + i\sqrt{59}}{2}\right) + 37}$$

$$\overset{?}{=} -64 - 16\left(\frac{-8 + i\sqrt{59}}{2}\right)$$

$$2\left(\frac{64 - 16i\sqrt{59} - 59}{4}\right) - \sqrt{\frac{64 - 16i\sqrt{59} - 59 - 128 + 16i\sqrt{59} + 148}{4}}$$

$$\overset{?}{=} -64 + 64 - 8i\sqrt{59}$$

$$\frac{5 - 16i\sqrt{59}}{2} - \frac{5}{2} \overset{?}{=} -8i\sqrt{59}$$

$$\tfrac{5}{2} - 8i\sqrt{59} - \tfrac{5}{2} = -8i\sqrt{59} \checkmark$$

Since substituting the other solution merely amounts to changing the algebraic sign of $i$, we see that

$$x = \frac{-8 - i\sqrt{59}}{2}$$

is also a solution. Thus the answer is

$$x = \frac{-8 \pm i\sqrt{59}}{2}.$$

## EXERCISES

*Solve the following:*

1. $x^4 - 5x^2 + 6 = 0$

2. $36y^4 - 25y^2 + 4 = 0$

3. $\sqrt[6]{x + 10} + \sqrt[3]{x + 10} - 2 = 0$

4. $\frac{x - 3}{2} - \frac{17}{4} + \frac{2}{x - 3} = 0$

5. $x - 2\sqrt{x} + 1 = 0$

6. $6\sqrt{z} + \frac{6}{\sqrt{z}} = 13$

**7.** $3y - 5 + 2\sqrt{3y - 5} - 8 = 0$      **8.** $y^4 + 4y^2 - 5 = 0$

**9.** $x^3 + 7\sqrt{x^3} = 8$      **10.** $3y^{-\frac{3}{2}} - 20y^{-\frac{3}{4}} = 32$

**11.** $y^{\frac{1}{4}} + y^{\frac{1}{2}} = 6$      **12.** $2y - 3 = 7\sqrt{2y - 3} - 12$

**13.** $\left(x + \dfrac{1}{x}\right)^2 + 6\left(x + \dfrac{1}{x}\right) - 16 = 0$

**14.** $(y^2 + 2y - 1)^2 - 37(y^2 + 2y - 1) + 322 = 0$

**15.** $2z^2 + 5z - 17 + 3\sqrt{2z^2 + 5z - 17} = 28$

**16.** $y^2 + 5y - 10 = \sqrt{y^2 + 5y + 2}$

**17.** $y^2 - 3y + 5 - 3\sqrt{y^2 - 3y + 8} = -5$

**18.** $\sqrt{y} - 3\sqrt[4]{y} - 10 = 0$

**19.** $2z^2 + 4z + \sqrt{z^2 + 2z - 3} = 9$

**20.** $(2z + 5)^{-5} + 31(2z + 5)^{-\frac{5}{2}} = 32$

**21.** $\dfrac{5}{v} + \dfrac{1}{3\sqrt{v}} - \dfrac{16}{15} = -0.4$      **22.** $2\sqrt[3]{y^{-2}} - 3\sqrt[3]{y^{-1}} = 2$

**23.** $6\sqrt{z^2 - 2z + 6} = 21 + 2z - z^2$

**24.** $\sqrt{\dfrac{3y + 2}{3y - 4}} - 6\sqrt{\dfrac{3y - 4}{3y + 2}} + 1 = 0$

**25.** $\left(z - \dfrac{15}{z}\right)^2 - 16\left(\dfrac{15 - z^2}{z}\right) + 28 = 0$

**26.** $(4y - 1)^6 - 26(4y - 1)^3 - 27 = 0$

**27.** $\left(5 - \dfrac{2}{y}\right) - \sqrt{\dfrac{5y - 2}{y}} = 6$      **28.** $y^2 - 8 + y + \dfrac{12}{y^2 + y} = 0$

**41. Applications.** The same procedure is followed here as in previous applications.

EXAMPLE I. The sum of the reciprocals of two consecutive odd integers is $\frac{12}{35}$. Find the numbers.

**Solution.** Let $x$ be one of the integers, then $x + 2$ is the other and we have

$$\frac{1}{x} + \frac{1}{x + 2} = \frac{12}{35}$$

$$\frac{x + 2 + x}{x(x + 2)} = \frac{12}{35}$$

$$35(2x + 2) = 12(x^2 + 2x)$$

$$70x + 70 = 12x^2 + 24x$$

$$-12x^2 + 46x + 70 = 0$$

$$6x^2 - 23x - 35 = 0$$

$$(6x + 7)(x - 5) = 0$$

$$x = 5, \; x = -\tfrac{7}{6}$$

*Check.*   $\frac{1}{5} + \frac{1}{7} = \frac{7}{35} + \frac{5}{35} = \frac{12}{35}$ ✓

Thus the integers are 5 and 7. (Ans.)

Since the other root, $x = -\frac{7}{6}$, is not an integer, it cannot be a solution.

EXAMPLE II.   The hypotenuse of a right triangle is 25.   One leg is 17 feet shorter than the other.   Find the legs.

**Solution.**   Let $x$ be one leg, then $x - 17$ is the other and we have

$$x^2 + (x - 17)^2 = (25)^2$$
$$x^2 + x^2 - 34x + 289 = 625$$
$$2x^2 - 34x - 336 = 0$$
$$x^2 - 17x - 168 = 0$$
$$(x - 24)(x + 7) = 0$$
$$x = 24, \ x = -7$$

*Check.*   $(24)^2 + (24 - 17)^2 = 576 + 49 = 625 = (25)^2$ ✓

Since the side of a triangle is positive we discard $x = -7$, and the legs are 24 feet and 7 feet. (Ans.)

## EXERCISES

**1.** A rectangle is 5 inches wide and 12 inches long. How much must be added to the width to increase the diagonal by 2 inches?

**2.** The hypotenuse of a triangle is 26 feet. One leg is 14 feet shorter than the other. Find the legs.

**3.** In calculating the area of a circle a student used 3.41 instead of 3.14 for $\pi$. If his answer is 1.08 too large, find the radius of the circle.

**4.** Find the radius of a circle such that the number of feet in its circumference equals the number of square feet in its area.

**5.** A picture measured inside the frame is 9 by 12 inches. The area of the frame is 46 square inches. How wide is the framing strip?

**6.** A room is 2 feet longer than it is wide. At 4 cents per square foot a covering for the floor costs $14.40. Find the dimensions of the room.

**7.** A box is to be 3 feet long and 2 feet wide. How deep must it be in order to have a diagonal of 7 feet?

**8.** If the speed of a train is reduced 5 miles per hour, it takes 24 minutes longer to make 180 miles. Find the original speed.

**9.** A pedestrian walked 6 miles in a certain interval of time. If the time had been $\frac{1}{2}$ hour less, the rate would have been 2 miles per hour greater. Find the time and rate.

**10.** A crew whose rate in still water is 6 miles per hour rowed 10 miles downstream and returned in 6 hours from the time they started. Find the rate of the stream.

**11.** *A* can walk half a mile farther in an hour than *B* can, and it takes *A* an hour less to walk 15 miles than it takes *B*. How fast does each walk?

**12.** A cab driver agrees to accomplish a trip of 200 miles in a specified time. After traveling 125 miles at a rate which will just enable him to keep his agreement, his car is delayed 15 minutes. He then drives 10 miles per hour faster than before and arrives exactly on time. What was his original rate?

**13.** The towers along a certain transmission line are at equal intervals. If the intervals between the towers were increased by 20 feet, there would be 2 fewer in every mile. How many are there in a mile?

**14.** The cost of a dinner is $45.00, which was to have been divided equally among the members of a party. But as 5 of the members failed to appear, the others had to pay 30 cents each more than they would if all had been present. What was the number of persons in the party at the dinner?

**15.** A given number was to be subtracted from 4, but by mistake 4 was divided by the number. Nevertheless, the correct result was obtained. What was the number?

**16.** If 12 is divided into two parts whose product is $\frac{63}{4}$, find each part.

**17.** Divide the number 72 into two parts whose product is 1295.

**18.** Divide the number 32 into two parts such that their product will be 12 times their difference.

**19.** Find three successive integers whose sum is $\frac{2}{5}$ of the product of the first two.

**20.** A number is 24 greater than 5 times its square root. Find the number.

**21.** The denominator of a fraction exceeds its numerator by 2 and the sum of the fraction and its reciprocal is $\frac{74}{35}$. Find the fraction.

**22.** The denominator of a fraction is 2 greater than twice the numerator, and if $\frac{119}{60}$ be added to the fraction, the sum is equal to the reciprocal of the original fraction. Find the fraction.

**23.** It took a number of men as many days as there were men to accomplish certain work, but if there had been 4 more men working it could have been done in 9 days. How many men were employed?

**24.** A tank can be filled by one of its pipes in 4 hours less than by the other, and by both together in 5 hours and 50 minutes. How long will it take each pipe alone to fill it?

**25.** A man and a boy working together do a piece of work in 12 days. If the man could do it alone in 18 days less than the boy alone, how long would it take each to do it?

**26.** An audience of 640 persons is seated in rows each containing the same number of people. They might have been seated in 8 rows less had each row contained 4 more seats. How many rows were there?

**27.** The advance guard of a regiment was marching in regular column with 32 men more in depth than in front. On approaching the enemy the front was increased by 72 men, and the whole advance guard drawn up in 4 lines. Find the number of men.

**28.** By lowering the price of eggs and selling them 2 cents a dozen cheaper, a grocer finds that he can sell one more egg than he used to sell for 40 cents. At what price per dozen did he sell them at first?

**29.** A earned \$12 and B, who worked 4 days more than A, earned \$20. Had their wages per day been interchanged, they would have earned \$34. How many days did each work?

**30.** A merchant has a cask full of wine. He draws out 10 gallons, and fills the cask with water. Again he draws out 10 gallons and fills the cask with water. The mixture in the cask now contains 32 gallons of pure wine. What is the capacity of the cask?

**31.** A man paid \$800 for a shipment of pigs. By selling all but 40 of them at a profit of \$1.00 each, he received the amount paid for all the pigs. How many pigs were there?

**32.** Show that it is impossible to find three consecutive integers such that the sum equals the product of the first and last.

**33.** When $s$ feet of wire are stretched between two poles $L$ feet apart, the sag $d$ of the wire in feet is given by the formula $d = \sqrt{.375L(s - L)}$. Solve for $L$ and interpret your results. If $s = 100$, $d = 5$, prove $L = 99.3$.

**34.** If $n =$ number of telephone wires in a pipe of diameter $D$ and $d =$ diameter of the wire, then

$$n = .907\left(\frac{D}{d} - .94\right)^2 + 3.7.$$

Solve for $D$ and evaluate for $d = .125$, $n = 100$.

# CHAPTER VII

## SYSTEMS INVOLVING QUADRATICS

**42. Solution by substitution.** *The equation of the form*

$$ax^2 + bxy + cy^2 + dx + ey + f = 0,$$

*where a, b, c, d, e, and f are constants is called the* **general equation of the second degree in x and y,** *or* **the general quadratic equation in x and y.** We consider here the solution of *two such equations*, called a **quadratic system.**

If one of the equations of the system is linear, the solution can always be found by substitution.

EXAMPLE I. Solve: $x^2 + xy - 12 + y^2 = 0$
$$x + y + 2 = 0$$

**Solution.** (*a*) Solve the linear equation for one of the variables in terms of the other.

$$x = -y - 2.$$

(*b*) Substitute this value for the variable in the quadratic equation, thus obtaining a quadratic equation in one unknown. Solve this equation.

$$(-y - 2)^2 + (-y - 2)y - 12 + y^2 = 0$$
$$y^2 + 4y + 4 - y^2 - 2y - 12 + y^2 = 0$$
$$y^2 + 2y - 8 = 0$$
$$(y + 4)(y - 2) = 0$$
$$y = 2$$
$$y = -4.$$

(*c*) Substitute each value obtained in (*b*) in the linear equation and find the corresponding value of the other variable. Each pair of values thus obtained constitutes a solution of the system.

If $\qquad y = 2, \qquad x = -2 - 2 = -4.$

Thus a solution is $x = -4, y = 2.$

If $\qquad y = -4, \qquad x = -(-4) - 2 = 4 - 2 = 2.$

Thus a solution is $x = 2, y = -4.$

The solutions may be arranged in a table:

| $x$ | $-4$ | $2$ |
|---|---|---|
| $y$ | $2$ | $-4$ |

(Ans.)

It should be observed that a solution consists of a value of $x$ and the corresponding value of $y$.

(d) Check the solutions by substitution in the original equations.

$x = 2, y = -4$          $(2)^2 + (2)(-4) - 12 + (-4)^2 \overset{?}{=} 0$

$$4 - 8 - 12 + 16 \overset{?}{=} 0$$
$$20 - 20 = 0 \checkmark$$
$$2 + (-4) + 2 \overset{?}{=} 0$$
$$4 - 4 = 0 \checkmark$$

$x = -4, y = 2$          $(-4)^2 + (-4)2 - 12 + (2)^2 \overset{?}{=} 0$

$$16 - 8 - 12 + 4 \overset{?}{=} 0$$
$$20 - 20 = 0 \checkmark$$
$$(-4) + (2) + (2) \overset{?}{=} 0$$
$$-4 + 4 = 0 \checkmark$$

The quadratic system in which one equation is of the form

$$ax^2 + cy^2 + f = 0,$$

and the other is of the form

$$bxy + g = 0$$

can be solved by substitution.

EXAMPLE II.   Solve:      $x^2 - 2y^2 = 7$
$$xy - 15 = 0$$

**Solution.**   (a) Solve the equation containing the $xy$ term for $x$ in terms of $y$.

$$x = \frac{15}{y}$$

(b) Substitute this value of $x$ in the other equation and solve for $y$.

$$\left(\frac{15}{y}\right)^2 - 2y^2 = 7$$
$$225 - 2y^4 = 7y^2$$
$$-2y^4 - 7y^2 + 225 = 0$$
$$2y^4 + 7y^2 - 225 = 0$$
$$(2y^2 + 25)(y^2 - 9) = 0$$

$$2y^2 = -25 \qquad\qquad\qquad y^2 = 9$$
$$y^2 = -\tfrac{25}{2}$$
$$y = \frac{5i}{\sqrt{2}}, \ y = \frac{-5i}{\sqrt{2}} \qquad y = 3, y = -3$$

(*c*) Substitute each value obtained for $y$ in the $xy$ equation and find the corresponding value of $x$.

$$y = \frac{5i}{\sqrt{2}}, \; x = \frac{15}{\frac{5i}{\sqrt{2}}} = \frac{3\sqrt{2}}{i} = -3\sqrt{2}\,i$$

$$y = -\frac{5i}{\sqrt{2}}, \; x = 3\sqrt{2}\,i$$

$$y = 3, \; x = \tfrac{15}{3} = 5$$

$$y = -3, \; x = -5$$

| $x$ | $y$ |
|---|---|
| $-3\sqrt{2}\,i$ | $\dfrac{5i}{\sqrt{2}}$ |
| $3\sqrt{2}\,i$ | $-\dfrac{5i}{\sqrt{2}}$ |
| $5$ | $3$ |
| $-5$ | $-3$ |

(*d*) Check by substitution in both original equations.

$$x = -3\sqrt{2}\,i \qquad (-3\sqrt{2}\,i)^2 - 2\left(\frac{5i}{\sqrt{2}}\right)^2 \overset{?}{=} 7$$

$$y = \frac{5i}{\sqrt{2}} \qquad\qquad -18 - 2\left(-\frac{25}{2}\right) \overset{?}{=} 7$$

$$-18 + 25 = 7 \; \checkmark$$

$$(-3\sqrt{2}\,i)\left(\frac{5i}{\sqrt{2}}\right) - 15 \overset{?}{=} 0$$

$$15 - 15 = 0 \; \checkmark$$

$x = 3\sqrt{2}\,i$     This must satisfy the first equation because it differs

$y = -\dfrac{5i}{\sqrt{2}}$    from the first solution only in signs and all the powers of $x$ and $y$ are even.

$$(3\sqrt{2}\,i)\left(-\frac{5i}{\sqrt{2}}\right) - 15 \overset{?}{=} 0$$

$$15 - 15 = 0 \; \checkmark$$

$x = 5$

$y = 3$

$$(5)^2 - 2(3)^2 \overset{?}{=} 7$$

$$25 - 18 = 7 \; \checkmark$$

$$5(3) - 15 \overset{?}{=} 0$$

$$15 - 15 = 0 \; \checkmark$$

$x = -5$     First equation is satisfied as above.

$y = -3$

$$(-5)(-3) - 15 \overset{?}{=} 0$$

$$15 - 15 = 0 \; \checkmark$$

A quadratic system in which both equations are of the form $ax^2 + cy^2 + f = 0$ can be solved like a system of linear equations for $x^2$ and $y^2$ by substitution, addition and subtraction, or by determinants. Of course, in finding $x$ and $y$ both square roots are included in the solutions.

**Example III.** Solve: $7x^2 - 10 = 2y^2$ $\qquad$ (1)

$$3y^2 = 31 - x^2 \qquad (2)$$

**Solution.** Solving equation (2) for $x^2$ we have

$$x^2 = 31 - 3y^2 \qquad (3)$$

Substituting this value for $x^2$ in (1)

$$7(31 - 3y^2) - 10 = 2y^2$$
$$217 - 21y^2 - 10 = 2y^2$$
$$- 23y^2 = - 207$$
$$y^2 = 9$$
$$y = + 3, y = - 3$$

Substituting in (3) $y = 3$, $\qquad x^2 = 31 - 3(3)^2 = 31 - 27 = 4$

$$x = + 2, x = - 2$$
$$y = - 3, \qquad x = + 2, x = - 2$$

Thus the solutions are:

| $x$ | 2 | 2 | $-2$ | $-2$ | |
|---|---|---|---|---|---|
| $y$ | 3 | $-3$ | 3 | $-3$ | |

$\qquad$ (Ans.)

*Check.* $\quad y = \pm 3, x = \pm 2 \qquad 7(\pm 2)^2 - 10 \overset{?}{=} 2(\pm 3)^2$

$$28 - 10 = 18 \checkmark$$
$$3(\pm 3)^2 \overset{?}{=} 31 - (\pm 2)^2$$
$$27 = 31 - 4 \checkmark$$

Since all powers of $x$ and $y$ are even in the original equations it is clear that if $x = 2$, $y = 3$ is a solution, then $x = \pm 2$, $y = \pm 3$ are solutions.

A system of equations in which one of the equations is of the form $ax^2 + ey + f = 0$ and the other is of the form $ax^2 + cy^2 + f = 0$ can be solved by eliminating the term in $x^2$ by subtraction and solving the resulting quadratic equation in $y$.

## EXERCISES

*Solve the following systems:*

**1.** $x^2 - 2y^2 = 1$
$\quad x - y - 1 = 0$

**2.** $u^2 + v^2 = 25$
$\quad u - 3v = - 5$

**3.** $\dfrac{w + z}{z} = 6$
$\quad wz = 45$

**4.** $u - 3v = 1$
$\quad uv + v^2 = 5$

**5.** $u^2 + v^2 = 89$
$u - v = 3$

**6.** $w + x = 4$
$2w^2 + 2x^2 = 17$

**7.** $u^2 = 4v$
$u + 2v = 4$

**8.** $5w - 5x = 3$
$25wx = 4$

**9.** $u^2 + v^2 - 8u - 4v - 5 = 0$
$3u + 4v + 5 = 0$

**10.** $u^2 - v^2 = 80$
$u + v = 10$

**11.** $2x - 3y = -2$
$x^2 + xy + y^2 - 20 = 0$

**12.** $x^2 - 9y = 0$
$x + 2y = 6$

**13.** $\dfrac{1}{x^2} + \dfrac{1}{y^2} = \dfrac{45}{4}$

$\dfrac{1}{x} - \dfrac{1}{y} = \dfrac{3}{2}$

**14.** $\dfrac{1}{u} + \dfrac{1}{v} = 5$

$\dfrac{1}{u^2} + \dfrac{1}{v^2} = 13$

**15.** $u^2 + v^2 = 5$
$uv = 2$

**16.** $u^2 + 9v^2 = 25$
$uv = 4$

**17.** $\dfrac{1}{xy} + \dfrac{1}{6} = 0$
$x^2 + y^2 = 13$

**18.** $\dfrac{1}{x^2} + \dfrac{1}{y^2} = 4c^2 + d^2$

$xy + \dfrac{1}{2cd} = 0$

**19.** $u^2 + v^2 = 40$
$uv = 12$

**20.** $x^2 + y^2 = 16$
$2xy = 9$

**21.** $x^2 + y^2 = 25$
$x^2 - y^2 = 7$

**22.** $2u^2 - v^2 = 4$
$3u^2 + 4v^2 = 12$

**23.** $x + 8 - 2y^2 = 0$
$x^2 + 16 = 4y^2$

**24.** $3u^2 - 4v^2 = 24$
$u^2 + 8 = 4v^2$

**25.** $v^2 = 4u + 3$
$9u^2 = 4v^2 - 9$

**26.** $6x^2 + 5y^2 = 58$
$x^2 - 2y^2 = 4$

**27.** $4x^2 - 6y^2 = -1$
$4x^2 + 2y^2 = 5$

**28.** $2u^2 + v^2 = 7$
$u^2 - 2v^2 = -4$

**29.** $4x^2 + y^2 = 13$
$8x^2 - 3y^2 = 6$

**30.** $8xy - 9y^2 = 119$
$4x - 9y = 7$

**31.** $u^2 - v^2 = 9$
$u^2 = 4(v + 3)$

**32.** $x^2 + y^2 = 13$
$2x^2 - y = 16$

**33.** $\dfrac{1}{u^2} + \dfrac{1}{v^2} = 2$

$\dfrac{1}{u} + \dfrac{1}{v} = 0$

**34.** $\dfrac{1}{x^2} + \dfrac{1}{y^2} = 74$

$\dfrac{1}{x} - \dfrac{1}{y} = 2$

**35.** $x^2 - 3y^2 = 4$
$2x - 3y = 1$

**36.** $xy = -21$
$4x + 3y = 19$

**37.** $4x^2 + 25y^2 = 89$
$5x^2 - 9y^2 = 71$

**38.** $7v^2 - 3u^2 = 15$
$3u^2 - 4v^2 = 12$

**39.** $u^2 - v^2 = 16$
$2u^2 - 5v^2 = 5$

**40.** $u^2 + 4v^2 = 20$
$4u^2 + v^2 = 20$

**41.** $2x^2 + 3y^2 = 30$
$x^2 - y = 7$

**42.** $5x^2 + 4y^2 - 8y = 17$
$x^2 + 3y + 2 = 0$

**43.** $6x^2 + 3y^2 - 27 = 0$
$y^2 - 3x + 6 = 1$

**44.** $3x^2 + y^2 + 4x = 29$
$x^2 + y^2 - x = 1$

**45.** $2x^2 - y^2 + 3x - y = 8$
$5x + y = 7$

**46.** $x^2 + y^2 + 2x + 3y = 10$
$x - y = 5$

**43. Reduction to simpler systems.** *A quadratic system in which both equations are of the form* $ax^2 + bxy + cy^2 + f = 0$ *is sometimes called a* **homogeneous system** *since every term involving the unknowns is of the same degree.* Examples I and II illustrate two methods of solving this system.

EXAMPLE I. Solve: $\quad 2x^2 - 3xy + y^2 = 4 \quad\quad$ (1)
$\qquad\qquad\qquad\quad x^2 + xy - 2y^2 = 7 \quad\quad$ (2)

**Solution.** (*a*) Eliminate the constant from the two equations by multiplying and adding.

Multiply (1) by 7 $\qquad 14x^2 - 21xy + 7y^2 = 28 \quad\quad$ (3)
Multiply (2) by $-4 \quad\; -4x^2 - 4xy + 8y^2 = -28 \quad\quad$ (4)
Add (3) and (4) $\qquad 10x^2 - 25xy + 15y^2 = 0$
$\qquad\qquad\qquad\qquad\;\; 2x^2 - 5xy + 3y^2 = 0 \quad\quad$ (5)

(*b*) Factor the resulting equation.
Factor (5) $\qquad\qquad (2x - 3y)(x - y) = 0 \quad\quad$ (6)

(*c*) Form two systems consisting of either original equation and one of the factors of (*b*) put equal to zero, and solve these two systems. These are solutions of the original system.

| | |
|---|---|
| $x^2 + xy - 2y^2 = 7$ | $x^2 + xy - 2y^2 = 7$ |
| $2x - 3y = 0$ | $x - y = 0$ |
| $x = \frac{3}{2}y$ | $x = y$ |
| $\frac{9}{4}y^2 + \frac{3}{2}y^2 - 2y^2 = 7$ | $y^2 + y^2 - 2y^2 = 7$ |
| $\frac{7}{4}y^2 = 7$ | $0 = 7$ |
| $y^2 = 4$ | |
| $y = 2, \quad y = -2$ | This is impossible and hence |
| $x = 3, \quad x = -3$ | this system has no solution. |

*Check.*    $x = 3,$        $2(3)^2 - 3(3)(2) + (2)^2 = 18 - 18 + 4 = 4$ $\checkmark$

        $y = 2,$            $(3)^2 + 3(2) - 2(2)^2 = 9 + 6 - 8 = 7$ $\checkmark$

The solution $x = -3$, $y = -2$ will satisfy the system because each term involving $x$ and $y$ is of degree 2, and $-x$ can be substituted for $x$ and $-y$

for $y$ without changing the equations. $\quad \dfrac{x}{y}\begin{array}{c|c} 3 & -3 \\ \hline 2 & -2 \end{array}$    (Ans.)

EXAMPLE II.  Solve:        $x^2 + xy = 12$             (7)

                $xy - 2y^2 = 1$             (8)

**Solution.**  Let $y = ux$, then

(7) becomes                $x^2 + ux^2 = 12$             (9)

(8) becomes            $ux^2 - 2u^2x^2 = 1$             (10)

Solve (9) for $x^2$        $x^2 = \dfrac{12}{1 + u}$             (11)

and (10) for $x^2$        $x^2 = \dfrac{1}{u - 2u^2}$             (12)

Equate (11) and (12)            $\dfrac{12}{1 + u} = \dfrac{1}{u - 2u^2}$

and solve for $u$.

$$12u - 24u^2 = 1 + u$$
$$-24u^2 + 11u - 1 = 0$$
$$24u^2 - 11u + 1 = 0$$
$$(8u - 1)(3u - 1) = 0$$
$$u = \tfrac{1}{3} \qquad\qquad u = \tfrac{1}{8}$$

Substitute $u = \dfrac{1}{3}$ in (11)    $x^2 = \dfrac{12}{1 + \frac{1}{3}} = \dfrac{36}{4} = 9, x = +3, x = -3$

Since $y = ux$, we have    $y = \tfrac{1}{3}(3) = 1, y = \tfrac{1}{3}(-3) = -1$.

Substitute $u = \dfrac{1}{8}$ in (11)    $x^2 = \dfrac{12}{1 + \frac{1}{8}} = \dfrac{96}{9}, x = \dfrac{4\sqrt{6}}{3}, x = \dfrac{-4\sqrt{6}}{3}$

Since $y = ux$, we have    $y = \dfrac{1}{8}\left(\dfrac{4\sqrt{6}}{3}\right) = \dfrac{\sqrt{6}}{6}, y = \dfrac{-\sqrt{6}}{6}$.

Thus the solutions are:

$$\dfrac{x}{y}\begin{array}{c|c|c|c} 3 & -3 & \dfrac{4\sqrt{6}}{3} & -\dfrac{4\sqrt{6}}{3} \\ \hline 1 & -1 & \dfrac{\sqrt{6}}{6} & -\dfrac{\sqrt{6}}{6} \end{array}$$    (Ans.)

*Check.*  $x = 3, y = 1$          $(3)^2 + (3)(1) = 9 + 3 = 12$ ✓

$(3)1 - 2(1)^2 = 3 - 2 = 1$ ✓

$$x = \frac{4\sqrt{6}}{3}, y = \frac{\sqrt{6}}{6} \qquad \frac{96}{9} + \frac{24}{18} = \frac{108}{9} = 12 \checkmark$$

$$\tfrac{24}{18} - 2(\tfrac{1}{6}) = \tfrac{4}{3} - \tfrac{1}{3} = 1 \checkmark$$

An equation is symmetrical in $x$ and $y$ if, when $x$ and $y$ are interchanged, the equation is unchanged. The following example illustrates a method of solution.

EXAMPLE III.  Solve:  $x^2 + y^2 + x + y = 14$          (13)

$$xy + x + y = -5 \qquad (14)$$

**Solution.**  Let $x = u + v$ and $y = u - v$, then

(13) becomes          $2u^2 + 2v^2 + 2u = 14$          (15)

(14) becomes          $u^2 - v^2 + 2u = -5$          (16)

Eliminate $v^2$ by multiplying (16) by 2 and adding to (15). Then we have

$$4u^2 + 6u = 4 \qquad (17)$$

Solve (17) for $u$          $2u^2 + 3u - 2 = 0$

$$(2u - 1)(u + 2) = 0$$
$$u = \tfrac{1}{2} \qquad u = -2$$

Find the corresponding values of $v$ from (16)

$$u = \tfrac{1}{2} \qquad \tfrac{1}{4} - v^2 + 1 = -5$$
$$1 - 4v^2 + 4 = -20$$
$$4v^2 = 25$$
$$v = -\tfrac{5}{2}, v = \tfrac{5}{2}$$
$$u = -2 \qquad 4 - v^2 - 4 = -5$$
$$v^2 = 5$$
$$v = -\sqrt{5}, v = \sqrt{5}$$

Since $x = u + v$, $y = u - v$, we have

| | |
|---|---|
| $u = \tfrac{1}{2}, v = \tfrac{5}{2}$ | $x = 3, y = -2$ |
| $u = \tfrac{1}{2}, v = -\tfrac{5}{2}$ | $x = -2, y = 3$ |
| $u = -2, v = \sqrt{5}$ | $x = -2 + \sqrt{5}, y = -2 - \sqrt{5}$ |
| $u = -2, v = -\sqrt{5}$ | $x = -2 - \sqrt{5}, y = -2 + \sqrt{5}$ |

*Check.*

$x = 3, y = -2$          $9 + 4 + 3 - 2 = 16 - 2 = 14$ ✓

$$-6 + 3 - 2 = -5 \checkmark$$

Since $x$ and $y$ may be interchanged, $x = -2$, $y = 3$ also checks.

$x = -2 + \sqrt{5}$, $y = -2 - \sqrt{5}$

$$9 - 4\sqrt{5} + 4\sqrt{5} + 9 - 2 + \sqrt{5} - 2 - \sqrt{5} = 14 \ \checkmark$$
$$4 - 5 - 2 + \sqrt{5} - 2 - \sqrt{5} = -5 \ \checkmark$$

Thus $x = -2 - \sqrt{5}$, $y = -2 + \sqrt{5}$ is also a solution.

The answer is:

| $x$ | $3$ | $-2$ | $-2 + \sqrt{5}$ | $-2 - \sqrt{5}$ |
|---|---|---|---|---|
| $y$ | $-2$ | $3$ | $-2 - \sqrt{5}$ | $-2 + \sqrt{5}$ |

The following examples illustrate further methods of obtaining simpler systems.

**EXAMPLE IV.**   Solve:  $(x + y)^2 + (x + y) = 12$       (18)

$$3x^2 + y^2 - x - y = 4 \qquad (19)$$

**Solution.**   Solve (18) for $(x + y)$

$$(x + y)^2 + (x + y) - 12 = 0$$
$$(x + y + 4)(x + y - 3) = 0$$

Now solve the two systems:

$$\begin{array}{ll} x + y + 4 = 0 & x + y - 3 = 0 \\ 3x^2 + y^2 - x - y = 4 & 3x^2 + y^2 - x - y = 4 \end{array}$$

**EXAMPLE V.**   Solve:  $x^2 + y^2 - 12x - 8y + 42 = 0$       (20)

$$x^2 + y^2 - 6x - 2y + 6 = 0 \qquad (21)$$

**Solution.**   By subtracting (20) from (21) we have

$$6x + 6y - 36 = 0$$
$$x + y - 6 = 0$$

Now solve the system:

$$x + y - 6 = 0$$
$$x^2 + y^2 - 6x - 2y + 6 = 0$$

### EXERCISES

*Solve the following:*

1.  $x^2 + xy + y^2 = 7$
    $xy + 6 = 0$

2.  $36u^2 + 36v^2 = 13$
    $6uv = 1$

3.  $x^2 + 6xy = 28$
    $xy + 8y^2 = 4$

4.  $7x^2 - 8xy = 15$
    $3xy - 7y^2 = -10$

5.  $x^2 - xy = 8$
    $xy - y^2 = 7$

6.  $u^2 + uv - 12 = 0$
    $uv - v^2 = 2$

**7.** $u^2 + uv = 10$
$3uv + 4v^2 = 54$

**8.** $x^2 + 4y^2 = 3xy + 11$
$xy = 10$

**9.** $2x^2 + 5xy - y^2 = 11$
$3x^2 + 7xy + 2y^2 = 22$

**10.** $7xy + 15y^2 = 156$
$12x^2 + 5xy = 3y^2$

**11.** $u^2 + 3uv + 2v^2 = 3$
$2u^2 = 6 - v^2$

**12.** $y^2 - x^2 = 12$
$xy - 8 = 0$

**13.** $xy + 3y^2 = 6$
$x^2 + y^2 = 10$

**14.** $2u^2 - 5uv + 3v^2 = 20$
$2u^2 - uv = 8$

**15.** $x^2 + 20y^2 + xy = 130$
$5x^2 - 4xy + y^2 = 65$

**16.** $x^2 + xy + 10y^2 = 22$
$xy - 2y^2 + 6 = 0$

**17.** $u^2 - 2uv = 5$
$u^2 + v^2 = 29$

**18.** $2x^2 + xy = 15$
$y^2 - 2xy = 7$

**19.** $u^2 + uv + v^2 = 129$
$uv - v^2 = 15$

**20.** $y^2 - 3yz - z^2 = 9$
$2y^2 + 2yz + 3z^2 = 7$

**21.** $x^2 - xy + y^2 = 20$
$12x^2 - 13xy + 3y^2 = 0$

**22.** $2u^2 - 3uv + v^2 = 4$
$u^2 - 2uv + 3v^2 = 9$

**23.** $w(w - z) = 3$
$z(z - w) = -2$

**24.** $x^2 + xy + y^2 = 19$
$2x^2 + xy + 2 = 0$

**25.** $3u^2 + 4uv + 3v^2 = 54$
$u^2 + v^2 = 30$

**26.** $u^2 + v^2 - 12u - 8v + 42 = 0$
$u^2 + v^2 - 6u - 2v + 6 = 0$

**27.** $u^2 + uv = 63$
$3uv - u = 35$

**28.** $3x^2 + 2xy = 7$
$2x^2 - 3xy = -4$

**29.** $x^2 + 7xy + 12y^2 = 0$
$x^2 = (y - 2)^2$

**30.** $9x^2 + 18xy + y^2 = 2$
$xy + 1 = 0$

**31.** $14x^2 + 21xy + 9y^2 = 8$
$140x^2 - 280xy - 183y^2 + 32 = 0$

**32.** $4u^2 + 3uv + 5v^2 = 27$
$7u^2 + 5uv + 9v^2 = 47$

**33.** $4x^2 - 9xy = 28y^2$
$x^2 + 2y^2 = 18$

**34.** $a^2 = a + b$
$b^2 = 3b - a$

**35.** $y - xy + x = 1$
$y^2 + x^2 = 5$

**36.** $u^2 + v^2 + u + v = 8$
$uv + u + v = 5$

**44. Applications.** The following examples are illustrative:

EXAMPLE I. The hypotenuse of a right triangle is 5. If one side is increased by 2 and the other by 8, the hypotenuse will be 13. Find the sides of the triangle.

**Solution.** Let $x$ and $y$ be the two sides. Then

$$x^2 + y^2 = (5)^2 \tag{1}$$

and
$$(x + 2)^2 + (y + 8)^2 = (13)^2 \tag{2}$$

or
$$x^2 + y^2 + 4x + 16y - 101 = 0 \tag{2}$$

Subtracting (1) from (2) we have

$$4x + 16y - 101 = -25$$
$$x + 4y - 19 = 0$$

Solving the system

$$x^2 + y^2 = 25$$
$$x + 4y = 19$$

we obtain

| $x$ | $-\frac{13}{7}$ | 3 |
|---|---|---|
| $y$ | $-$ | 4 |

Since a side cannot have negative length, we discard the value

$$x = -\frac{13}{7}.$$

*Check.*          $(3)^2 + (4)^2 = 9 + 16 = 25 \checkmark$
                  $(5)^2 + (12)^2 = 25 + 144 = 169 \checkmark$

Thus the answer is a triangle with one side 3 and the other 4.

EXAMPLE II.  Simplify:  $\sqrt{7 + 4\sqrt{3}}$.

**Solution.**  If we can write $\sqrt{7 + 4\sqrt{3}}$ as a binomial square, i.e., $(x + y)^2$, then the simplification of $\sqrt{7 + 4\sqrt{3}}$ is immediate.  In this case $x$ and $y$ may involve square roots which appear in the $xy$ term of the expansion, while $x^2$ and $y^2$ are rational.  Thus, let

$$x^2 + y^2 = 7 \qquad (3)$$
$$2xy = 4\sqrt{3}$$
$$xy = 2\sqrt{3}$$
$$x = \frac{2\sqrt{3}}{y}$$

and substituting in (3) we have

$$\left(\frac{2\sqrt{3}}{y}\right)^2 + y^2 = 7$$
$$12 + y^4 = 7y^2$$
$$y^4 - 7y^2 + 12 = 0$$
$$(y^2 - 3)(y^2 - 4) = 0$$

| $y^2 = 3$ | | $y^2 = 4$ | |
|---|---|---|---|
| $y = +\sqrt{3}$ | $y = -\sqrt{3}$ | $y = 2$ | $y = -2$ |
| $x = 2$ | $x = -2$ | $x = \sqrt{3}$ | $x = -\sqrt{3}$ |

Thus the solutions are:

| $x$ | 2 | $-2$ | $\sqrt{3}$ | $-\sqrt{3}$ |
|---|---|---|---|---|
| $y$ | $\sqrt{3}$ | $-\sqrt{3}$ | 2 | $-2$ |

*Check.*   $x = 2, y = \sqrt{3}$   $(2)^2 + (\sqrt{3})^2 = 4 + 3$ ✓
$2(2)(\sqrt{3}) = 4\sqrt{3}$ ✓

Thus all solutions check.

Hence   $\sqrt{7 + 4\sqrt{3}} = \sqrt{(2 + \sqrt{3})^2} = 2 + \sqrt{3}$   (Ans.)

## EXERCISES

*Simplify:*

**1.** $\sqrt{11 + 2\sqrt{28}}$   **2.** $\sqrt{16 + 2\sqrt{55}}$   **3.** $\sqrt{18 - 8\sqrt{5}}$

**4.** $\sqrt{-5 + 12\sqrt{-1}}$   **5.** $\sqrt{16 + 5\sqrt{7}}$   **6.** $\sqrt{11 + 6\sqrt{2}}$

**7.** $\sqrt{10 - 4\sqrt{6}}$   **8.** $\sqrt{442 - 24\sqrt{30}}$   **9.** $\sqrt{37 + 20\sqrt{3}}$

*Solve:*

**10.** Find the sides of the rectangle whose area is 6000 square feet and whose diagonal is 130 feet.

**11.** The area of a rectangle is 12 square feet and its perimeter is 14 feet. Find its length and breadth.

**12.** The hypotenuse of a right triangle is 25 inches and its area is 84 inches. Find the legs of the triangle.

**13.** The sum of the perimeters of two squares is 76 feet. The sum of their areas is 193 square feet. Find their sides.

**14.** A tank can be filled by two pipes in $11\frac{1}{9}$ minutes. If the first pipe is open 12 minutes and the second 10 minutes, it will be filled. How long will it take each pipe to fill it?

**15.** One number is 3 greater than another, and its cube is 279 greater than the cube of the other. Find the numbers.

**16.** The perimeter of a right triangle is 30 and its area is 30. Find its sides.

**17.** The diagonal of a certain rectangular field is 250 feet and its area is 16,800 square feet. Find the cost of enclosing it by a fence at 25 cents a foot.

**18.** The sum of two numbers multiplied by the lesser is 300 and their difference multiplied by the greater is 13. Find the numbers.

**19.** A fraction is less than 1. The difference of the squares of its terms is 16, and the difference of its terms is 2. Find the fraction.

**20.** A workman and his assistant can do a piece of work in $4\frac{4}{5}$ days. It would take the assistant 2 days longer to do the work alone than it would take the master workman. How long would it take each to do the work alone?

**21.** The diagonal of a rectangle is 25 inches. If the rectangle were

4 inches shorter and 8 inches wider, the diagonal would still be 25 inches. Find the area of the rectangle.

**22.** The area of a rectangle is 108 square inches and if the sides are both diminished by 1 inch the area is diminished by 20 square inches. Find the diagonal of the rectangle.

**23.** A plane flying with the wind goes 125 miles per hour, and flying against a wind twice as strong it goes 80 miles per hour. What is the rate of the wind in each case?

**24.** A person can travel a certain distance by auto in 1 hour and 20 minutes, or by horse in 4 hours. If he is to cover the same distance traveling equal times by auto and by horse, when must he leave the auto?

**25.** The product of two numbers is 72 and the sum of their squares is 145. Find the numbers.

**26.** Find two numbers such that three times the first is 15 greater than the second, and three times the square of the first is 111 greater than the square of the second.

**27.** The sum of the squares of two numbers is 74, and their difference is 2. Find the numbers.

**28.** The sum of two numbers exceeds the product of their square roots by 21. If the product of their square roots is added to the sum of the numbers the result is 61. Find the numbers.

**29.** The yearly interest on a sum of money is $60. If the sum were $400 larger and the rate 1 per cent less, the interest would be $10 more. Find the principal and the rate.

**30.** A person has $6000 which he divides into two portions and lends at different rates of interest, so that the two portions produce equal returns. If the first portion had been lent at the second rate of interest, it would have produced $320; and if the second portion had been lent at the first rate of interest, it would have produced $80. Find the rates of interest.

**31.** The dimensions of a rectangular steel plate are $a$ and $b$. Find the dimensions of a plate having twice the perimeter, and twice the area.

**32.** The radius of a circular arch is $r$ and the span is $2s$. Find a formula for the height $h$ of the arch.

**33.** The top of a mountain is just visible from a point $d$ miles distant by airline. Find the height of the mountain in terms of $d$ and the radius of the earth $r$.

**34.** The sides of a triangle are $a$, $b$, $c$. A perpendicular $x$ is drawn to the side $c$ from the opposite vertex. Find $x$ in terms of $a$, $b$, $c$ and $s$ where $2s = a + b + c$, and give a geometric interpretation of your result.

**35.** A long horizontal pipe is connected with the bottom of a reservoir. If $H$ is the depth of water in the reservoir in feet, $d$ the diameter of the pipe in inches, $L$ the length of the pipe in feet, and $v$ the velocity of the water in the pipe in feet per second, then

$$\frac{Hd}{L} = \frac{4v^2 + 5v - 2}{1200}.$$

Find the velocity of water in a 5-inch pipe, 1000 feet long, connected with a reservoir containing 49 feet of water.

# CHAPTER VIII

## FUNCTIONS AND GRAPHS

**45. Rectangular coordinates.** In Chapter I we saw how a point on a line corresponds to a single real number and we plotted the real numbers as points on a line. *A point in a plane corresponds to a pair of real numbers and we plot pairs of real numbers as points*

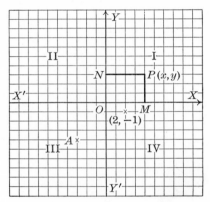

Fig. 2

*in a plane* in the following manner: In a plane let $X'X$ and $Y'Y$ be two straight lines intersecting at right angles in the point $O$. *The lines $X'X$ and $Y'Y$ divide the plane into four parts, called* **quadrants,** numbered I, II, III, IV in Figure 2. Let the *positive direction* on $X'X$ be to the *right* (and *negative* to the *left*), and let the *positive direction* on $Y'Y$ be *upward* (and *negative downward*). Lay off on $X'X$ and $Y'Y$ numbered scales with $O$ as the zero point and an arbitrary unit of length. Let $P$ be any point in the plane and from $P$ drop perpendiculars $MP$ and $NP$ to $X'X$ and $Y'Y$, respectively. *The number represented by $OM$ (positive, negative, or zero) is called the* **abscissa** *of $P$, and the number represented by $ON$ is called the* **ordinate** *of $P$. The abscissa and ordinate of $P$ are*

110

*called the* **rectangular coordinates** *of P.* The point $P$, whose abscissa is $x$ and whose ordinate is $y$, is written $(x, y)$ or $P(x, y)$, with the abscissa always first. *The abscissa of a point P is its directed (signed) distance from Y'Y and the ordinate of P is its directed distance from X'X.* Thus the point $(2, -1)$ is 2 units to the *right* of $Y'Y$ and 1 unit *below* $X'X$. *The point O is called the* **origin**, $X'X$ *the* **x-axis,** *and* $Y'Y$ *the* **y-axis.**

EXAMPLE I. Plot the point $A(-3, -4)$.

**Solution.** (See Fig. 2.) $A$ may be plotted by going 3 units to the left from $O$ along $X'X$ and then down 4 units parallel to $Y'Y$. Or $A$ may be plotted by going 4 units down $Y'Y$ from $O$ and 3 units to the left parallel to $X'X$. $A$ is the intersection of a line 3 units to the left of and parallel to $Y'Y$ with a line 4 units below and parallel to $X'X$.

## EXERCISES

*Plot the following points:*

**1.** $(3, -1)$, $(2, 4)$, $(-1, 7)$, $(6, 2)$, $(-1, -4)$, $(2, -5)$, $(-5, 2)$.

**2.** $(3\frac{1}{2}, 2)$, $(0, -1)$, $(2, 0)$, $(-\frac{1}{2}, \frac{1}{2})$, $(\sqrt{2}, 0)$, $(3\frac{1}{4}, 2\frac{1}{2})$, $(0, -0.5)$.

**3.** $(\pi, e)$, $(\sqrt{5}, 0)$, $\left(-\dfrac{\sqrt{2}}{2}, -\dfrac{\sqrt{2}}{2}\right)$, $(0, 3e)$, $(1 + \sqrt{2}, 1 - \sqrt{2})$.

**4.** Draw a triangle whose vertices are $(0, 0)$, $(2, 5)$, and $(-1, 7)$.

**5.** Draw the circle whose center is $(0, 0)$ and whose radius is 5. Find the coordinates of 6 points on the circle.

**6.** Where is every point whose ordinate is 0? Where is every point whose abscissa is 0?

**7.** Where is every point whose ordinate is (a) 4, (b) $-2$, (c) $2\frac{1}{3}$?

**8.** Where is every point whose abscissa is (a) 7, (b) $1\frac{1}{2}$, (c) $-3$?

**9.** Find the distance from $(1, 2)$ to $(6, 14)$. Find the distance from $(-1, 2)$ to $(2, -2)$.

**10.** Plot the points in the following table and draw a smooth curve through them. Here $x$ is the abscissa and $y$ the ordinate.

| $x$ | $-2$ | $-1$ | $-\frac{1}{2}$ | 0 | 1 | 3 | $3\frac{1}{2}$ | 4 |
|---|---|---|---|---|---|---|---|---|
| $y$ | $-13$ | $-9$ | $-7$ | $-5$ | $-1$ | 7 | 9 | 11 |

**11.** Draw the line $l_1$ through $(0, 0)$ and $(5, 5)$, and the line $l_2$ through $(0, 4)$ and $(4, 0)$. What is the point of intersection of these two lines?

**12.** Draw the circle with center 0 and radius 5, and a line through 0 and the point $(8, 6)$. In what points do the circle and the line intersect?

**46. Graphs and graphical solution of equations.**   In the equation
$y - x - 3 = 0$, if $x = 1$, $y = 4$, and we say that the coordinates
of the point (1, 4) **satisfy the equation** $y - x - 3 = 0$.   We can
find any number of points whose coordinates satisfy this equation
by assuming various values for $x$ and finding the corresponding
values of $y$.   All these points lie on a curve which is called the
**graph of the equation.**   *The* **graph of an equation** *contains every
point whose coordinates satisfy the equation and no other points.*

EXAMPLE I.   Plot the graph of the equation $y - x - 3 = 0$.

**Solution.**   (a) Solve for $y$ in terms of $x$.   $y = x + 3$.

(b) Assume values of $x$ and find the corresponding values of $y$ and
arrange these values in a table.

| $x$ | $-5$ | $-4$ | $-2$ | 0 | 2 | 3 | 5 |
|---|---|---|---|---|---|---|---|
| $y$ | $-2$ | $-1$ | 1 | 3 | 5 | 6 | 8 |

(c) Plot these points:

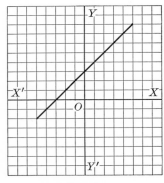

FIG. 3

(d) Draw a smooth curve through these points.

*The graph of an equation of the first degree is a straight line and
hence the name* **linear equation.**   In solving a system of two equations in two unknowns, $x$ and $y$, we found values of $x$ and the
corresponding values of $y$ which satisfied the two equations simultaneously.   Thus we found the coordinates of points which were
on both graphs, or the points of intersection of the graphs of the

two equations. Hence the graphical solution of a system of equations consists in finding the points of intersection of the graphs of the equations. Of course, all the points on the graphs have real coordinates and, consequently, *we cannot find graphically those solutions which are complex or imaginary.*

EXAMPLE II. Solve graphically: $2x - y = 4$
$$x + 2y = 7$$

**Solution.** Plot the graphs of $2x - y = 4$ and $x + 2y = 7$ as in Example I (see Fig. 4). It is seen from the graphs that these lines intersect in the point (3, 2). Hence the solution is $x = 3, y = 2$.

*The graph of an expression in x (function of x) is the graph of the equation formed by setting y equal to the expression in x.*

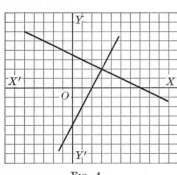

FIG. 4

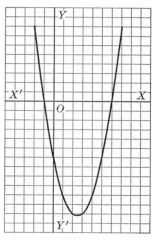

FIG. 5

EXAMPLE III. Plot the graph of the function $x^2 - 5x - 6$.

**Solution.** Set $y = x^2 - 5x - 6$ and plot the graph of the equation (see Fig. 5).

| $x$ | $-2$ | $-1$ | 0 | 1 | 2 | 3 | 4 | 5 | 6 | 7 |
|---|---|---|---|---|---|---|---|---|---|---|
| $y$ | 8 | 0 | $-6$ | $-10$ | $-12$ | $-12$ | $-10$ | $-6$ | 0 | 8 |

*The graph of the quadratic function (polynomial of the second degree in x) is a parabola (see Fig. 5).*

*To find graphically the real roots of a polynomial in x simply means to find the abscissas of the points where the graph of the polynomial crosses the x-axis.*

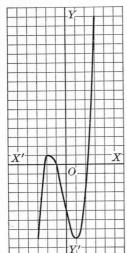

FIG. 6

EXAMPLE IV.  Find graphically the real roots of

$$x^3 + x^2 - 5x - 5 = 0.$$

**Solution.**  Put $y = x^3 + x^2 - 5x - 5$ and plot the graph of this equation.

| $x$ | $-3$ | $-2$ | $-1$ | $0$ | $1$ | $2$ | $3$ |
|---|---|---|---|---|---|---|---|
| $y$ | $-8$ | $1$ | $0$ | $-5$ | $-8$ | $-3$ | $16$ |

The graph crosses the x-axis at $(-2.2, 0)$, $(-1, 0)$, and $(2.2, 0)$ and hence the roots are $x = -2.2$, $x = -1$, and $x = 2.2$.

Of course, the accuracy of the solution depends upon the accuracy of plotting the points and the number of points plotted. Any desired accuracy can be attained by plotting a sufficient number of points.

### EXERCISES

*Plot the graphs of the following functions:*

1. $x + 3$    2. $2x - 7$    3. $x^3$    4. $x^2 - 7x$

5. $2$    6. $\dfrac{x}{2} - 5$    7. $x^3 + x - 4$    8. $x^4 + 3x^2$

9. $\sqrt{36 - x^2}$    10. $\pm\sqrt{16 - x^2}$    11. $\pm\sqrt{4 + x}$    12. $x^5$

*Find the real roots of the following polynomials to the nearest tenth:*

13. $x^2 - 2x - 3$      14. $x^3 - x$        15. $x^4 - 1$
16. $2x^3 - 3x^2 + 9x$    17. $3x^2 + 2 - 5x$    18. $x^4 + x^2 + 1$
19. $2x^2 - 6x - 9$      20. $x^2 - 4x + 5$    21. $x^2 - x - 4$
22. $8x^2 - 5$          23. $2x^2 - 10x + 4$    24. $x^2 + x - 4$

*Graph the following equations:*

25. $y - 3x + 7 = 0$    26. $2y - 8x = 1$      27. $3y + 2x - 7 = 0$
28. $y^2 + x^2 = 25$    29. $y^2 - x^2 = 0$    30. $25x^2 + 16y^2 = 400$
31. $y^2 = 8x$          32. $x^2 - 4y = 0$      33. $16x^2 - 9y^2 = 144$

**34.** $y = x^3$        **35.** $y = x^2$        **36.** $y = x^4$

**37.** $x^2 + y^2 = 0$        **38.** $x^2+y^2-6x-8y=0$        **39.** $xy + y^2 = 0$

**40.** $x^2+y^2-6x-7=0$        **41.** $xy = 1$        **42.** $y = \dfrac{x-2}{x+3}$

**43.** The system $x - 3y = 7$, $2x - 6y = 9$ has no solution. Explain geometrically.

**44.** The system $x^2 + y^2 = 25$, $x + y = 12$ cannot be solved graphically. Why?

**45.** For what value or values of $x$ is there no corresponding value of $y$ in the equation $y = \dfrac{x+3}{x-4}$?

**46.** Solve the exercises of §§ 30, 31 graphically.

**47.** Solve the exercises of § 33 graphically.

**48.** Find the real roots of the equations in the exercises of §§ 37, 38 graphically.

**49.** Solve graphically as far as possible the exercises of §§ 42, 43.

# CHAPTER IX

## RATIO, PROPORTION, AND VARIATION

**47. Ratio and proportion.** The **ratio of a number $a$ to a number $b$** *is the quotient $a \div b$.* The ratio of $a$ to $b$ is also written $a : b$, read "*a* is to *b*." Thus

$$a : b = a \div b = \frac{a}{b}.$$

*A* **proportion** *is a statement that two ratios are equal,* thus

$$a : b = c : d, \text{ read } ``a \text{ is to } b \text{ as } c \text{ is to } d."$$

We say that $a$, $b$, $c$, and $d$ are in proportion; *a and d are called the* **extremes,** *and b and c the* **means** *of the proportion, and d is called the* **fourth proportional** *to a, b, and c.* If $b = c$, the proportion becomes $a : b = b : d$ and in this case *d is called the* **third proportional** *to a and b, and b is a* **mean proportional** *between a and d.* In working problems in ratio and proportion we simply write the ratios as fractions and apply the laws of algebra.

EXAMPLE I. Find the fourth proportional to 3, 5, and 9.

**Solution.** Let $x$ be the required proportional, then

$$3 : 5 = 9 : x,$$

or

$$\frac{3}{5} = \frac{9}{x}$$

$$3x = 45$$

$$x = 15 \quad \text{(Ans.)}$$

EXAMPLE II. If $a : b = c : d$, prove that $\dfrac{a + b}{a - b} = \dfrac{c + d}{c - d}$.

**Solution.** Given $\dfrac{a}{b} = \dfrac{c}{d}$.

Then

$$\frac{a}{b} + 1 = \frac{c}{d} + 1$$

or

$$\frac{a + b}{b} = \frac{c + d}{d} \tag{1}$$

Also,                   $\dfrac{a}{b} - 1 = \dfrac{c}{d} - 1$

or                      $\dfrac{a - b}{b} = \dfrac{c - d}{d}$                  (2)

From (1) we have        $\dfrac{d}{b} = \dfrac{c + d}{a + b}$

From (2) we have        $\dfrac{d}{b} = \dfrac{c - d}{a - b}$

Hence                   $\dfrac{c - d}{a - b} = \dfrac{c + d}{a + b}$

Multiplying both members by $\dfrac{a + b}{c - d}$, we have

$$\dfrac{a + b}{a - b} = \dfrac{c + d}{c - d} \quad \text{Q.E.D.}$$

## EXERCISES

*Solve for x or y:*

**1.** $2 : 4 = 18 : x$        **2.** $(x - 1) : (x - 3) = 18 : 6$

**3.** $\frac{1}{5} : x = 4 : 20$        **4.** $(a + b) : y = y : 4(a + b)^3$

**5.** $(ab - b^2) : (a^3 - b^3) = y : (a^3 + a^2b + ab^2)$

*Find the required proportional:*

**6.** Third proportional to 2 and $- 5$.

**7.** Fourth proportional to $b$, $2c$, and $3bc$.

**8.** Mean proportional between 6 and 54.

**9.** Fourth proportional to 17, 19, and 187.

**10.** Third proportional to $\frac{5}{36}$ and $\frac{5}{12}$.

**11.** Mean proportional between $(a^2 + b^2)$ and $(c^2 + d^2)$.

**12.** Fourth proportional to $a^3$, $ab$, and $5a^2b$.

**13.** Mean proportional between $12ab^2$ and $3a^3$.

*If $a : b = c : d$, prove:*

**14.** $a(c + d) = c(a + b)$        **15.** $\dfrac{a}{b} = \dfrac{c}{d} = \dfrac{a + c}{b + d}$

**16.** $\dfrac{a + b}{b} = \dfrac{c + d}{d}$        **17.** $\dfrac{a + b}{a} = \dfrac{c + d}{c}$

**18.** $a : (b - a) = c : (d - c)$

**19.** $(3a + 4b) : (3a - 4b) = (3c + 4d) : (3c - 4d)$

**20.** $(a - c) : (a + c) = (b - d) : (b + d)$

**21.** $(a + mb) : (a - mb) = (c + md) : (c - md)$

**22.** $a^2 - ab : c^2 - cd = ab : cd$

**23.** $(a \pm b)^2 : ab = (c \pm d)^2 : cd$    **24.** $a : b = \sqrt{ac} : \sqrt{bd}$

**25.** $\dfrac{a + b^2}{a - b^2} = \dfrac{c + bd}{c - bd}$    **26.** $\dfrac{a}{b} = \dfrac{c}{d} = \dfrac{\sqrt{a^2 + c^2}}{\sqrt{b^2 + d^2}}$

**27.** $\left(\dfrac{a}{b}\right)^2 + \left(\dfrac{c}{d}\right)^2 = \dfrac{2ac}{bd}$

**28.** $(a^2 + c^2) : (ab + cd) = (ab + cd) : (b^2 + d^2)$

**29.** $(a^2 + ac + c^2) : (a^2 - ac + c^2) = (b^2 + bd + d^2) : (b^2 - bd + d^2)$

**30.** $(a^2 + ab^2 - b^2) : b^2 = (ac + abd - bd) : bd$

**31.** A line 12 feet long is divided into two segments so that the longer segment is to the shorter segment as 2 : 1. Find the lengths of the two segments. $8$ ✓

**32.** Divide 25 in the ratio 2 : 3. $\frac{5}{2} = \frac{25}{x}$

**33.** What number added to 2, 4, 12, and 18 will give four numbers which are in proportion? $3$

**34.** If four quantities are in proportion and the second is a mean proportional between the third and the fourth, prove that the third is a mean proportional between the first and the second.

**35.** What number must be added to 4, 7, and 8 in order that the fourth proportional to the sums may be 15?

**36.** $A$ and $B$ are 17 and 26 years old, respectively. In how many years will the ratio of their ages be 3 : 4?

**37.** Two numbers are in the ratio 2 : 3. If each be increased by 9, the new numbers will be in the ratio 3 : 4. Find the numbers.

**38.** The sum of two numbers is 8, and the square of their sum is to the sum of their squares as 32 : 17. Find the numbers.

**39.** A business worth $28,000 is owned by three partners. The share of one partner, $8000, is a mean proportional between the shares of the other two. Find the share of each. $\frac{8000}{x} = \frac{x}{20\,000}$  $x^2 = 160\,000\,000$  $x = 14\,000$

**40.** What number must be subtracted from each of the numbers 6, 7, 8, and 10, so that the resulting differences shall form a proportion when taken in the given order?

**48. Variation.** Let $x$, $y$, and $z$ denote variable quantities. *We say that $y$* **varies directly as $x$,** *or $y$* **varies as $x$,** *if for every value of $x$ there is a corresponding value of $y$ given by*

$$y = kx,$$

*where $k$ is the constant of variation,* e.g., the perimeter $p$ of a square varies directly as the side $d$, $p = 4d$. *We say that $y$* **varies inversely**

**as** *x* *if for every value of x there is a corresponding value of y given by*

$$y = \frac{k}{x},$$

*where k is the constant of variation,* e.g., the time required for an automobile to travel 100 miles at a uniform velocity varies inversely as the velocity. *We say that y* **varies jointly as** *x* **and** *z if* *y* = *kxz*, i.e., *y varies directly as the product xz*, e.g., the area *A* of a rectangle of breadth *b* and height *h* varies jointly as *b* and *h*, *A* = *bh*. Other types of variation are:

$y = \dfrac{10x^3}{z},$   *y* varies directly as $x^3$ and inversely as *z*;

$V = \pi r^2 h,$   *V* varies jointly as $r^2$ and *h*;

$y = \dfrac{kx^2\sqrt[3]{z}}{\sqrt{w}},$   *y* varies jointly as $x^2$ and $\sqrt[3]{z}$, and inversely as $\sqrt{w}$.

The following examples illustrate the applications of variation:

EXAMPLE I. The illumination from a source of light varies inversely as the square of the distance from the light. If a picture, now 10 inches from the light, is moved to 20 inches away, what is the ratio of the new illumination to the old?

**Solution.** Let *I* be the original illumination and *I'* the new illumination. Then the problem is to find $\dfrac{I'}{I}$. But $I = \dfrac{k}{s^2}$, where *s* is the distance from the light, and *k* is the constant of variation.

Hence   $I = \dfrac{k}{100}, \; I' = \dfrac{k}{400}.$

Therefore,   $\dfrac{I'}{I} = \dfrac{\dfrac{k}{400}}{\dfrac{k}{100}} = \dfrac{1}{4}$   (Ans.)

EXAMPLE II. The safe load of a horizontal beam supported at the ends varies jointly as the breadth and the square of the depth, and inversely as the length between supports. A beam 24 feet long, 4 inches wide, and 6 inches deep has a safe load of 1200 pounds. Find the minimum depth of a 30-foot beam of the same material, 6 inches wide, to carry 2 tons.

**Solution.** $S = \dfrac{kbd^2}{l}$, where $S$ is the safe load in pounds, $b$ is the breadth and $d$ the depth in inches, $l$ is the length in feet, and $k$ the constant of variation.

Hence
$$1200 = \frac{k(4)(36)}{24} = 6k \tag{1}$$
$$k = 200$$

Since the new beam is of the same material, $k$ is the same, and we have, with 2 tons $= 4000$ pounds,
$$4000 = \frac{200(6)d^2}{30} \tag{2}$$
$$d^2 = \frac{(4000)30}{200(6)} = 100$$
$$d = 10 \text{ inches} \quad \text{(Ans.)}$$

It should be observed that with $S$ in pounds, $b$ and $d$ in inches, and $l$ in feet, we found $k = 200$. This value of $k$ holds so long as the beam is of the same material and the units consistent with those used in the original evaluation. Thus, $S$ for equation (2) must be expressed in pounds and not in tons.

### EXERCISES

*Express the relationship between the variables by an equation using $k$ for the constant of variation, if it is not known:*

  **1.** The area $A$ of a circle and its radius $r$.   $A = \pi r^2$

  **2.** The perimeter $P$ of a square and a side $s$.   $P = 4s$

  **3.** The volume $V$ of a sphere and its radius $r$.   $V = \frac{4\pi r^3}{3}$

  **4.** The circumference $S$ of a circle and its diameter $d$.   $S = \pi d$

  **5.** The area $A$ of a triangle, its base $b$, and its altitude $h$.   $A = \frac{1}{2} bh$

  **6.** The lateral area $S$ of a cylinder, its altitude $h$, and the radius $r$ of its base.   $S = 2\pi r h$

  **7.** $V$ varies directly as $x$ and inversely as $y^2$.   $V = \frac{kx}{y^2}$

  **8.** $z$ varies jointly as $x$ and $y^2$ and inversely as $\sqrt[3]{w}$.   $z = \frac{kxy^2}{\sqrt[3]{w}}$

  **9.** $s$ varies directly as $t^2$.   $S = kt^2$

**10.** $w$ varies directly as $x^{\frac{2}{3}}$ and inversely as $\sqrt{y}$.   $w = \frac{x^{2/3}}{\sqrt{y}}$

*Write an equivalent statement in the language of variation:*

**11.** $s = kt^2$      **12.** $A = \pi r^2$      **13.** $P = 4s$

**14.** $w = \dfrac{kx^2 \sqrt[3]{z}}{\sqrt{u}}$      **15.** $S = \pi r l$      **16.** $v = \dfrac{1}{p}$

**17.** $w = \dfrac{5xy}{z^3}$      **18.** $A = \frac{1}{2}bh$      **19.** $A = \frac{1}{2}(b_1 + b_2)h$

**20.** The distance through which a body falls from rest varies as the square of the time. If a body falls 144 feet in the first three seconds, how far will it fall in the first five seconds? During the fifth second?

**21.** Assuming that the power to drive a motorboat is proportional to the square of the speed, how much power will it take to drive at 12 miles per hour a boat that a 4-horsepower engine drives at 8 miles per hour?

**22.** The time required by a pendulum to make one vibration is proportional to the square root of its length. If a pendulum 100 centimeters long vibrates once in a second, find the time of one vibration of a pendulum 64 centimeters long.

**23.** The volume of a gas varies inversely as the pressure. A tank contains 4 cubic feet of air under a pressure of 60 pounds per square inch. How much space will be occupied by the air when expanded so as to be under a pressure of 20 pounds per square inch?

**24.** If the intensity of light varies inversely as the square of the distance from its source, how much farther away from a lamp must a book which is now 2 feet away be removed so as to receive one fourth as much light?

**25.** Kepler's third law of planetary motion states that the square of a planet's time of revolution varies as the cube of its mean distance from the sun. The mean distances of the earth and Mercury from the sun are 93 and 36 millions of miles, respectively. Find the time of Mercury's revolution.

**26.** The weight of a body above the surface of the earth varies inversely as the square of its distance from the center of the earth, and its weight below the surface varies directly as its distance from the center. A body weighs 100 pounds at the surface of the earth. What would it weigh 5000 miles above the surface? What would it weigh 1500 miles below the surface? (Assume radius of earth = 4000 miles.)

**27.** The interest on a fixed sum of money varies as the length of the time it is invested. If a certain sum draws $145 in 3 months, how much will it draw in 10 months?

**28.** A disk 1 foot in diameter held 2 feet from the eye just obscures a ball whose center is 14 feet from the eye. If the ball is moved away, so that the distance of its center from the eye is 26 feet, where must the disk be placed to just obscure the ball?

**29.** The fixed charge per hour of running a freight train is $100, and the additional cost per hour is proportional to the square of the speed $s$ at which the train is run. This additional cost is $10 per hour when the speed is 12 miles per hour. Find an expression in terms of $s$ for the total cost $C$ of a trip of 500 miles.

**30.** The deflection of a beam supported at both ends varies directly as the fourth power of the length and inversely as the square of the depth. If the length is increased 25 per cent, how much must the depth be changed to decrease the deflection 15 per cent? (Give your answer correct to 0.1 per cent.)

**31.** The safe load $S$ of a horizontal beam supported at both ends varies jointly as the breadth $b$ and the square of the depth $d$, and inversely as the length $l$ between supports. If a $2 \times 6$ beam, 16 feet between supports, can bear a maximum load of 1000 pounds, find a law connecting $S$, $b$, $d$, and $l$.

**32.** The pressure of water on the bottom of a containing vessel varies jointly as the area of the bottom and the depth of the water. When the water is 1 foot deep, the pressure on 1 square foot of the bottom is 62.5 pounds. Find the pressure on the bottom of a circular tank 12 feet in diameter in which the water is 5 feet deep.

**33.** The volume of a gas varies directly as the absolute temperature and inversely as the pressure. When the pressure is 15 pounds per square inch and the temperature 260°, the volume is 200 cubic inches. What will be the volume when the pressure becomes 24 pounds per square inch and the temperature 390°?

**34.** The pressure of the wind on a plane surface varies jointly as the area of the surface and the square of the wind's velocity. The pressure on 1 square foot is 18 pounds when the wind blows 15 miles per hour. Find the velocity when the pressure on a surface 2 feet square is 20 pounds.

**35.** The force of attraction between two bodies varies directly as the product of their masses and inversely as the square of the distance between them. When two masses, 2 and 15, are separated by 100 inches, the force is 24 units. If the distance between them is diminished by 3 feet and the larger mass tripled, what must be the smaller mass if the force is to remain the same?

**36.** The number of vibrations of a stretched string varies directly as the square root of the stretching force and inversely as the product of its length and diameter. If a string 4 feet long and $\frac{1}{8}$ inch in diameter vibrates $n$ times per second under a stretching force of 15 pounds, what change in the stretching force would cause the string to vibrate $2n$ times per second?

**37.** The stiffness of a beam varies jointly as the breadth and the depth, and inversely as the square of the length. If the breadth is increased 25 per cent and the depth decreased 30 per cent, what change must be made in the length in order to increase the stiffness 50 per cent?

# CHAPTER X

## PROGRESSIONS

**49. Arithmetic progressions.** *A set of numbers such that there is a first, a second, a third, etc., is called a* **sequence** *and each number is called a* **term of the sequence.** *An* **arithmetic progression** (A.P.) *is a sequence of numbers each of which after the first is derived from the preceding by adding to it a fixed number called the* **common difference.**

Let $a$ be the first term and $d$ the common difference, then $a + d$ is the second term, $a + 2d$ the third term, and $a + (n-1)d$ the $n$th term, where $n$ is any positive integer. Let $S$ represent the sum of the first $n$ terms of this A.P., then

$$l = a + (n-1)d$$

is the last term and, writing the sum forward and backward, we have

$$S = a + a + d + a + 2d + \cdots + l - d + l$$
$$S = l + l - d + l - 2d + \cdots + a + d + a$$

$$2S = (a + l) + (a + l) + (a + l) + \cdots + (a + l) + (a + l)$$
$$= n(a + l)$$

Thus
$$S = \frac{n}{2}(a + l)$$

$$\text{or } S = \frac{n}{2}(a + a + (n-1)d) = \frac{n}{2}(2a + (n-1)d)$$

EXAMPLE I.  Find $l$ and $S$ for 2, 4, 6, $\cdots$ to 8 terms.

**Solution.**  Here $a = 2$, $d = 2$, $n = 8$.
$$l = 2 + (8 - 1) \cdot 2 = 2 + 14 = 16$$
$$S = \tfrac{8}{2}(2 + 16) = 4(18) = 72 \quad \text{(Ans.)}$$

EXAMPLE II.  If $a = 3$, $l = 121$, $n = 60$ in an A.P., find $d$ and $S$.

**Solution.**  $l = a + (n-1)d = 3 + (60 - 1)d = 3 + 59d$
$$121 = 3 + 59d$$
$$59d = 118$$
$$d = 2 \quad \text{(Ans.)}$$
$$S = \frac{n}{2}(a + l) = \frac{60}{2}(3 + 121) = 30(124) = 3720 \quad \text{(Ans.)}$$

## EXERCISES

*Find l and S of each of the following* A.P.:

**1.** 1, 2, 3, $\cdots$ to 12 terms.       **2.** 3, 1, $-$ 1, $\cdots$ to 6 terms.

**3.** 2, 5, 8, $\cdots$ to 27 terms.       **4.** $-$ 3, $-$ 8, $-$ 13, $\cdots$ to 40 terms.

**5.** 3, $-$ 1, $-$ 5, $\cdots$ to 18 terms.    **6.** 2, 4, 6, 8, $\cdots$ to 60 terms.

**7.** 7, 12, 17, $\cdots$ to 20 terms.     **8.** $\frac{1}{2}$, $\frac{3}{2}$, $\frac{5}{2}$, $\cdots$ to 18 terms.

*Of a, d, l, n, and S, find the ones not given:*

**9.** $a = -24$, $d = 4$, $S = -80$.       **10.** $l = 57$, $d = 4$, $n = 17$.

**11.** $d = -3$, $l = -21$, $S = -66$.      **12.** $a = \frac{2}{3}$, $n = 16$, $S = \frac{232}{3}$.

**13.** $a = 1$, $n = 6$, $S = 16$.          **14.** $a = -7$, $n = 23$, $d = 4$.

**15.** $d = 5$, $l = -47$, $S = -357$.       **16.** $a = 1$, $d = 7$, $S = 12$.

**17.** $l = 19$, $n = 9$, $S = 27$.          **18.** $a = 12$, $l = -76$, $S = -640$.

**19.** $a = 5$, $l = 395$, $d = 5$.          **20.** $l = 8$, $S = 44$, $n = 8$.

**21.** $a = 8$, $l = -9.1$, $n = 20$.        **22.** $a = 20$, $d = -6$, $S = 30$.

**23.** $a = 3$, $n = 6$, $S = -12$.          **24.** $n = 15$, $S = 600$, $d = 5$.

**25.** The sum of the first 5 terms of an A.P. is 40 and the sum of the first 12 is 222. Find the progression.

**26.** The sum of the first 6 terms of an A.P. is 48 and the sum of the first 20 is 440. Find the progression.

**27.** Find four numbers in A.P. such that the product of the first and fourth shall be 52 and the product of the second and third shall be 70.

**28.** The sum of three numbers in A.P. is 15, and their product is 105. Find the progression.

**29.** The second term of an A.P. is $\frac{1}{3}$ of the seventh and the sum of 20 terms is 440. Find the progression.

**30.** The sum of three numbers in A.P. is 12, and the sum of their squares is 56. Find the numbers.

**31.** An A.P. consists of 11 terms. The sum of the three terms in the middle is 33, and of the last three is 57. Find the progression.

**32.** The eighth term of an A.P. is 67 and the twelfth term is 59, the sum of $n$ terms is 952. Find $n$.

**33.** The fifth term of an A.P. is 1 and the thirteenth is 2. Find the sum of 23 terms.

**34.** The sum of the first 8 terms of an A.P. is 124, and the sum of the second and fifth terms is 5 times the first term. Find the progression.

**35.** A ball starting from rest rolls down an inclined plane, passing over 6 inches in the first second, 14 inches in the second second, 22 inches in the third second, etc. How long will it take the ball to pass over a distance of 156 inches?

**36.** A clerk received \$100 a month for the first year and an annual increase of \$25 for the next 10 years. Treat as a progression and find his salary for the eleventh year and the total amount he received.

**37.** Divide 20 into four parts which are in A.P. and such that the product of the first and fourth is to the product of the second and third as 2 : 3.

**38.** Twelve eggs are placed in line at distances 5, 10, 15, $\cdots$ feet from a basket. A boy, starting from the basket, picks up the eggs and carries them one at a time to the basket. How far must he run to complete the race?

**39.** How much will it cost to have a horse shod, paying 2 cents for the first nail, 4 cents for the second, 6 for the third, and so on? Each shoe has 8 nails.

**40.** A body falls 16 feet in the first second, three times as far in the next second, five times as far in the third second, and so on. How far would it fall in a minute?

**50. Geometric progressions.** *A geometric progression* (G.P.) *is a sequence each term of which after the first is obtained by multiplying the preceding term by a fixed number called the* **common ratio.** Let $a$ be the first term and $r$ the common ratio, then $ar$ is the second term, $ar^2$ the third term, and $ar^{n-1}$ the $n$th term, where $n$ is any positive integer. Thus

$$l = ar^{n-1},$$

where $l$ is the last term in a G.P. of $n$ terms, whose first term is $a$, and common ratio is $r$. Let $S$ represent the sum of the first $n$ terms of this G.P., then

$$S = a + ar + ar^2 + \cdots + ar^{n-2} + ar^{n-1}$$
$$rS = \quad ar + ar^2 + \cdots + ar^{n-2} + ar^{n-1} + ar^n$$
$$S - rS = a - ar^n$$
$$S(1 - r) = a(1 - r^n)$$
$$S = \frac{a(1 - r^n)}{1 - r}, \ r \neq 1,$$

or

$$S = \frac{a - rar^{n-1}}{1 - r} = \frac{a - rl}{1 - r}, \ r \neq 1.$$

$$S = \frac{a - rl}{1 - r}, \ r \neq 1$$

**EXAMPLE I.** The first term of a G.P. is 3 and the common ratio is 2. Find the fifth term and the sum of the first five terms.

**Solution.** $a = 3$, $r = 2$, $n = 5$.

$$l = ar^{n-1} = 3(2)^{5-1} = 3 \cdot 2^4 = 48 \quad \text{(Ans.)}$$

$$S = \frac{a - rl}{1 - r} = \frac{3 - 2 \cdot 48}{1 - 2} = \frac{-93}{-1} = 93 \quad \text{(Ans.)}$$

EXAMPLE II. In a G.P. $a = -3$, $S = -468$, $r = 5$. Find $n$ and $l$.

**Solution.**

$$S = \frac{a(1 - r^n)}{1 - r}$$

$$-468 = \frac{-3(1 - 5^n)}{1 - 5}$$

$$(-4)(-468) = -3 + 3 \cdot 5^n$$
$$1872 = -3 + 3 \cdot 5^n$$
$$3 \cdot 5^n = 1875$$
$$5^n = 625$$

Hence
$$n = 4 \quad \text{(Ans.)}$$
$$l = (-3)5^3 = -375 \quad \text{(Ans.)}$$

### EXERCISES

*Find l and S of each of the following* G.P.:

**1.** 2, 4, 8, $\cdots$ to 5 terms

**2.** 3, 6, 12, $\cdots$ to 6 terms

**3.** 0.2, 0.02, 0.002, $\cdots$ to 5 terms

**4.** $\sqrt{3}$, $\sqrt{6}$, $2\sqrt{3}$, $\cdots$ to 6 terms

**5.** 1, 2, 4, $\cdots$ to 12 terms

**6.** $-4$, 2, $-1$, $\cdots$ to 5 terms

**7.** $\frac{1}{36}$, $-\frac{1}{12}$, $\frac{1}{4}$, $\cdots$ to 8 terms

**8.** $-\frac{3}{2}$, 3, $-6$, $\cdots$ to 7 terms

*Of a, l, n, r, and S, find those not given:*

**9.** $a = -2$, $n = 5$, $l = -32$

**10.** $a = 1$, $r = -2$, $n = 7$

**11.** $S = 750$, $r = 2$, $l = 400$

**12.** $S = 255$, $l = 1$, $r = \frac{1}{2}$

**13.** $a = 2$, $l = 512$, $r = 2$

**14.** $r = 3$, $n = 5$, $S = 363$

**15.** $a = 3$, $l = 81$, $n = 4$

**16.** $r = 5$, $l = 625$, $S = 775$

**17.** $a = -3$, $l = -243$, $S = -183$

**18.** $a = 48$, $l = 243$, $n = 5$

**19.** $n = 5$, $a = 2$, $l = 162$

**20.** $r = 2$, $S = 635$, $n = 7$

**21.** $a = 2$, $n = 5$, $S = 242$

**22.** $a = 1$, $l = \frac{1}{16}$, $S = \frac{11}{16}$

**23.** The sum of three numbers in G.P. is 21 and their product is 216. Find the numbers.

**24.** The second term of a G.P. is 8 and the fifth is 1. Find the first and sixth terms and the sum of six terms.

**25.** Of a G.P. the sum of the first and second terms is 8, and the sum of the third and fourth terms is 72. Find the ratio and the sum of the first 5 terms.

**26.** The sum of the first 4 terms of a G.P. is 80, and the sum of the first 8 terms is 6560. Find the progression.

**27.** Find three numbers in G.P. such that their sum is 21 and the sum of their squares is 189.

**28.** Find the sum of 10 terms of a G.P. if the third term is 16 and the fifth term is 64.

**29.** If the first, third, and sixth terms of a G.P. are 12, 3, $\frac{3}{8}$, respectively, find the ratio and the sum of the first 6 terms.

**30.** A swinging pendulum is brought gradually to rest by friction of the air. If the length of the first swing is 20 inches and the length of each succeeding swing is one tenth less than the preceding one, what is the distance passed over in the sixth swing?

**31.** Each stroke of an air pump removes one sixth of the air then in the cylinder. What part of the air originally in the cylinder is removed in the first 6 strokes? How much is removed in the sixth stroke?

**32.** If a man puts one cent in the bank the first day, two cents the second day, four cents the third day, and so on, how much will his balance be at the end of ten days?

**33.** If $100 were deposited in a savings bank, which would pay 3 per cent interest compounded annually, and allowed to remain 8 years, how much would it amount to at the end of that time?

# CHAPTER XI

## THE BINOMIAL THEOREM

**51. Mathematical induction.** The following equalities are easily verified:

$$\frac{1}{1 \cdot 2} = \frac{1}{1 + 1}$$

$$\frac{1}{1 \cdot 2} + \frac{1}{2 \cdot 3} = \frac{2}{2 + 1}$$

$$\frac{1}{1 \cdot 2} + \frac{1}{2 \cdot 3} + \frac{1}{3 \cdot 4} = \frac{3}{3 + 1}$$

$$\frac{1}{1 \cdot 2} + \frac{1}{2 \cdot 3} + \frac{1}{3 \cdot 4} + \frac{1}{4 \cdot 5} = \frac{4}{4 + 1}$$

A careful inspection of these relations leads one to suspect that

$$\frac{1}{1 \cdot 2} + \frac{1}{2 \cdot 3} + \frac{1}{3 \cdot 4} + \cdots + \frac{1}{n(n + 1)} = \frac{n}{n + 1}, \quad (1)$$

where $n$ is any positive integer. Certainly (1) is valid for $n = 1, 2,$ 3, 4. Let us assume that it is valid for $n = r - 1$, where $r$ is any integer, then

$$\frac{1}{1 \cdot 2} + \frac{1}{2 \cdot 3} + \cdots + \frac{1}{(r - 1)(r - 1 + 1)} = \frac{r - 1}{r}$$

Now adding $\dfrac{1}{r(r + 1)}$ to both sides, we have

$$\frac{1}{1 \cdot 2} + \frac{1}{2 \cdot 3} + \cdots + \frac{1}{(r - 1)r} + \frac{1}{r(r + 1)} = \frac{r - 1}{r} + \frac{1}{r(r + 1)}$$

$$= \frac{(r - 1)(r + 1) + 1}{r(r + 1)}$$

$$= \frac{r^2 - 1 + 1}{r(r + 1)}$$

$$= \frac{r}{r + 1},$$

which is precisely (1) for $n = r$. Thus we have shown that *if* (1) *is valid for* $n = r - 1$, *where r is any positive integer, it is valid for* $n = r$, *the next positive integer.* But we know from arithmetic that (1) is valid for $n = 1$, consequently, (1) holds for $n = 1 + 1 = 2$, and since it is valid for $n = 2$, it holds for $n = 2 + 1 = 3$, and so on. Thus we have established (1) for every positive integer. *This method of proof is called* **mathematical induction** *and consists of the following steps:*

(a) *Verifying the theorem for the first few values of n.*

(b) *Proving that if the theorem is true for* $n = r - 1$, *where r is any integer for which the theorem has been verified, then it is true for* $n = r$.

EXAMPLE I. Prove by mathematical induction that
$$2 + 4 + 6 + \cdots + 2n = n(n + 1). \tag{2}$$
**Proof.**
$$2 = 1(1 + 1)$$
$$2 + 4 = 2(2 + 1) = 2 \cdot 3 = 6$$
$$2 + 4 + 6 = 3(3 + 1) = 3 \cdot 4 = 12$$
If $\quad 2 + 4 + 6 + \cdots + 2(r - 1) = (r - 1)r,$
then $\quad 2 + 4 + 6 + \cdots + 2(r - 1) + 2r = (r - 1)r + 2r = r^2 - r + 2r$
$$= r^2 + r$$
$$= r(r + 1).$$

But this is precisely (2) for $n = r$ and the theorem is proved.

### EXERCISES

*Prove by mathematical induction, n being any positive integer:*

**1.** $1 + 2 + 3 + \cdots + n = \frac{1}{2}(n)(n + 1)$

**2.** $3 + 6 + 9 + \cdots + 3n = \dfrac{3n}{2}(n + 1)$

**3.** $1^3 + 2^3 + 3^3 + \cdots + n^3 = (1 + 2 + 3 + \cdots + n)^2 = \dfrac{1}{4}n^2(n + 1)^2$

**4.** $1^2 + 2^2 + 3^2 + \cdots + n^2 = \frac{1}{6}n(n + 1)(2n + 1)$

**5.** $2 \cdot 4 + 4 \cdot 6 + 6 \cdot 8 + \cdots + 2n(2n + 2) = \frac{1}{3}n(2n + 2)(2n + 4)$

**6.** $2 + 2^2 + 2^3 + \cdots + 2^n = 2(2^n - 1)$

**7.** The formula for the sum of the first $n$ terms of an A.P.

**8.** The formula for the sum of the first $n$ terms of a G.P.

**9.** That $(x^n - y^n)$ has $(x - y)$ as a factor.

*Hint.* Use the identity
$$x^{r+1} - y^{r+1} = x(x^r - y^r) + y^r(x - y).$$

**10.** That $(x^{2n-1} + y^{2n-1})$ has $(x + y)$ as a factor.
**11.** That $(x^{2n} - y^{2n})$ has $(x + y)$ as a factor.

**52. The binomial theorem.** *The* **binomial formula** *is*

$$(a + b)^n = a^n + na^{n-1}b + \frac{n(n - 1)}{1 \cdot 2} a^{n-2}b^2 + \frac{n(n - 1)(n - 2)}{1 \cdot 2 \cdot 3} a^{n-3}b^3$$

$$+ \cdots + \frac{n(n - 1)(n - 2) \cdots (n - k + 2)}{1 \cdot 2 \cdot 3 \cdots (k - 1)} a^{n-k+1}b^{k-1}$$

$$+ \cdots + nab^{n-1} + b^n,$$

*where a and b are any numbers, n is any positive integer, and k is a positive integer between 1 and n. The product* $1 \cdot 2 \cdot 3 \cdots n$ *is often written* $n!$ *or* $\lfloor n$ *and read "*n *factorial."*

*The* **binomial theorem** *states that the above formula is true and we shall prove it by mathematical induction.*

For       $n = 1$,   $(a + b) = a + b$,
          $n = 2$,   $(a + b)^2 = a^2 + 2ab + b^2$,
          $n = 3$,   $(a + b)^3 = a^3 + 3a^2b + 3ab^2 + b^3$,

and thus the formula is valid for $n = 1, 2, 3$. Now let us assume that it holds for $n = r - 1$, i.e.,

$$(a + b)^{r-1} = a^{r-1} + (r - 1)a^{r-2}b + \frac{(r - 1)(r - 2)}{2!} a^{r-3}b^2 + \cdots$$

$$+ \frac{(r - 1)(r - 2) \cdots (r - 1 - k + 2)}{(k - 1)!} a^{r-1-k+1}b^{k-1}$$

$$+ \frac{(r - 1)(r - 2) \cdots (r - 1 - k + 1)}{k!} a^{r-1-k}b^k$$

$$+ \cdots + (r - 1)ab^{r-2} + b^{r-1}.$$

Multiplying each side by $(a + b)$, we have

$$(a + b)^r = a^r + (r - 1)a^{r-1}b + \frac{(r - 1)(r - 2)}{2!} a^{r-2}b^2 + \cdots$$

$$+ \frac{(r - 1)(r - 2) \cdots (r - k)}{k!} a^{r-k}b^k + \cdots + ab^{r-1} + a^{r-1}b$$

$$+ (r - 1)a^{r-2}b^2 + \cdots + \frac{(r - 1)(r - 2) \cdots (r - k + 1)}{(k - 1)!} a^{r-k}b^k$$

$$+ \cdots + (r - 1)ab^{r-1} + b^r$$

Adding, we have

$$(a + b)^r = a^r + ra^{r-1}b + \frac{r(r - 1)}{2!}\, a^{r-2}b^2 + \cdots$$

$$+ \frac{r(r - 1)(r - 2) \cdots (r - k + 1)}{k!}\, a^{r-k}b^k + \cdots + rab^{r-1} + b^r,$$

and the theorem is true for $n = r$, and hence for every positive integral value of $n$ by mathematical induction.

The details of the simplification of the general term are:

$$\frac{(r - 1)(r - 2) \cdots (r - k)}{k!} + \frac{(r - 1)(r - 2) \cdots (r - k + 1)}{(k - 1)!}$$

$$= \frac{(r - 1)(r - 2) \cdots (r - k + 1)}{(k - 1)!} \left\{ \frac{r - k}{k} + 1 \right\}$$

$$= \frac{(r - 1)(r - 2) \cdots (r - k + 1)}{(k - 1)!} \left(\frac{r}{k}\right)$$

$$= \frac{r(r - 1)(r - 2) \cdots (r - k + 1)}{k!}$$

*In the binomial expansion of $(a + b)^n$ the coefficients of the terms are called the* **binomial coefficients.** *The coefficient of the first term is* 1, *the coefficient of the second term is* $n$, *the coefficient of the k-th term is*

$$\frac{n(n - 1)(n - 2) \cdots (n - k + 2)}{(k - 1)!}$$

These coefficients can be obtained from an arrangement called **Pascal's triangle:**

| | | | | | | |
|---|---|---|---|---|---|---|
| $(a + b)^0$ | | | | 1 | | |
| $(a + b)^1$ | | | 1 | | 1 | |
| $(a + b)^2$ | | | 1 | 2 | 1 | |
| $(a + b)^3$ | | 1 | 3 | 3 | 1 | |
| $(a + b)^4$ | 1 | 4 | 6 | 4 | 1 | |
| . . . . . . . | 1 | 5 | 10 | 10 | 5 | 1 |

The numbers in each row of this triangular array are the coefficients in the expansion of the binomial at the left of the row. Each row begins and ends with the number 1. To find the intermediate numbers add the two numbers to the left and right above, e.g., the second number in the sixth row is $1 + 4 = 5$, the third number is $4 + 6 = 10$.

**EXAMPLE I.** Expand and simplify: $\left(2x^2 - \dfrac{1}{x}\right)^5$

**Solution.** $\left(2x^2 - \dfrac{1}{x}\right)^5 = \left[(2x^2) + \left(-\dfrac{1}{x}\right)\right]^5$

Thus $a = 2x^2$, $b = -\dfrac{1}{x}$, $n = 5$, and we have

$$\left[(2x^2) + \left(-\dfrac{1}{x}\right)\right]^5 = (2x^2)^5 + 5(2x^2)^4\left(-\dfrac{1}{x}\right) + \dfrac{5(5-1)}{1 \cdot 2}(2x^2)^3\left(-\dfrac{1}{x}\right)^2$$

$$+ \dfrac{5(5-1)(5-2)}{1 \cdot 2 \cdot 3}(2x^2)^2\left(-\dfrac{1}{x}\right)^3$$

$$+ \dfrac{5(5-1)(5-2)(5-3)}{1 \cdot 2 \cdot 3 \cdot 4}(2x^2)\left(-\dfrac{1}{x}\right)^4 + \left(-\dfrac{1}{x}\right)^5$$

$$= 32x^{10} - 80x^7 + 80x^4 - 40x + \dfrac{10}{x^2} - \dfrac{1}{x^5} \quad \text{(Ans.)}$$

**EXAMPLE II.** Find the sixth term in the expansion of $\left(3x - \dfrac{5}{x}\right)^8$.

**Solution.** Here $n = 8$, $a = 3x$, $b = -\dfrac{5}{x}$, $k = 6$, and we have

$$\dfrac{8(8-1)(8-2)(8-3)(8-4)}{1 \cdot 2 \cdot 3 \cdot 4 \cdot 5}(3x)^3\left(-\dfrac{5}{x}\right)^5$$

$$= \dfrac{8 \cdot 7 \cdot 6 \cdot 5 \cdot 4}{1 \cdot 2 \cdot 3 \cdot 4 \cdot 5} 27x^3\left(-\dfrac{3125}{x^5}\right)$$

$$= -\dfrac{4725000}{x^2} \quad \text{(Ans.)}$$

## EXERCISES

*Expand by the binomial theorem and simplify:*

1. $(x + y)^5$    2. $(u - v)^3$    3. $(a + b)^4$    4. $(2x - 3y)^4$

5. $(x^2 + 2)^3$    6. $(1 - 2x)^5$    7. $(a - 2)^7$    8. $(2x + 3)^4$

9. $\left(\dfrac{2}{3} - \dfrac{3x}{2}\right)^6$    10. $(x - 2y)^{12}$    11. $\left(\dfrac{1}{a} + \dfrac{1}{y}\right)^5$    12. $\left(\dfrac{2x}{y} - \dfrac{3y}{x}\right)^5$

13. $\left(\dfrac{x^2}{y} + \dfrac{y^2}{x}\right)^4$    14. $\left(\dfrac{a^2}{x^3} - \dfrac{y^{\frac{1}{2}}}{a^3}\right)^6$    15. $\left(2x + \dfrac{1}{\sqrt{x}}\right)^5$

16. $(x + 0.1)^8$    17. $\left(\dfrac{2}{x} + x^2\right)^5$    18. $(x^{-\frac{1}{2}} + x^{\frac{3}{2}})^3$

19. $\left(\dfrac{1}{2}x^{\frac{2}{3}} + \sqrt{\dfrac{2}{x}}\right)^4$    20. $\left(\sqrt{x} - \sqrt{\dfrac{x}{y}}\right)^7$    21. $\left(\sqrt{a^3} + \dfrac{2}{\sqrt{a}}\right)^6$

*Use the binomial theorem to find the numerical value of the following correct to five significant figures:*

**22.** $(1.02)^6$  **23.** $(101)^3$  **24.** $(98)^4$  **25.** $(100.5)^3$  **26.** $(99.3)^4$  **27.** $(20.1)^5$

*Find the indicated terms of the following expansions and simplify:*

**28.** $(x - 3y)^8$; fourth.  **29.** $(a - b)^{14}$; middle.

**30.** $\left(x + \dfrac{1}{x}\right)^{10}$; middle.  **31.** $(x^2 + y^{\frac{1}{6}})^{31}$; twenty-sixth.

**32.** $(b^{-\frac{1}{4}} - 2c^{\frac{1}{5}})^{20}$; sixth.  **33.** $\left(\sqrt[3]{x} - \dfrac{1}{\sqrt{x}}\right)^{18}$; fifth.

**34.** $\left(\dfrac{3}{4x} - \dfrac{x^{\frac{3}{2}}}{\sqrt{2}}\right)^{12}$; middle  **35.** $\left(\dfrac{1}{\sqrt{xy}} - \dfrac{x^2}{y^{-\frac{1}{2}}}\right)^7$; fourth

**36.** $\left(\dfrac{3}{2x} - \dfrac{x^2}{2}\right)^9$; fourth.  **37.** $\left(\dfrac{4x}{5} - \dfrac{5}{2x}\right)^7$; third.

**38.** $(x^{\frac{3}{2}}a^{\frac{1}{2}} - y^{\frac{5}{2}}b^{-\frac{3}{2}})^6$; fourth.  **39.** $\left(\dfrac{3\sqrt{a}}{2\sqrt[3]{b}} - \dfrac{2\sqrt{b}}{3\sqrt[3]{a}}\right)^{19}$; tenth.

**40.** Find the coefficient of $x^3$ in $(1 - 2\sqrt{x})^8$.

**41.** Find the coefficient of $x^{15}$ in $x^3(1 - x^2)^{12}$.

**42.** Find the coefficient of $b^4$ in $(\sqrt{a} - \frac{1}{2}\sqrt{b})^{10}$.

**43.** Find the coefficient of $y^{10}$ in $(x - y^2)^7$.

**44.** Find the coefficient of $y^{12}$ in $(2x^2 + y^3)^8$.

**45.** In the expansion of $\left(2y + \dfrac{1}{3y}\right)^6$ the ratio of the fourth term to the fifth is $2:1$. Find $y$.

**46.** The sum of two numbers $a$ and $b$ is 5; and the sum of the two middle terms in the expansion of $(a + b)^3$ is equal to the sum of the first and last terms. Find $a$ and $b$.

**47.** In the expansion of $\left(y - \dfrac{2}{3y^2}\right)^9$ find the value of the term which does not contain $y$.

**48.** Find the term of $\left(\dfrac{4y}{5} - \dfrac{5}{4y}\right)^{10}$ which is independent of $y$.

**49.** The sum of the first two terms in the expansion of $(13 - 7y)^5$ is equal to $13^4 \cdot 6$. Find $y$.

**50.** Find the ratio of the seventh term of $\left(1 + \dfrac{u}{2}\right)^{10}$ to the fourth term of $\left(1 + \dfrac{u^2}{2}\right)^{12}$.

**51.** The sum of the coefficient of $y^5$ in the expansion of $(2 - \frac{1}{2}y)^8$ and of the coefficient of $y^2$ in $(1 + y)^n$ is $-4$. Find $n$.

# REVIEW EXERCISES

## PART A (Chaps. I, II)

*Simplify:*

**1.** $-2\{3x - y - \frac{1}{2}[y - (5x - 2y) + 3x] - 4x\}$

**2.** $\dfrac{2^{h-1}}{(2^h)^{h+1}} \cdot \dfrac{(2^{h+1})^h}{4^{h-1}}$

**3.** $\left(\dfrac{a}{6b}\right)^2 \left(\dfrac{2a}{b}\right)^2 \left(\dfrac{3b}{a}\right)^3$

**4.** $\dfrac{9 \cdot 3^{3n-3}}{9^{n-1} \cdot 3^{n-1} \cdot 9 - 27^n}$

**5.** $\left(\dfrac{x^{4n+1}}{4^{3n+1}} \cdot \dfrac{x^4}{4^{n+3}}\right)\left(\dfrac{16^2}{x^{3n}}\right)$

**6.** $\left(\dfrac{x^{-\frac{1}{2}}y^{-\frac{1}{3}}}{xy^{-\frac{4}{3}}}\right)^2 \left(\dfrac{x^{-\frac{1}{2}}y}{x^{\frac{3}{2}}y^{-1}}\right)$

**7.** $y^{-2}\left[\dfrac{4(2x^{\frac{1}{3}})^2 x^0 y}{x^{-\frac{2}{3}}y^{-3}}\right]^{\frac{3}{4}}$

**8.** $x^{-1}\left[\dfrac{9(3a^{\frac{1}{2}})^3 x^3}{a^{-1}x^{-2}y^0}\right]^{\frac{2}{5}}$

**9.** $\sqrt{2\sqrt[3]{24}}$

**10.** $\left[\dfrac{x^{-\frac{1}{2}}\sqrt[3]{y^{-1}}}{\sqrt[12]{x^{-2}}\,y^{-1}} \cdot \dfrac{(xy)^{-3}}{x^{-2}\sqrt[6]{y^3 x^0}}\right]^{-3}$

**11.** $\left\{\left[\dfrac{a\sqrt[3]{b^{-2}}\,a^{-4}c^2\sqrt{a^{-1}c^{-1}}}{\sqrt{a^6}\,b^{-1}(ab)^{-2}\sqrt[4]{c^{12}}}\right]^{-3}\right\}^{-\frac{1}{3}}$

**12.** $\left[\dfrac{\sqrt[3]{y^{-2}\sqrt{x}}\,\sqrt[4]{x^{-1}\sqrt[3]{y^{-2}}}}{\{(x^{-1}\sqrt{y^{-1}})^{\frac{1}{6}}\}^2\,(y^{-2}\sqrt[3]{x^{-\frac{9}{2}}})^{\frac{1}{4}}}\right]^{-1}$

## PART B (Chap. III)

*Simplify:*

**1.** $\dfrac{x\sqrt{x^2-a^2}}{(x^2-a^2)^{\frac{3}{2}}} + \dfrac{\frac{1}{a}}{\frac{x^2}{a^2}-1}$

**2.** $\dfrac{x(x^2-a^2)^{-\frac{1}{2}}}{\sqrt{x^2-a^2}} + \dfrac{\frac{1}{a}}{1-\frac{x^2}{a^2}}$

**3.** $-y^2(9-y^2)^{-\frac{1}{2}} + \sqrt{9-y^2} + \dfrac{3}{\sqrt{1-\left(\frac{y}{3}\right)^2}}$

**4.** $\dfrac{b^{-2}+a^{-1}b^{-1}}{ab^{-2}-a^{-1}}$

**5.** $\dfrac{(a^2-x^2)^{\frac{1}{2}}(3x^2) - x^3(a^2-x^2)^{-\frac{1}{2}}(-3x)}{(a^2-x^2)^{\frac{3}{2}}}$

**6.** $\dfrac{(a^2+x^2)^{\frac{1}{2}}(4x) - x^2(a^2+x^2)^{-\frac{1}{2}}(-2x)}{2(a^2+x^2)}$

**7.** $\sqrt{\dfrac{12}{3}} - \sqrt{\dfrac{3}{25}} + \dfrac{8}{5}\sqrt{\dfrac{1}{3}}$

**8.** $4\sqrt{\dfrac{a}{b}} - 3\sqrt{\dfrac{4b}{a}} + 5\sqrt{\dfrac{1}{ab}}$

**9.** $2\sqrt{\dfrac{4a}{b}} + 5\sqrt{\dfrac{b}{a}} - 3\sqrt{\dfrac{1}{ab}}$

**10.** $2\sqrt{242} + \sqrt{\dfrac{121}{2}} - \sqrt{\dfrac{1}{8}} - \sqrt[4]{4}$

**11.** $3\left(\dfrac{-2 + \sqrt{10}}{3}\right)^2 + 4\left(\dfrac{-2 + \sqrt{10}}{3}\right) + 1$

**12.** $\sqrt{4a^2 - 4b^2}\,\sqrt{a^4 - b^4}$

**13.** $(3\sqrt{2} - 2\sqrt{3})(2\sqrt{2} + 3\sqrt{3})$

**14.** $\sqrt{19 + \sqrt{72}}\,\sqrt{19 - \sqrt{72}}$

**15.** $2 - \left[\dfrac{1 - \sqrt{3}}{2}\right] - 2\left[\dfrac{1 - \sqrt{3}}{2}\right]^2$

**16.** $(\sqrt{2} - 2\sqrt{-3})(\sqrt{-3} - 3\sqrt{2})$

**17.** $(4i - 3) \div (2 + 3i)$

**18.** $(i^5 - 5i^2 - i)(i^2 - i^6 - i^3 + 2)$

**19.** $(i^3 + i + 3)(i^5 - 3 - i^2 - 2i^6)$

**20.** $\dfrac{(20x^2 - 10x + 5)(2x^2 - x - 1)(3x - 1)}{(8x^3 + 1)(5x - 5)(1 - 9x^2)}$

**21.** $\dfrac{3x - 3 - 3x^2}{1 + x^3}$

**22.** $\dfrac{6a^2 + 9ab - 6b^2}{18ab - 6b^2 - 12a^2}$

**23.** $\dfrac{x - 1}{x^2 + x - 6} + \dfrac{x + 4}{x^2 + 4x + 3} - \dfrac{x - 4}{x^2 - x - 2}$

**24.** $\dfrac{a}{a^2 - b^2} + \dfrac{b}{a^2 + ab} - \dfrac{1}{a - b}$

**25.** $\left[\dfrac{x - 4n}{x^2 - 9n^2} \cdot \dfrac{x^2 - 2nx - 3n^2}{4n - x}\right] \div \dfrac{x + n}{(x - 2n)^2}$

**26.** $\dfrac{9a^2 - b^2}{b^3 - 16a^2b} \cdot \dfrac{b^2 - 4ab}{b - 3a}$

**27.** $\dfrac{1}{\sqrt{3} - \sqrt{2}} - \dfrac{1}{\sqrt{2} + 1} - 1$

**28.** $\dfrac{\sqrt{2} - 3}{\sqrt{2} + 1}$

**29.** $4\sqrt{3} + \sqrt{27} - 6\sqrt{\dfrac{1}{3}}$

**30.** $\dfrac{5 + 2\sqrt{-3}}{3 - 4\sqrt{-3}}$

**31.** $5\sqrt{2} + \sqrt{32} - 4\sqrt{\dfrac{1}{2}}$

**32.** $\dfrac{[1 + (-x^{-\frac{1}{3}}y^{\frac{1}{3}})^2]^{\frac{3}{2}}}{\dfrac{x^{\frac{2}{3}} + y^{\frac{2}{3}}}{3x^{\frac{1}{3}}y^{\frac{1}{3}}}}$

**33.** $\dfrac{3x + 2}{6x^2 - x - 1} - \dfrac{x - 2}{2x^2 + 3x - 2}$

**34.** $(a^5 + 5a^4b + 3a^3b^2 + a^2b^3 - 6ab^4 - 24b^5) \div (a^2 + 3ab - 6b^2)$

**35.** $\dfrac{\dfrac{2b}{a - b} + 1}{\dfrac{3a - b}{a - b} - 2}$

**36.** $\dfrac{\dfrac{x^2}{a^2} - \dfrac{x}{a} - 2}{\dfrac{x^2}{a^2} - \dfrac{3x}{a} + 2}$

**37.** $\dfrac{2 - \dfrac{6}{x + 2}}{x - 2 - \dfrac{1}{x - 2}}$

**38.** $1 - \dfrac{1}{3 - \dfrac{1}{6 - \dfrac{1}{a - 1}}}$

**39.** $\dfrac{(x - y) - 2y\left(\dfrac{x - y}{x + y}\right)}{\left(\dfrac{x^2 + y^2}{xy + y^2} - 1\right)\left(1 - \dfrac{y}{x}\right)}$

**40.** If $x = \dfrac{1 - \sqrt{-31}}{4}$, find $2x^2 - x + 1$.

**41.** If $x = \dfrac{1 - \sqrt{-11}}{2}$, find $x^2 - x + 3$.

**42.** If $x = \dfrac{2 - \sqrt{-5}}{2}$, find $x^2 - 2x + 2$.

### PART C (Chaps. IV, V, VI, VII)

*Solve for x:*

**1.** $\dfrac{x + 3}{x^2 - 3x + 2} = \dfrac{x + 1}{x - 2} - \dfrac{x + 2}{x - 1}$     **2.** $\dfrac{28x^2 + 4}{16x^2 - 25} = \dfrac{5x}{5 + 4x} - \dfrac{2x}{5 - 4x}$

**3.** $\dfrac{2x^2 - x + 3}{3x + 2} + \dfrac{2x^2 + 3x - 1}{2 - 3x} = \dfrac{-20x^2 - 6x + 3}{9x^2 - 4}$

**4.** Solve for $x$ and $y$ by substitution:

$$\frac{x}{8} + \frac{3y}{4} = 1$$
$$3x - 2y = 4$$

**5.** Solve for $x$ and $y$ by determinants:

$$\frac{x}{2} - \frac{6y}{4} = 1$$
$$\frac{2x}{3} = 2y - \frac{10}{3}$$

**6.** Solve for $x$ and $y$ by addition and subtraction:

$$\frac{x}{y} = \frac{5}{3}$$
$$\frac{x + 2}{y + 2} = 1 + \frac{4}{y + 2}$$

**7.** Solve for $x$, $y$, and $z$ by determinants:

$$x + y - 7 = 0$$
$$2y - z - 11 = 0$$
$$y - x + z = -6$$

**8.** Solve for $x$, $y$, and $z$:

$$\frac{3}{x} + \frac{5}{y} = 1$$
$$\frac{9}{x} + \frac{5}{z} = -7$$
$$\frac{9}{y} + \frac{3}{z} = 2$$

*Solve for x:*

**9.** $\dfrac{x + 3}{4x - 9} = \dfrac{3x - 1}{x + 1}$

**10.** $3x^2 - 4x = 2$

**11.** $ax^2 - 2bx + c = 0$

**12.** $x(y + 2x) = 3y(y - 1) - 2x$

**13.** $\sqrt{8x + 1} - \sqrt{3x - 2} = \sqrt{3x + 1}$

**14.** $\sqrt{x + 20} - \sqrt{x - 1} - 3 = 0$

**15.** $9x^4 - 148x^2 + 64 = 0$

**16.** $x^2 - x + \dfrac{12}{x^2 - x} = 8$

**17.** $2x^2 + 3x = 5\sqrt{2x^2 + 3x + 9} - 3$

**18.** $2x^2 = 4\sqrt{x^2 - 4x - 5} + 26 + 8x$

*Solve and group answers:*

**19.** $x + 3y - 15 = 0$
$x^2 + y^2 = 25$

**20.** $xy + 54 = 0$
$x + y + 3 = 0$

**21.** $2x^2 - 3y^2 + 2y = 2$
$x^2 - 2y^2 = 1$

**22.** $x^2 + xy = ay$
$(a - x)y - 2ax = 0$

**23.** $x^2 + y^2 + x + y = 14$
$xy + x + y = -5$

**24.** $x^2 + xy + y^2 = 37$
$x^2 + y^2 = 25$

**25.** A tax of $5000 was paid by four men $A$, $B$, $C$, and $D$, $A$ paying $\frac{4}{5}$ as much as $B$, $C$ half as much as $A$ and $B$ together, and $D$ $400 less than $A$ and $B$ together. How much did each pay?

**26.** A boy rows 18 miles down a stream and back in 12 hours. He finds that he can row 3 miles with the stream in the same time that it takes him to row 1 mile against it. Find his rate and that of the stream.

**27.** If a wagon wheel 11 feet in circumference took $\frac{1}{12}$ of a second less to revolve, the rate of the wagon would be 1 mile more per hour. At what rate is the wagon traveling?

**28.** A merchant bought a number of yards of cloth for $140; he kept 8 yards and sold the remainder at a profit of $1.50 a yard, and gained $20. How many yards did he buy?

### PART D (Chap. VIII)

**1–7.** Solve by graphical methods Exercises 4, 5, 6, 9, 10, 15, 16 of Part C.

**8–13.** Solve by graphical methods Exercises 19 through 24 of Part C.

### PART E (Chaps. IX, X, XI)

**1.** Find two numbers such that if 7 be added to each they will be in the ratio of 2 to 3; and if 2 be subtracted from each, they will be in the ratio of 1 to 3.

**2.** Find the ratio of $x$ to $y$ if $7x - 3y = 4x + y$.

**3.** Solve for $x$: $(2x + 3) : (3x - 1) = (3x + 1) : (2x + 1)$.

**4.** If $a : b = c : d$ prove $a : b = \sqrt{a^2 + 3c^2} : \sqrt{b^2 + 3d^2}$.

**5.** If $x$ varies inversely as $y$, and equals 2 when $y$ is 4, find $y$ when $x = 5$.

**6.** The volume of a right circular cylinder varies as the altitude and the square of the radius. What must be the altitude of a cylinder with a 3-inch radius, if it is to contain three times as much as another cylinder 6 inches high and 2 inches in radius?

**7.** Find the sum of the progression $\frac{5}{6}$, $\frac{3}{4}$, $\frac{2}{3}$, $\cdots$ to 96 terms.

**8.** A man travels $2\frac{1}{3}$ miles the first day, $2\frac{2}{3}$ the second, 3 the third, and so on. At the end of his journey he finds that if he had traveled $6\frac{1}{6}$ miles every day he would have required the same time. How many days was he walking?

**9.** In an arithmetic progression $a = -3\frac{1}{4}$, $l = 9\frac{1}{4}$, $S = 48$. Find $n$ and $d$.

**10.** In an arithmetic progression $l = 2$, $d = -\frac{1}{4}$, $S = 19\frac{1}{4}$. Find $a$ and $n$.

**11.** In a geometric progression $n = 6$, $r = 3$, $l = 486$. Find $a$ and $S$.

**12.** In a geometric progression $a = -2$, $l = 2048$, $n = 6$. Find $r$.

**13.** Three numbers whose sum is 24 are in arithmetic progression, but if 3, 4, and 7 be added to them respectively, these sums will be in geometric progression. Find the numbers.

**14.** Write the middle term in the expansion of $(x^2 - 6y^{\frac{3}{2}})^8$.

**15.** Write the term which does not contain $x$ in the expansion of $(y^3 + 3y^{-2})^{15}$.

**16.** Compute $(1.01)^4$ by the binomial theorem.

**17.** Prove by mathematical induction that

$$1 + 3 + 6 + 10 + \cdots + \frac{n(n + 1)}{2} = \frac{n}{6}(n + 1)(n + 2).$$

**18.** The safe load of a horizontal beam of given length varies jointly as the breadth and the square of the depth. What percentage loss of load is caused if a $3 \times 6$ inch beam placed on edge is tipped over to make the smaller dimension the depth?

### PART F. (General Review)

**1.** *Simplify:*

$$\frac{(4x^2 - 4)(x^3 + x^2 + x)(2x^2 - 7x + 6)}{(x^3 - 1)(2x^2 - x - 3)(2x^2 - 4x)}$$

**2.** Solve for $x$ and $y$:

$$\frac{2x - 3y}{4} + \frac{4x + 6y}{3} + \frac{1}{2} = 0$$

$$\frac{5x + 2y}{2} + \frac{7y - 3x}{5} = \frac{39}{10}$$

**3.** Find the value of $2x + 3 - 3x^2$ if $x = \dfrac{1 + 2i\sqrt{2}}{3}$.

**4.** Simplify and then evaluate the result if $x = -1$:

$$\frac{2x^4(x^3 + 5)^{-\frac{1}{3}} + 2x(x^3 + 5)^{\frac{2}{3}}}{\sqrt[3]{(x^3 + 5)^2}}$$

**5.** Solve for $x$ by determinants, then substitute and solve for $y$ and $z$:

$$x + y + z = 9$$
$$3x - y + 2z = 11$$
$$4x + 3y - z = 13$$

**6.** Solve for $x$: $\quad \dfrac{3x}{2x + 3} + \dfrac{2x}{3 - 2x} = \dfrac{2x^2 - 15}{4x^2 - 9}$

**7.** Simplify: $\quad \dfrac{\dfrac{2}{x + y} - \dfrac{1}{x}}{y - \dfrac{xy}{2x + y}} - \dfrac{\dfrac{1}{y} - \dfrac{2}{x + y}}{x - \dfrac{xy}{x + 2y}}$

**8.** Express $\dfrac{a}{a + 1} + \dfrac{b}{b + 1} + \dfrac{c}{c + 1}$ in terms of $p$, $q$, and $r$, where $p = a + b + c$, $q = ab + bc + ac$, $r = abc$.

**9.** Solve for $x$: $\sqrt{2x + 5} - \sqrt{x + 2} = \sqrt{x - 1}$

**10.** $A$, $B$, and $C$ move around a circular track. At the start $A$ is the same distance from $B$ as $B$ is from $C$. If it takes $A$ 15 minutes to overtake $B$ and 20 minutes to overtake $C$, how long does it take $B$ to overtake $C$?

**11.** Expand $\left(x - \dfrac{1}{2y^2}\right)^5$ by the binomial theorem.

**12.** Simplify: $\left[\dfrac{y}{3x - y} + \dfrac{3x}{3x + y}\right]\left[\dfrac{3x - y}{9x^2 + y^2}\right] \div \left[\dfrac{1}{3x - y} - \dfrac{1}{3x + y}\right]$

**13.** Solve for $x$: $\dfrac{5}{2x + 3} - \dfrac{8x^2 - 13x - 64}{6x^2 + x - 12} = \dfrac{7}{4 - 3x}$

**14.** Simplify by rationalizing the denominators and then compute to two decimals:

$$\frac{2\sqrt{2}}{\sqrt{3} - 1} - \frac{\sqrt{3}}{\sqrt{2} + 1} - \frac{1}{\sqrt{3} - \sqrt{2}} + \frac{1}{\sqrt{3}}$$

**15.** Given:

$$a = \frac{1}{u}$$

$$b = \frac{1}{u} + \frac{1}{v}$$

$$c = \frac{1}{u} + \frac{1}{v} + \frac{1}{w}$$

$$d = \frac{1}{u} + \frac{1}{v} + \frac{1}{w} + \frac{1}{z}$$

Express $u$, $v$, $w$, and $z$ in terms of $a$, $b$, $c$, and $d$.

**16.** Solve for $x$: $x^2 + 5x - \sqrt{x^2 + 5x + 2} - 10 = 0$

**17.** Find the dimensions of a rectangle whose area is five times the area of a square of side $a$, and whose perimeter is three times the perimeter of the square.

**18.** Simplify:
$$\frac{\left[\dfrac{x^2 + y^2}{xy + y^2} - 1\right]\left[1 - \dfrac{y}{x}\right]}{(x - y) - 2y\left[\dfrac{x - y}{x + y}\right]}$$

**19.** Solve and group answers: $2x^2 - xy = 6y^2$
$$2x - 3y = 1$$

**20.** Find the sum of the first 51 terms of the progression 3, 6, 9, $\cdots$

**21.** Solve for $x$, $y$, and $z$ by determinants:
$$x - 2y - 3z = 9$$
$$2x + y - z = 8$$
$$x - 3y + 4z = -13$$

**22.** Simplify:
$$\left[\frac{x^{-2}y^3}{xy^{-1}}\right]^{-2} \div \frac{xy^{-2}}{x^{-2}y}$$

**23.** An express train which runs 55 miles an hour leaves a station 4 hours after a freight traveling 11 miles an hour. How many miles from the station will the express be when it overtakes the freight?

**24.** Find two numbers in the ratio of 2 to 5, such that when each is increased by 5 they shall be as 3 to 5.

**25.** Simplify:
$$\frac{\dfrac{x^2}{\sqrt{x^2 + 4a^2}} - \sqrt{x^2 + 4a^2}}{x^2\sqrt{\dfrac{x^2 + 4a^2}{x^2}} - 1} \div \frac{3}{\sqrt{x^3 + 4a^2x}}$$

**26.** If $z$ varies as $y$ and inversely as $x$, and if $z = 28$ when $y = 14$ and $x = 2$, find $z$ when $y = 42$ and $x = 3$.

**27.** A beam resting on a fulcrum balances when it carries weights of 100 lb. and 130 lb. at its respective ends. It will also balance if instead it carries weights of 80 lb. and 110 lb. respectively two feet from its ends. Find the distance of the fulcrum from the ends of the beam.

**28.** Simplify: $\sqrt{91 - 40\sqrt{3}}$

**29.** Rationalize the denominator and simplify:

$$\frac{\sqrt{3} - \sqrt{4} + \sqrt{1}}{\sqrt{12} + \sqrt{2}}$$

**30.** Reduce to a single radical and find the value to 2 decimals:

$$\frac{30}{\sqrt{2}} - 2\sqrt{50} + 2\sqrt{\tfrac{1}{2}} - 2\sqrt{32}$$

**31.** Solve: $\sqrt{x+1} - \sqrt{2x-3} - \sqrt{3x-2} = 0$

**32.** The safe load of a horizontal beam 10 feet long, supported at both ends, varies jointly as its breadth and the square of its depth. If a $2 \times 6$ beam of this length, standing on edge, will safely hold 900 lb., how much will a $2 \times 10$ beam of the same material and in the same position hold?

**33.** Three men, $A$, $B$, and $C$, can do a piece of work together in 1 hour and 20 minutes. To do the work alone $C$ would require twice as long as $A$ and two hours longer than $B$. How long would it take each to do the work alone?

**34.** Solve: $\dfrac{1}{x+1} + \dfrac{3}{x-1} = \dfrac{10}{3}$

**35.** The coefficient of $x^3$ in the expansion of $(1 + x)^n$ is 5 times the coefficient of $x$. Find $n$.

**36.** Reduce to the simplest possible form without evaluating the radicals:

$$\frac{1}{\sqrt{3} + 2} - 6\sqrt{\tfrac{1}{3}} + \sqrt{27}$$

**37.** Solve: $2x^2 - 4x + 3\sqrt{x^2 - 2x + 6} = 15$

**38.** Simplify: $\sqrt{14 - 6\sqrt{5}}$

**39.** Kepler's third law states that the square of the number of years it takes a planet to revolve about the sun is proportional to the cube of the distance of the planet from the sun. Let the distance of the earth from the sun be 1. How long would it take a planet whose distance from the sun was 100 to complete a revolution?

**40.** Derive the formula for the sum of the first $n$ terms of an A.P. by mathematical induction.

**41.** Solve for $x$:

$$\frac{2}{2x^2 - x - 6} + \frac{3}{8 - 2x^2} + \frac{1}{2x + 3} = 0$$

**42.** Solve for $x$:

$$\frac{3x}{x + 1} - \frac{15}{3x^2 + x - 2} = \frac{10}{3x - 2} - 5$$

**43.** Find the positive root of $x^3 + x^2 - 2x - 2 = 0$ by graphical methods.

**44.** Two towns on opposite sides of a lake are 30 miles apart, by water. At 8 A.M. from each town a boat starts for the other town traveling at uniform speed. The boats pass each other six hours later. One boat arrives at its destination five hours earlier than the other. What is the speed of each boat?

**45.** Simplify:       $\sqrt{13 - 4\sqrt{3}}$

**46.** Each stroke of an air pump exhausts one tenth of the air in the receiver. What part of the air originally in the receiver is left after 5 strokes?

**47.** The electrical resistance of a wire varies directly as its length and inversely as its area. If a copper wire 1 centimeter in diameter has a resistance of 1 unit per mile, how many units of resistance will a copper wire have which is 500 feet long and 3 millimeters in diameter?

**48.** Find the 5th term of $(a^{\frac{1}{3}} + 2x^{-\frac{3}{2}})^{16}$.

**49.** Two farmers, $A$ and $B$, have together 30 calves, which they sell for \$336, $A$ receiving as many dollars for each of his as $B$ had calves; if each one had sold his calves for as many dollars apiece as the other received for each of his, they would have received only \$324. How many calves did $A$ have, and at what price did he sell them?

**50.** Solve for $x$:     $\sqrt{5x + 11} = \sqrt{3x + 1} + 2$

**51.** A man is rowing upstream. At a point $A$ his hat falls out of the boat. He discovers that his hat is missing 10 minutes later and rows back to recover it. At a point $B$ one mile below $A$ he overtakes his hat. How fast is the stream flowing?

**52.** A contractor buys \$12,270 worth of fire hydrants, valves, and pipe sections at \$60, \$35, and \$25 each, respectively. The number of valves exceeds the number of fire hydrants by twelve, and the number of pipe sections is five times the number of hydrants and valves together. How many of each did he buy?

**53.** A man and a boy have to row 4 miles up a stream and back. The man rows twice as fast as the boy. If the man rows up and the boy rows back, it will take 2 hours and 40 minutes. If the boy rows up and the man rows back, it will take 4 hours and 48 minutes. How fast can each row and what is the rate of the stream?

**54.** Two bodies move toward each other from points 120 feet apart and meet after 6 seconds; it takes one 16 seconds longer than the other to traverse the entire distance. Find the rates.

# INDEX

Abscissa, 110.
Absolute value, 3.
Applications
  linear equations, 60.
  linear systems, 77.
  quadratic equations, 92.
  quadratic systems, 105.
Axes, coordinate, 110.

Binomial, 18.
Binomial coefficients, 131.
Binomial formula, 130.
Binomial theorem, 130.

Cancellation, 28, 53.
Coefficient, 18.
  binomial, 131.
Completing a square, 83.
Conjugate complex number, 49.
Constant, 52.
Coordinates, 110.

Decimal representation of a real
  number, 2.
Denominator, 27.
  lowest common, 34.
Determinant of the system, 75.
Determinants, 72.
Division by zero, 6.

Equality, conditional, 22–23.
Equation (*see* Systems), 22–23.
  defective, 54.
  derived, 53.
  equivalent, 53.
  graph of an, 112.
  in quadratic form, 89.
  involving radicals, 86.
  irrational, 86.
  linear, 55, 112.
  polynomial, 53.
  quadratic, 81.
  rational integral, 53.
  reducible to linear, 56.

  redundant, 54, 86.
  roots of an, 53.
  solution of an, 53.
  symmetrical in $x$ and $y$, 103.
Exponents
  fractional, 11.
  laws of, 9.
  negative, 13.
  positive integral, 9.
  zero, 12.
Extraneous roots, 54.

Factor, 18, 24.
  prime, 24.
  rational, 24.
Factoring, 18.
Factoring a quadratic, 82.
Fractions, 27.
  complex, 36.
  product of, 31.
  quotient of, 31.
  sum and difference of, 33.
Functions, graphs of, 113.

Homogeneous, 101.

$i$, 16.
Identity, 23.
Induction, mathematical, 128.
Integer, 1.

Laws of algebra, 4.
Linear systems
  in three unknowns, 70.
  in two unknowns, 65.
  solution of, by addition and sub-
    traction, 65.
  solution of, by determinants, 72.
  solution of, by substitution, 65.
Lowest common denominator, 34.
Lowest common multiple, 26.

Mathematical induction, 128.
Mean proportional, 116.

Monomial, 18.
Multiple, lowest common, 26.

Numbers, 1.
  complex, 49.
  imaginary, 16.
  irrational, 2.
  rational, 2.
  real, 1.
Numerator, 27.

Operations, fundamental, 4.
Ordinate, 110.

Parabola, 113.
Pascal's triangle, 131.
Plotting points, 3, 110.
Polynomial, 18.
  degree of a, 52.
  in $x$, 52.
  roots of a, 52.
Polynomials
  product of, 19.
  quotient of, 20.
Prime factors, 24.
Product of polynomials, 19.
Progressions
  arithmetic, 123.
  geometric, 125.
Proportion, 116.
  extremes of a, 116.
  means of a, 116.
Proportional
  fourth, 116.
  mean, 116.
  third, 116.

Quadrant, 110.
Quadratic
  form, 89.
  formula, 83.
  graph of the function, 113.
  systems, 96.
Quadratic equation
  equations involving radicals, 86.

factoring a, 82.
  solution of, by completing the
    square, 83.
  solution of, by factoring, 81.
  solution of, by formula, 83.
Quotient of polynomials, 20.

Radicals, 14, 39.
  equations involving, 86.
  product of, 43.
  quotient of, 47.
  sum and difference of, 45.
Ratio, 116.
  of a geometric progression, 125.
Rational integral equation, 53.
Rationalizing the denominator, 47.
Reciprocal, 32.
Roots, 11.
  extraneous, 86.
  graphical method of finding, 114.
  of an equation, 53.
  of a real number, 11.

Signs, 5.
  changing, before a fraction, 29.
Simultaneous solutions, see Systems.
Symbols of grouping, 4.
  removing, 6.
Symmetrical equation, 103.
System
  determinant of the, 75.
  homogeneous, 101.
Systems involving quadratics
  reduction to simpler, 101.
  solution of, by substitution, 96.
Systems of linear equations, 65.

Term, 18.
  degree of a, 65.
Terms, reduction to lowest, 27.
Transposition, 53.
Trinomial, 18.

Variable, 52.
Variation, 118.

# ANSWERS

## SEWELL'S
## REVIEW COURSE IN ALGEBRA

D. C. HEATH AND COMPANY

BOSTON

# REVIEW COURSE IN ALGEBRA

## ANSWERS

### Exercises.  Page 1

**1.** (a) 9   (b) 1   (c) $\frac{5}{4}$   (d) 3        **2.** 5, 1, $\frac{3}{2}$, $\sqrt{5}$
**3.** 7, 5, 6, $\sqrt{7}$        **4.** 20, 6, $\frac{1}{7}$, $\sqrt{20}$        **5.** 12, 4, 2, $\sqrt{12}$
**6.** 138, 64, $\frac{101}{37}$, $\sqrt{138}$        **7.** 227, 225, 226, $\sqrt{227}$        **8.** 81, 79, 80, 9
**9.** 25, 5, $\frac{3}{2}$, 5        **10.** 16, 8, 3, 4        **11.** $\frac{2}{3}$

### Exercises.  Pages 2–3

**1.** Irr., irr., int., int., int., irr., irr., rat., rat.
**2.** Rat., irr., rat., irr., rat., rat., int., rat.
**3.** $0.333\cdots$        **4.** $0.0769230769\cdots$
**5.** $1.14285714\cdots$        **6.** $0.933\cdots$
**7.** 0.125        **8.** 2.5
**9.** 4.721        **10.** 2.25
**11.** $4.14285714\cdots$        **12.** 17.2
**13.** 2.75        **14.** 0.022
**15.** Ex. 7, 8, 9, 10, 12, 13, 14        **16.** Ex. 3, 4, 5, 6, 11
**17.** Ex. 3: 3;  Ex. 4: 076923;  Ex. 5: 142857;  Ex. 6: 3;  Ex. 11: 142857

### Exercises.  Page 4

**2.** $-e$, $-\frac{1}{2}$, 0, $\frac{2}{7}$, $\frac{1}{3}$, $|\frac{3}{4}|$, $\frac{e}{2}$, 1.4, 2, $\frac{7}{3}$, $2\frac{1}{2}$, $|-e|$, $\pi$, $|-5|$, $2\pi$, 7
**3.** 3, $\frac{5}{12}$, $-\frac{1}{10}$, 1.45, 3.1

### Exercises.  Page 5

**1.** $3\cdot5$        **2.** $x+4$        **3.** $a+2b+3$        **4.** $(3y+7)2$        **5.** $zyx$
**6.** $(5)(4)(x)$        **7.** $3x+y+4$        **8.** $(a+b)\cdot2$        **9.** $4+17x+5y$

### Exercises.  Pages 7–8

**1.** 15        **2.** $-4$        **3.** $6x$        **4.** $-xyz$        **5.** $-a+3b$
**6.** $-\frac{2}{5}$        **7.** $-5$        **8.** $\frac{x}{y}$        **9.** $x$        **10.** 0
**11.** 5        **12.** 0        **13.** Meaningless        **14.** $a$        **15.** 6
**16.** $-\frac{2}{7}$        **17.** $-24$        **18.** 0        **19.** $2a+x-c$
**20.** $3+2x-4y-7$        **21.** $a+3b-2c+d$
**22.** $8-2c-d$        **23.** $x-ay+z$

1

**24.** $a - bx - 7c$          **25.** $a + 7 - 4c - 4d$

**26.** $9 - 3c$          **27.** $24x - 3y - 8 + 7c$

**28.** $- x + 3y - a + u - v + z + w - 5$

**29.** $896$          **30.** $1107$          **31.** $9b - 3a - 18c$          **32.** $- 240$

**33.** $a - b + c + d - e + f$          **34.** $3x - 5y + 7z + 9a + 3b - 4$

**35.** $- a - b + c + d - 1$          **36.** $4$

**37.** (1) $a^2 + b^2 + c^2 + (- ab - bc - ca)$, (2) $a^2 + b^2 + c^2 - (ab + bc + ca)$

**38.** (1) $63x^4 + x^3 + (49x^2 - 16x + 20)$, (2) $63x^4 + x^3 - (- 49x^2 + 16x - 20)$

**39.** (1) $x^3 + 2x^2y^2 + (4x - 3xy^2 - 7y^2)$, (2) $x^3 + 2x^2y - (3xy^2 - 4x + 7y^2)$

**40.** (1) $a + b + (d - c - e)$, (2) $a + b - (c - d + e)$

**41.** (1) $x^2 + (z^2 - y^2 - 3)$, (2) $x^2 - (y^2 - z^2 + 3)$

**42.** (1) $3x^2 - ax + c + (bx + y^2 - 3x)$, (2) $3x^2 - ax + c - (3x - bx - y^2)$

**43.** (1) $a^2 + 2ab + (b^3 - c^2 + d^2)$, (2) $a^2 + 2ab - (c^2 - b^3 - d^2)$

**44.** (1) $a^4 + (3b^2d^2 + 2bd - c)$, (2) $a^4 - (c - 3b^2d^2 - 2bd)$

**45.** (1) $x^5 - 5xy^4 + (6xy^3 - 7x + 3)$, (2) $x^5 - 5xy^4 - (7x - 6xy^3 - 3)$

**46.** (1) $ax + (2bcy - 3ay + 2z)$, (2) $ax - (3ay - 2bcy - 2z)$

**47.** (1) $3x^2 + (7x - 2y + z)$, (2) $3x^2 - (2y - 7x - z)$

**48.** (1) $2x + (7y - 4z + 6)$, (2) $2x - (4z - 7y - 6)$

## Exercises. Pages 10–11

**1.** 9          **2.** 8          **3.** 32          **4.** 72          **5.** 128          **6.** 8

**7.** 4          **8.** 1          **9.** 1          **10.** $- 1$          **11.** $\frac{1}{2}$          **12.** 27

**13.** $x^8$          **14.** $x^6$          **15.** $x^4$          **16.** $x^n$          **17.** $\frac{x^4}{y^4}$

**18.** $\frac{1}{(a + b)^2}$          **19.** $\frac{x^8}{y^{12}}$          **20.** $(2 + x)^3$          **21.** $(x + 3y - 7)^2$          **22.** $\frac{1}{2}$

**23.** 8          **24.** $- 6$          **25.** 5          **26.** $x = 6$          **27.** $x = 10$

## Exercises. Page 12

**1.** $x$          **2.** $x^{\frac{1}{4}}$          **3.** $x$          **4.** $\frac{x^{\frac{3}{4}}}{y^{\frac{3}{4}}}$          **5.** $y^{\frac{7}{6}}$          **6.** $\frac{1}{x^{\frac{7}{12}}}$

**7.** $a^{1\frac{1}{3}}x^{1\frac{7}{5}}$          **8.** $\frac{x^{\frac{1}{5}}}{a^{1\frac{2}{5}}}$          **9.** $\frac{a^{1\frac{5}{2}}x^{\frac{3}{4}}}{y^{\frac{1}{3}}}$          **10.** $(a^2 + b^4)^{\frac{1}{2}}$

**11.** $(a^3 - b^3)^{\frac{1}{3}}$          **12.** $x^2(a + b)^4$          **13.** $a(a + b)$          **14.** $\frac{y^{18}z^3}{(y^3 + z^{\frac{1}{2}})^2}$

**15.** $y$          **16.** $- 2a^{\frac{5}{4}}$          **17.** $\frac{y^{\frac{5}{6}}(x + y)^{\frac{1}{2}}}{(x^{\frac{1}{2}} + y^{\frac{1}{2}})}$          **18.** $\frac{x^{\frac{3}{3}}}{y^2}$

## Exercises. Pages 12–13

**1.** 1          **2.** $\frac{1}{2}$          **3.** $\frac{1}{y}$          **4.** $y$          **5.** 15          **6.** 1

**7.** 4          **8.** 2          **9.** 1          **10.** $x^{\frac{1}{2}}y^{\frac{1}{3}}z^3$          **11.** 6          **12.** 3

**13.** $y^2z^{\frac{5}{2}}$          **14.** $\frac{1 + y}{1 + x}$          **15.** $xy$          **16.** $\frac{7}{2}$          **17.** 1          **18.** $- 6$

## Exercises. Page 14

**1.** $a^{\frac{1}{4}}$    **2.** $\dfrac{2^{\frac{1}{4}}}{a^{\frac{3}{2}}}$    **3.** $\frac{1}{2}$    **4.** $\frac{1}{4}$    **5.** $\dfrac{1}{x^{10}}$

**6.** $x^{\frac{3}{8}}$    **7.** $\dfrac{1}{x^{\frac{17}{10}}y^{\frac{19}{6}}}$    **8.** $1$    **9.** $x^{\frac{3}{8}}y^{\frac{9}{8}}$    **10.** $\dfrac{4}{x^{\frac{5}{3}}y^{\frac{2}{9}}}$

**11.** $\dfrac{u^3 w^{\frac{3}{2}}}{c^{\frac{2}{3}}}$    **12.** $\dfrac{243b^{10}}{32a^{10}y^4}$    **13.** $\dfrac{729c^6}{16x^2}$    **14.** $\dfrac{3}{xy^{\frac{1}{2}}}$

**15.** $\dfrac{yz^3}{x^2}$    **16.** $a^{\frac{5}{2}}c^{\frac{5}{6}}$    **17.** $\dfrac{a^9 b^2}{c^{\frac{1}{2}}}$    **18.** $\dfrac{x^{\frac{3}{8}}}{a^{\frac{35}{32}}}$

**19.** $\dfrac{z^3}{x^{\frac{5}{7}}y^{\frac{19}{6}}}$    **20.** $\dfrac{1}{a^9}$    **21.** $a^4 y$    **22.** $\dfrac{b^{\frac{7}{3}}}{a^{\frac{9}{2}}c^{\frac{3}{2}}}$

## Exercises. Pages 15–16

**1.** $\sqrt{2}$    **2.** $\sqrt[3]{12}$    **3.** $\dfrac{1}{\sqrt[5]{x}}$    **4.** $\sqrt{x^5}$

**5.** $\sqrt{512}$    **6.** $\sqrt[6]{5}\sqrt[3]{x}$    **7.** $\sqrt{\dfrac{a}{x^3}}$    **8.** $\sqrt{xy^3}$

**9.** $\sqrt[8]{x^4}$    **10.** $2\sqrt{a}+\sqrt{b}$    **11.** $\sqrt{4a^2+b^2}$    **12.** $\dfrac{1}{\sqrt{x^9 y^{15}}}$

**13.** $x^{\frac{3}{2}}$    **14.** $x^{\frac{2}{3}}y^{\frac{1}{3}}$    **15.** $(3a^2+b^2)^{\frac{1}{2}}$    **16.** $a^{\frac{3}{2}}b^{-\frac{5}{2}}$
**17.** $a^{-6}$    **18.** $a^{\frac{1}{6}}$    **19.** $x^{\frac{2}{3}}$    **20.** $x^2 y^3$
**21.** $x^{\frac{1}{2}}$    **22.** $14.000$    **23.** $10.333$    **24.** $-3.000$
**25.** $329.000$    **26.** $6.000$    **27.** $8.750$    **28.** $0.333$
**29.** $11.639$    **30.** $-3.5$    **31.** $49.2$    **32.** $8.25$

**33.** $0.001$    **34.** $3.697$    **35.** $\dfrac{a^{\frac{2}{3}}}{b^{\frac{3}{2}}}$    **36.** $\dfrac{b^{\frac{1}{3}}}{x^{\frac{1}{3}}z^{\frac{1}{3}}}$

**37.** $32x^5 y^2$    **38.** $\dfrac{2^{\frac{4}{3}}3^{\frac{7}{3}}x^{\frac{1}{2}}}{y^2}$    **39.** $\dfrac{3y^{\frac{1}{9}}}{2a^{\frac{5}{3}}}$    **40.** $1$

**41.** $\dfrac{z^3}{x^4}$    **42.** $a^{\frac{2}{3}}$    **43.** $\dfrac{49y^4}{9x^2 z^{\frac{3}{2}}}$    **44.** $\dfrac{a^{\frac{1}{6}}}{x^{\frac{5}{8}}}$

## Exercises. Page 17

**1.** $\sqrt{7}i$    **2.** $4i$    **3.** $ai$    **4.** $2xi$    **5.** $a+bi$    **6.** $b+ai$

**7.** $10i$    **8.** $\dfrac{1}{xi}$    **9.** $a+bi$    **10.** $1$    **11.** $1+i$    **12.** $-8$

**13.** $i$    **14.** $0$    **15.** $1$    **16.** $1$    **17.** $1$    **18.** $1$

## Exercises. Page 18

**1.** Binomial    **2.** Trinomial    **3.** Trinomial
**4.** Polynomial    **5.** Binomial    **6.** Trinomial
**7.** Monomial    **8.** Monomial    **9.** Binomial

## Exercises. Page 19

**1.** $5a + 3b$      **2.** $2x - 2xy$      **3.** $a + 2b + 5c$

**4.** $5x - y$      **5.** $x - 7$      **6.** $2a + 5b - 5c$

**7.** $5y - 6z + 3$      **8.** $3x - a - 6c + 9$      **9.** $-8x^2 - 5ax - 8$

**10.** $-a$      **11.** $4x - 8y + 6z$      **12.** $xy + y^2$

**13.** $9a^2 - 9b - a + 9$      **14.** $8a - 2x - 2a^2 - 16$      **15.** $a - 3y - 3c$

**16.** $18a^2 - 7b^3 - b - 10$      **17.** $x - 2b + 2c$      **18.** $13a - 6b - c$

**19.** $4x + 2z$      **20.** $-4x - 14z$      **21.** $6x + 2$

**22.** $6x - 5y$      **23.** $10a - 5b$      **24.** $4$      **25.** $6n + 3$

## Exercises. Page 20

**1.** $x^2 - y^2$      **2.** $x^2 + x - 12$      **3.** $2x^2 - 9x - 35$

**4.** $x^2 + 2xy - 8y^2$      **5.** $2ax^2 + 2bx$

**6.** $x^2 + 3xy - 4xz - 7x - 21y + 28z$      **7.** $9x^4y^2 + 15x^4 + 27x^2y^2 + 45x^2$

**8.** $2x^3 - 12x^2 - 38x + 168$      **9.** $-12x^4y^4z^3$

**10.** $6x^2 - 40y^2 - 28z^2 - 3w^2 - xy - 13xz - 3xw + 76yz - 23yw + 25wz$

**11.** $x^4 - 16x^2 + 33x - 36$

**12.** $2x^5 + 10x^4y - 62x^3y^2 + 48x^2y^3 - 18xy^4$

**13.** $x^2 + 2xy + y^2 - 4$

**14.** $2a^2 + 12c^2 + 2d^2 + 3ab - 10ac + 5ad - 9bc + 6bd - 11cd + 10a + 15b - 20c + 5d$

**15.** $-a^4 + 3a^2 - 1$      **16.** $x^2 + y^2 + z^2 + 2xy + 2xz + 2yz$

**17.** $x^3 + y^3 + z^3 + 3x^2y + 3x^2z + 3xy^2 + 3xz^2 + 3y^2z + 3yz^2 + 6xyz$

**18.** $y^4 - (a + b + c + d)y^3 + (ab + ac + ad + bc + bd + cd)y^2 - (abc + abd + acd + bcd)y + abcd$

**19.** $65a^2 - 12a^2b^2 - 47a^2b - 101ab + 35ab^2 + 80a + 3b^2 - 14b + 15$

**20.** $x^3 + y^3 + z^3 - 3xyz$      **21.** $x^4 + 4x^3y + 6x^2y^2 + 4xy^3 + y^4$

**22.** $x^4 + 4x^3y + 6x^2y^2 + 4xy^3 + y^4$      **23.** $6x^4 - 12x^2y^2 + 6y^4$

**24.** $18a^4 - 84a^3b + 26a^2b^2 + 168ab^3 + 72b^4$

## Exercises. Page 22

**1.** $x - y$    **2.** $x - y$    **3.** $x^2 - 2xy + 4y^2$    **4.** $b^2 + 7a^2$    **5.** $x - 4$

**6.** Quotient $= x - 4$; remainder $= 1$      **7.** $2x^2 - 3ax + 4a^2$

**8.** Quotient $= 5y + 2$; remainder $= -(10y + 4)$

**9.** $-2a^2 + 3ab - b^2$      **10.** $a^3 + 2a^2 - 6a + 5$      **11.** $x + y + z$

**12.** Quotient $= a(2y^2 - 1) + b$; remainder $= b^2$

**13.** $-y(6b + 4) + a(3b + 2)$      **14.** $y + 5x + 3$

**15.** $x^4 - 2x^3y + 4x^2y^2 - 8xy^3 + 16y^4$      **16.** $-u^2 + 2u - 3$

**17.** $\frac{1}{3}x^3 + \frac{2}{3}x^2y - \frac{1}{4}xy^2 + \frac{3}{4}y^3$      **18.** $2x^2 - 3xy + y^2$      **19.** $x - y + z$

**20.** Quotient $= -4$; remainder $= a^3 - 2a^2 + 5a$

**21.** $x^2 - 3x + 2$      **22.** $3x^2 - 7x + 4$

**23.** $2x^2 - 8x + 5$      **24.** $x^2 - 7x + 5$

## Exercises.  Pages 23–24

**1.** Equation  **2.** Identity  **3.** Identity  **4.** Equation
**5.** Equation  **6.** Identity  **7.** Identity  **8.** Equation
**9.** $a^2 - 4b^2$  **10.** $9x^2 - y^2$  **11.** $4a^2 + 4ab + b^2$
**12.** $4x^2 - 9xy - 9y^2$  **13.** $8a^3 + b^3$  **14.** $a^2 - 6ab + 9b^2$
**15.** $49x^2 + 42xy + 9y^2$  **16.** $x^2 + 2x - 15$
**17.** $3x^2 + 30x + 75$  **18.** $4x^2 - 12xy + 9y^2$
**19.** $x^2 - 4y^2 + 4yz - z^2$  **20.** $a^2x^2 + 2acx + c^2 - b^2$
**21.** $x^4 - y^4$  **22.** $a^6 + b^6$
**23.** $a^2 + 4ab + 4b^2 - 16c^2 - 8cd - d^2$  **24.** $45a^2 - 47ab + 12b^2$
**25.** $1 - 8a^3$  **26.** $x^3 - y^3$
**27.** $a^2 - 2ab + b^2 - c^2$  **28.** $x^2 - y^2 + 2yz - z^2$
**29.** $4x^4 - y^6$  **30.** $x - y$
**31.** $x + y$  **32.** $\dfrac{1}{x} - \dfrac{4}{y}$
**33.** $a^{\frac{3}{4}} + 8b^{\frac{3}{4}}$  **34.** $1 - x^4$
**35.** $a - b$  **36.** $-2$
**37.** $x + 2x^{\frac{1}{2}}y^{\frac{1}{2}} + y$  **38.** $x^6 + 2x^3y^2 + y^4$
**39.** $\dfrac{1}{x^6} + 2 + x^6$  **40.** $-49x^2 + 28xy - 4y^2$

## Exercises.  Pages 25–26

**1.** $(2 + x)(2 - x)$  **2.** $2(x - 2y)$  **3.** $(x + 3)(x^2 - 3x + 9)$
**4.** $(x - 2)^2$  **5.** $(y + 4)^2$  **6.** $(a - 9 + x)(a - 9 - x)$
**7.** $(a - \frac{1}{2})^2$  **8.** $(x^2 - 3y^2)(x^4 + 3x^2y^2 + 9y^4)$
**9.** $(2x - 9)(x - 3)$  **10.** $(x + y + 2z)(x + y - 2z)$
**11.** $2^2a(3a - 4b^2)$  **12.** $(x + 2y + z)(x + 2y - z)$
**13.** $(x^4 + 16)(x^2 + 4)(x + 2)(x - 2)$  **14.** $a(x - 7)(x + 5)$
**15.** $(x^2 + xy + y^2)(x^2 - xy + y^2)$  **16.** $(\frac{1}{5}a^2 + \frac{3}{7}c)(\frac{1}{5}a^2 - \frac{3}{7}c)$
**17.** $(2 + 3w)(4 - 6w + 9w^2)$  **18.** $(r^2 + 4rt + 8t^2)(r^2 - 4rt + 8t^2)$
**19.** $(y - 5 + 3x - z)(y - 5 - 3x + z)$  **20.** $s^2(2r + 5)(2r - 3)$
**21.** $(4a^2 + 2ab - 3b^2)(4a^2 - 2ab - 3b^2)$  **22.** $(5x^2 + 6)(8x - 7)$
**23.** $(2a - 3b + x - y)(2a - 3b - x + y)$
**24.** $(t + r + s)(t - r - s)$  **25.** $(2x + 3c - b)(5y - 4w)$
**26.** $(w + 1)(w - 2)(w^2 - w + 1)(w^2 + 2w + 4)$
**27.** $(9z + 2w - 5)(9z - 2w + 5)$  **28.** $(a + b + 3x)(a + b - 2x)$
**29.** $(2a^2 + 2a + 1)(2a^2 - 2a + 1)$
**30.** $(2m^2 + 3mn + 7n^2)(2m^2 - 3mn + 7n^2)$
**31.** $(3a^2 + 2ab + b^2)(3a^2 - 2ab + b^2)$  **32.** $(x + z - 3y)(2r - s)$
**33.** $(5x^2 - 6)(5x + 7)$  **34.** $(x + y)^3(x - y)$
**35.** $(x^2 + x + 1)(2x - y)$  **36.** $b(x^2 + y^2)(6a - b)$
**37.** $(x + y)(x^2 + xy + y^2)(x^2 - xy + y^2)$
**38.** $(a^2 + a - 6b)(a^2 - a + 6b)$  **39.** $(m^2 + 4)(2m + 3)(2m - 3)$
**40.** $2(x - y)(4x + 1)$  **41.** $3p(p + 3)^2(p - 3)^2$  **42.** $xy(xy + 1)(x^2 - 2y^2)$
**43.** $(3x + 4y + 7a - 2b)(3x + 4y - 7a + 2b)$

**44.** $(x^a + y^b)(x^b + y^a)$      **45.** $(3x + 1)^4$

**46.** $(2u^2 - 3v^3)(4u^4 - 6u^2v^3 + 9v^6)$      **47.** $2(a - d)(a + b + c + d)$

**48.** $m(m + n)(m^2 + mn + n^2)(m^2 - mn + n^2)$

**49.** $(x - z + y + 1)(x - z - y - 1)$    **50.** $3a^2(3a^2 + 4)(5a + 2)$

## Exercises. Page 27

**1.** $30$      **2.** $18x^3y$      **3.** $198y^4z$      **4.** $(x - y)^2(x + y)$

**5.** $4(x - 2)^2(x + 2)$      **6.** $(x - 2)^3(x + 3)$      **7.** $30(a - 2)(a + 3)$

**8.** $(y - 2)(y - 3)(y + 4)$      **9.** $(x - 4)(x + 6)(x + 7)(x - 7)$

**10.** $x(x + 1)(x - 1)(2x + 3)$      **11.** $4(x + 3)(2x - 1)(5x - 3)$

**12.** $(a + 2)(2a - 1)(3a + 1)$      **13.** $(a - 1)(a + 2)(a - 3)$

**14.** $(r - 3a)^2(r + 7a)$      **15.** $(x - 1)(x - 2)^2(2x - 5)$

**16.** $(x + 1)(x + 5)(x - 5)$      **17.** $70x^3y^2(x + y)^3(x - y)$

**18.** $a^3b(x + y)(x - y)^2$      **19.** $12a^2b(a^2 - 2b^2)(a^3 - 2b^2)$

**20.** $15(x+y)(x-y)(2x+5y)(2x-5y)$      **21.** $20xy(3x+2y)(6x+7y)(6x-7y)$

**22.** $(a + b)(a - b)(2a + 3)(a^2 - ab + b^2)$

**23.** $(x + y)(x - y)(3x + 5)(x^2 + xy + y^2)$

**24.** $18x^2(x - 2a)(2x^2 + 2x + 1)(2x^2 - 2x + 1)$

**25.** $x(x - 1)(x + 2)(x - 2)(x - 3)$      **26.** $(a + 1)(a + 2)(a - 2)^2$

**27.** $84x^3(x + 1)(x - 1)(x + 3)(x - 6)(x + 7)$

**28.** $12x^2y^2(x + y)(x - y)(3x - 2y)(2z - 5w)$

**29.** $150ax^3y^2(a + x)^2(a - x)^2(a - 2x)$

**30.** $42x^4y^3(a - 1)(a^2 + 2a + 2)(a^2 + 3a + 3)$

**31.** $2x(x + 1)(x + 2)(2x - 1)(2x - 3)(x^2 - x + 1)$

**32.** $(x + a)(x - a)(x - b)(2x + 3a)(x^2 + a^2)$

## Exercises. Pages 28-29

**1.** $\frac{5}{12}$      **2.** $\frac{3}{5}$      **3.** $x - y$      **4.** $\frac{3 + 4d}{4 + 5d}$

**5.** $\frac{1}{a + 2b}$      **6.** $3ab$      **7.** $\frac{4}{5x(a + b)}$      **8.** $d$

**9.** $x - y$      **10.** $\frac{x^2 + 2x + 4}{x^2 + 4}$      **11.** $\frac{a + 4b}{a + 7b}$

**12.** $\frac{a(m - n)}{m + n}$      **13.** $\frac{b(a - 2)}{c(a - 6)}$      **14.** $\frac{3 + r^2}{2(2 + r^2)}$

**15.** $\frac{x^4 + 1}{2x - 3}$      **16.** $\frac{a + 10}{a - 4}$      **17.** $\frac{a(y - 4)}{y + 5}$

**18.** $\frac{3x + 4y}{x + y}$      **19.** $\frac{x - 4}{a - 2}$      **20.** $\frac{8m}{(m^2 + 2)^2}$

**21.** $2(2y^4 - x^2)$      **22.** $\frac{x + 3}{x - 3}$      **23.** $\frac{a - 3b + c}{a - 3b - c}$

**24.** $\frac{a - 3}{a^2 - 7}$      **25.** $\frac{y + 1}{y + 5}$      **26.** $\frac{2x + 5}{3(x - 2)}$

**27.** $\frac{m + 1}{3m - 2}$      **28.** $\frac{a + 2}{a^2 - 2}$      **29.** $1$

**30.** $\dfrac{x-3}{x-1}$

**31.** $\dfrac{2x-1}{4x+1}$

**32.** 1

**33.** $x - 2y$

**34.** $\dfrac{2(a-3)(a-4)}{3a^2(a+2)(3a-2)}$

**35.** $\dfrac{(y-1)^2}{(y+1)^2}$

**36.** $\dfrac{2m-1}{3m+2}$

## Exercises. Page 30

**1.** $\frac{5}{3}$

**2.** $-\dfrac{ax}{c}$

**3.** $-\dfrac{10xy}{6cz}$

**4.** $\dfrac{10xy}{48x^2z}$

**5.** $-\dfrac{2abc}{2abc}$

**6.** $\dfrac{5cde^2}{2ab}$

**7.** $\dfrac{16xy}{8z^3}$

**8.** $\dfrac{108x^3y^2}{9y^3z^2}$

**9.** $-\dfrac{3xy}{y^3}$

**10.** $-a$

**11.** $-\dfrac{c-d}{c}$

**12.** $-\dfrac{x+2}{x+4}$

**13.** $-\dfrac{a^2+3}{2(a^2+2)}$

**14.** $-\dfrac{a}{2x+y}$

**15.** $-\dfrac{x+y}{2x+y}$

**16.** $\dfrac{3y+4a}{y+a}$

**17.** $\dfrac{a}{x^2+a^2}$

**18.** $\dfrac{b+c}{b}$

**19.** $\dfrac{(2x+5)}{3(x-2)}$

**20.** $\dfrac{a+10}{a-4}$

**21.** $(x+1)(y+1)$

**22.** $-(x^2+3xy+9y^2)$

**23.** $-\dfrac{x^2-3x+9}{4(x+3)}$

**24.** $\dfrac{y(x-4)}{x+5}$

**25.** $-(16a^4+24a^3y+36a^2y^2+54ay^3+81y^4)$

**26.** $-(x^2+y^2)$

**27.** $\dfrac{x-3y}{2x-y}$

## Exercises. Pages 32–33

**1.** $\frac{1}{7}$

**2.** $\frac{1}{3}$

**3.** $-\frac{1}{5}$

**4.** $\dfrac{1}{x+y}$

**5.** $\dfrac{1}{a+3b}$

**6.** $\dfrac{1}{2x-5y^2}$

**7.** $\dfrac{1}{x^2-3x+4}$

**8.** $\dfrac{1}{(x+y)(x-4y)}$

**9.** $\dfrac{1}{(a+b)(3a-5b)}$

**10.** $\dfrac{a}{x(x+a)(x-a)}$

**11.** $\dfrac{(a-1)^2}{a(a^2-a+1)}$

**12.** $\dfrac{a-1}{4a+7}$

**13.** $\dfrac{y^2}{x^2}$

**14.** $\dfrac{1}{a+7}$

**15.** $\dfrac{3x(x-y)}{2(x+y)^2}$

**16.** $\dfrac{3(y+3)}{2t^2(y-2)}$

**17.** $\dfrac{r(r+2s)^2}{s(r+s)}$

**18.** $\dfrac{a+b}{a(a+3b)}$

**19.** $\dfrac{(n+2)(2n+1)}{2n}$

**20.** $\dfrac{(2a-3b)(3a-5b)}{(3a-2b)(3a+5b)}$

**21.** $\dfrac{w^2(w-z)}{(4w-z)(9w^2+6wz+4z^2)}$

**22.** $\dfrac{2y+1}{4-y}$

**23.** $\dfrac{24(4x-1)}{25(4x+1)}$

**24.** $\dfrac{(x+y)(x-2y)}{x(x-y)}$

**25.** $\dfrac{x-3}{x-1}$

**26.** $\dfrac{(x+1)(x+3)(x-4)}{3(x^2-13)}$

**27.** $\dfrac{p^2+3}{p-3}$

**28.** $\dfrac{(a+1)(a-7)}{(a+3)(a^2+a+1)}$

**29.** $\dfrac{1}{x+7}$

**30.** 1

**31.** $\dfrac{(a+4)^2}{(a+2)^2}$

**32.** $\dfrac{(m-3)(m^2+3)}{(m^2+3m+9)}$

**33.** $(a-3)^2$

**34.** $-\dfrac{2b}{a+b}$

**35.** $\dfrac{b}{a-b}$

**36.** $\dfrac{(a-1)(a-6)}{a^2}$

**37.** $\dfrac{1+a}{(1-a)(1+a^2)}$

**38.** 1

**39.** 1

**40.** 1

**41.** $\dfrac{2(a-3)}{3(a+3)^2}$

**42.** 1

## Exercises.  Pages 35–36

**1.** $\tfrac{23}{12}$

**2.** $-\tfrac{25}{6}$

**3.** $\dfrac{4x-7}{4}$

**4.** $\dfrac{16y-6a+193}{48}$

**5.** $\dfrac{4x-83}{35}$

**6.** $\dfrac{3cx+by-bc}{bc}$

**7.** $\dfrac{27a^2-15ab-20a+24b}{12a^2b}$

**8.** $\dfrac{3a^2-20a^2c-24c^2+4ac^2}{4ac}$

**9.** $\dfrac{3a^2-23a-2}{3a}$

**10.** $\dfrac{(2x-1)^2}{x^2-1}$

**11.** $-\dfrac{4a^2+10a-1}{(a+3)(a-2)}$

**12.** $\dfrac{2x^3-8}{(x+2)(x-2)}$

**13.** $\dfrac{27x^2-15xy-20x+24y}{12x^2y}$

**14.** $\dfrac{a^2+17a+1}{(a-3)(a+4)}$

**15.** $-\dfrac{a^2+a+2}{(a+1)(2a+3)}$

**16.** $\dfrac{5y}{6(x-y)}$

**17.** $\dfrac{6(x+1)(x-1)}{2x-3}$

**18.** $\dfrac{32x+5y+7}{4x(4x+1)}$

**19.** $\dfrac{2m-mx-4x}{m(m+4)(m-4)}$

**20.** $-\dfrac{2a+15}{(a+3)(a-3)}$

**21.** $-\dfrac{1}{ab}$

**22.** $\dfrac{y^2-11y+29}{y(y-5)}$

**23.** $\dfrac{12}{(x-6)(x+10)}$

**24.** $\dfrac{2y^3}{x^2-xy+y^2}$

**25.** $\dfrac{2}{x+4}$

**26.** $\dfrac{a^3-3a^2-2a+48}{(a+3)(a+4)(a-4)}$

**27.** $\dfrac{6a-2}{a(2a+1)(2a-1)}$

**28.** 0

**29.** $\dfrac{2a+7}{(a+3)(a+4)}$

**30.** $\dfrac{y^2+5xy-4x^2}{(y-3x)^2(y+7x)}$

**31.** $\dfrac{4a^3+6a^2-1}{a(2a+1)(2a-1)}$

**32.** $\dfrac{y^2-3xy+2}{(x-y)(2x+y)}$

**33.** $\dfrac{a-b}{8(a+b)}$

**34.** $\dfrac{1}{(a+1)(a-1)}$

**35.** $\dfrac{x}{y}$

**36.** $-\dfrac{a}{a-2}$

**37.** 1

## Exercises. Pages 37–39

**1.** $\dfrac{3}{2}$  **2.** $\dfrac{4}{9}$  **3.** $\dfrac{21}{10}$  **4.** $\dfrac{5}{6}$  **5.** $\dfrac{5a^3}{8b^3}$

**6.** $\dfrac{15b}{2a}$  **7.** $\dfrac{(a+b)^2(a-b)}{4}$  **8.** $\dfrac{3x}{a+x}$

**9.** 1  **10.** $\frac{3}{2}$  **11.** $\frac{4}{7}$  **12.** $-\frac{109}{225}$

**13.** $\dfrac{(9x^2+y^2)(3x-y)}{(3x+y)(4x-y)}$  **14.** $x+y$  **15.** $\dfrac{1}{2x^2-1}$

**16.** $\dfrac{x-2}{x+2}$  **17.** $\dfrac{a}{a-1}$  **18.** 1  **19.** $\dfrac{a-2y}{a}$

**20.** $\dfrac{(x+a)(x^2-x-ax+2a)}{(x-a)(x^2-2x+ax-a)}$  **21.** $\dfrac{x^2+xy+y^2}{xy}$

**22.** $\dfrac{a(1+a^2)}{(1-a)^3}$  **23.** $\dfrac{4ax}{x^2+a^2}$  **24.** $\dfrac{x^4+a^4}{ax(x^2+a^2)}$

**25.** $\dfrac{1+a^4}{a(1+a^2)}$  **26.** $\dfrac{(x+2a)(x-2a)}{4a-x}$  **27.** $-\dfrac{a^2+1}{(a-1)^2}$

**28.** $\dfrac{2(x+y)}{x-y}$  **29.** $\dfrac{3}{5}$  **30.** 1

**31.** $x-1$  **32.** $\dfrac{x+y}{x-y}$  **33.** $x+y$

**34.** $x$  **35.** $x-1$  **36.** $\dfrac{x^2y}{x+y}$

**37.** $\dfrac{1}{2x^2-1}$  **38.** $y$  **39.** $\dfrac{2x}{1+x^2}$

**40.** $-3x^2(3x-7)$  **41.** $\dfrac{x(x^2+x-1)}{x^3+3x^2-1}$  **42.** $\dfrac{(a-1)^2(2a+1)}{a^2(2a^2-a-2)}$

## Exercises. Pages 41–43

**1.** $\sqrt[3]{2}$  **2.** $\sqrt[5]{9}\sqrt{y}$  **3.** $2\sqrt{a}+\sqrt{b}$  **4.** $\sqrt{a^2+b^2}$

**5.** $\sqrt[3]{x^4y}$  **6.** $3\sqrt{x^3}\sqrt[3]{x}$  **7.** $\sqrt[5]{\frac{1}{3}}$  **8.** $\sqrt[3]{(x^2+3y^2)^2}$

**9.** $\sqrt[3]{a^2x^4}+\sqrt[3]{b^2y^2}$  **10.** $2^{\frac{1}{2}}$  **11.** $(a^2+b^2)^{\frac{1}{2}}$

**12.** $(a+b)$  **13.** $x^{\frac{1}{2}}y^{\frac{5}{4}}$  **14.** $x^{\frac{1}{2}}5^{\frac{1}{6}}$

**15.** $2a^{\frac{3}{4}}$  **16.** $x^{\frac{2}{3}}y^{\frac{1}{4}}$  **17.** $3^{\frac{1}{6}}(5x)^{\frac{1}{12}}$

**18.** $x^{\frac{1}{3}}$  **19.** $6\sqrt{2}$  **20.** $2\sqrt[3]{3}$

**21.** $xy\sqrt[4]{x}$  **22.** $(x+y)\sqrt{x}$  **23.** $0.6x^3\sqrt{x}$

**24.** $-4x^2\sqrt[3]{2}$  **25.** $a\sqrt{b-c}$  **26.** $2\sqrt[3]{2a^3+a^2x^2}$

**27.** $\dfrac{x\sqrt[3]{6x^2}}{4z^3}$  **28.** $\sqrt[3]{32}$  **29.** $\sqrt[3]{(x+y)^4}$

**30.** $\sqrt[3]{\dfrac{32}{9}}$  **31.** $\sqrt{\dfrac{a}{x}}$  **32.** $\sqrt[4]{1}$

**33.** $\sqrt[3]{40}$  **34.** $\sqrt{10}$  **35.** $\sqrt{4x}+\sqrt[3]{125y}$

**36.** $\sqrt{9xy}$  **37.** $\sqrt{5x}$  **38.** $\sqrt[3]{ab^2}$

**39.** $\sqrt[4]{4y}$  **40.** $\sqrt{0.12a}$  **41.** $\sqrt{3ab^2}$

**42.** $\sqrt{7ab^2}$  **43.** $\sqrt{2xy}$  **44.** $\sqrt[6]{14x^4y^4}$

**45.** $\sqrt{15a^2xy}$  **46.** $\dfrac{\sqrt[3]{36}}{4}$  **47.** $-\dfrac{\sqrt[3]{6}}{3}$

**48.** $\dfrac{\sqrt{18a}}{4}$  **49.** $\dfrac{\sqrt{2}}{2}$  **50.** $\dfrac{\sqrt{3}}{3}$

**51.** $-\dfrac{3\sqrt[3]{3a}}{2a^2}$  **52.** $\dfrac{\sqrt{10}}{4x}$  **53.** $\dfrac{\sqrt[3]{2y}}{2y}$

**54.** $\dfrac{y\sqrt{10xy}}{2x^3}$  **55.** $\dfrac{\sqrt{5(x+y)}}{x+y}$  **56.** $-\tfrac{6}{5}$

**57.** $\dfrac{\sqrt{3x}}{3y}$  **58.** $\dfrac{2y^2\sqrt{6}}{9}$  **59.** $\dfrac{xy\sqrt{y(x-y)}}{x-y}$

**60.** $-\dfrac{\sqrt[5]{3z^4}}{3z}$  **61.** $\dfrac{\sqrt{(3a+b)(x^2-y^2)}}{x^2-y^2}$  **62.** $\dfrac{2\sqrt{(1+2a)(a+b)}}{(a+b)^2}$

**63.** $\dfrac{\sqrt[3]{(5y+7)(x+y)^2(x-3y)^2}}{(x+y)(x-3y)}$  **64.** $\dfrac{y\sqrt[6]{4a^2by^2}}{2b}$

**65.** $\dfrac{\sqrt{x^4+3x}}{x}$  **66.** $\dfrac{\sqrt[3]{27xy^3z^3-81y^2z^3+2y^3z}}{3yz}$

**67.** $\sqrt[12]{2^6},\ \sqrt[12]{3^4},\ \sqrt[12]{6^3}$  **68.** $\sqrt[12]{8^3},\ \sqrt[12]{5^6},\ \sqrt[12]{6^2}$  **69.** $\sqrt[6]{7},\ \sqrt[6]{4^3},\ \sqrt[6]{5^2}$

**70.** $\sqrt[30]{(x-1)^{15}},\ \sqrt[30]{(x+1)^{10}},\ \sqrt[30]{x^{18}y^{24}}$  **71.** $3\sqrt[5]{3},\ \sqrt[5]{3}$

**72.** $\sqrt[60]{x^{20}},\ \sqrt[60]{x^{15}},\ \sqrt[60]{x^{12}}$  **73.** $y\sqrt[6]{x^3},\ \sqrt[6]{x^4},\ \sqrt[6]{y^3}$

**74.** $2\sqrt[6]{8},\ 2\sqrt[6]{4}$  **75.** $ab\sqrt[6]{a^3b^3},\ \sqrt[6]{a^2b^2},\ \sqrt[6]{a^2b^2}$

**76.** $\dfrac{\sqrt{5x-x^2}}{x}$  **77.** $\dfrac{a}{x^2+a^2}$  **78.** $\dfrac{1}{\sqrt{a^2-x^2}}$

**79.** $\dfrac{a}{\sqrt{a^2+x^2}}$  **80.** $\dfrac{y}{\sqrt{2ay-y^2}}$  **81.** $\dfrac{x+4y}{4x^{\frac{3}{2}}}$

**82.** $\dfrac{x+\sqrt{x^2+1}}{x^2+1+\sqrt{x^2+1}}$  **83.** $\tfrac{1}{4}$  **84.** $\dfrac{3-2ax}{2x}$

**85.** $\dfrac{x+a}{x^2+a^2}$  **86.** $\dfrac{1}{b^2}$  **87.** $\dfrac{1}{(2x-x^2)^{\frac{3}{2}}}$

**88.** $2\sqrt{9-x^2}$  **89.** $x$  **90.** $\dfrac{3a^3y^2}{(a^3-y^3)^{\frac{7}{6}}}$

**91.** $-\dfrac{8xy^2}{(4y^2-x^2)^{\frac{13}{6}}}$  **92.** $-\dfrac{a^3+x^3}{2x^{\frac{3}{2}}(a^3-x^3)^{\frac{2}{3}}}$  **93.** $\dfrac{a^5-7x^5}{4x^{\frac{3}{4}}(a^5+x^5)^{\frac{7}{5}}}$

**94.** $-\dfrac{3a^2}{(1+2a^3)^{\frac{5}{4}}(1-2a^3)^{\frac{3}{4}}}$  **95.** $\dfrac{8a^2}{(x^2+4a^2)\sqrt{x^2-4a^2}}$

**96.** $\dfrac{x}{y}$  **97.** $\sqrt{x}$  **98.** $a$  **99.** $2xy(3y+2x)$  **100.** $\dfrac{8}{(4+x^2)^{\frac{3}{2}}}$

## Exercises. Pages 44–45

**1.** $\sqrt{2x+2y}$  **2.** $\sqrt[4]{12}$  **3.** $5\sqrt{42}$  **4.** $\sqrt[6]{4a^3b^2}$

**5.** $\dfrac{\sqrt[10]{48}}{3}$  **6.** $2$  **7.** $\dfrac{8\sqrt{15}}{45}$  **8.** $\sqrt[6]{\tfrac{1}{6}}$

**9.** $-3\sqrt[6]{3^2 \cdot 2^5}$    **10.** $\sqrt[6]{\frac{1}{16}}$    **11.** $\frac{8}{ab^5}$    **12.** $2x\sqrt[6]{800x^4y^4}$

**13.** $144x^3y^3$    **14.** $\sqrt[12]{24a}$    **15.** $9$    **16.** $\sqrt{2} + \sqrt{6}$

**17.** $-1$    **18.** $10 + 5\sqrt{6}$    **19.** $11 + 5\sqrt{5}$    **20.** $17 - 12\sqrt{2}$

**21.** $3 + 4x\sqrt{3} + 4x^2$    **22.** $12 - ay$    **23.** $3\sqrt[3]{a^2} - 5\sqrt[3]{a}$    **24.** $11$

**25.** $6 - 4a + \sqrt{a^2 - a}$    **26.** $5y - 4$    **27.** $\frac{11 - 6\sqrt{2}}{8}$    **28.** $2$

**29.** $\frac{1 - 2\sqrt{xy} + xy}{\sqrt{xy}}$    **30.** $\sqrt{x^2 - y}$

**31.** $\sqrt{3} - \sqrt{5} + 2\sqrt{15} - 8$    **32.** $a - b$

**33.** $3\sqrt{x^2 - xy} + 5y - 3x$    **34.** $22a - 23\sqrt{a^2 - 1} + 2$

**35.** $\sqrt[12]{a}\,(5a^2 - 41ab + 42b^2)$    **36.** $98$

**37.** $18 - 12\sqrt{6}$    **38.** $0$

**39.** $x^2 + xy + b^2$    **40.** $\frac{3 + \sqrt{3}}{2}$

**41.** $\frac{48 + 10\sqrt{5}}{9}$    **42.** $0$    **43.** $0$    **44.** $0$

## Exercises. Pages 46–47

**1.** $7\sqrt{2}$    **2.** $-\sqrt{2} - \sqrt{6}$    **3.** $3\sqrt{21}$    **4.** $3\sqrt[3]{3}$

**5.** $0$    **6.** $4\sqrt{2}$    **7.** $\frac{22\sqrt{3}}{3}$    **8.** $\sqrt{10} + 6\sqrt{2}$

**9.** $(x + y + 3)\sqrt{2}$    **10.** $(1 - 9xy)\sqrt[3]{ab}$    **11.** $(3a + ab)\sqrt[4]{a}$

**12.** $0$    **13.** $4\sqrt[3]{3} + 4\sqrt[3]{2}$    **14.** $9\sqrt{7}$

**15.** $\frac{21\sqrt{5}}{20}$    **16.** $-\frac{87\sqrt{2}}{4} - 1$    **17.** $\sqrt[3]{2x} - \frac{\sqrt{2x}}{2}$

**18.** $\left(\frac{15xy - 8xy^2 + 4}{3y}\right)\sqrt{3xy} - \frac{2\sqrt[3]{3xy}}{3z}$

**19.** $\left(\frac{8x^2y - 3x^3y + 60}{4y}\right)\sqrt[3]{y}$    **20.** $(a + b - 1)\sqrt{ab}$

**21.** $(6a^2 + 54)\sqrt{a^2 + 9}$    **22.** $9\sqrt{x + 3}$

**23.** $\frac{x\sqrt{xy}}{3} + (2x - y)\sqrt{3y}$    **24.** $4a\sqrt{6a}$

**25.** $\frac{10x\sqrt{3x}}{3} - 6x\sqrt{6x} + \frac{2\sqrt[3]{2x}}{x} + \frac{7x\sqrt[3]{x}}{2z}$

**26.** $-\frac{4\sqrt{a^2 - 1}}{a^2 - 1}$    **27.** $(\frac{7}{3} - 10x + 3y)\sqrt{6}$

**28.** $9cm\sqrt{x - z}$    **29.** $12ab\sqrt{2} - b\sqrt{2a}$    **30.** $(2a + 6c)\sqrt[3]{a - c}$

**31.** $\frac{3a\sqrt{3}}{2b} + \frac{(2a - 1)\sqrt{3a}}{3b}$    **32.** $\frac{2}{3} + 2\sqrt{2} + 2\sqrt[3]{2}$

**33.** $\left(\dfrac{a}{2} - \dfrac{y}{4} + \dfrac{z}{5}\right)\sqrt{3}$

**34.** $(x^{\frac{3}{4}} - y^{\frac{3}{4}})\sqrt{x^{\frac{1}{2}} + y^{\frac{1}{2}}}$

**35.** $\dfrac{15a\sqrt[3]{2a}}{2} + (21x^2 - 16y^2)\sqrt{xy}$

**36.** $5 + 6\sqrt{3}$

### Exercises. Pages 48–49

**1.** $\dfrac{3\sqrt{2}}{4}$

**2.** $\dfrac{\sqrt{2}}{2}$

**3.** $\dfrac{2\sqrt{3}}{3}$

**4.** $\dfrac{\sqrt{7}}{7}$

**5.** $4\sqrt[3]{2}$

**6.** $\dfrac{3\sqrt{55}}{11}$

**7.** $\dfrac{\sqrt{35a}}{7a}$

**8.** $-\dfrac{\sqrt[3]{10x^2}}{2x}$

**9.** $\dfrac{b\sqrt{5a}}{10}$

**10.** $\dfrac{\sqrt[3]{18x^2y^2}}{3y}$

**11.** $\dfrac{y\sqrt{10xy}}{2x^3}$

**12.** $\dfrac{\sqrt{30xy}}{6y}$

**13.** $\dfrac{\sqrt{a^4 + 3a}}{a}$

**14.** $\dfrac{y\sqrt[6]{4x^2y^2z}}{2z}$

**15.** $\dfrac{\sqrt{5b}}{5ab}$

**16.** $-\dfrac{\sqrt[5]{3x^4}}{3x}$

**17.** $\dfrac{2x\sqrt[3]{9y^2}}{3y^2}$

**18.** $\dfrac{\sqrt{3xy(z-w)}}{z-w}$

**19.** $2 - \sqrt{3}$

**20.** $6 - 2\sqrt{2} - 3\sqrt{3} + \sqrt{6}$

**21.** $5 + 2\sqrt{6}$

**22.** $-\dfrac{5 + 2\sqrt{6}}{2}$

**23.** $-5$

**24.** $6 - \sqrt{35}$

**25.** $3 + 2\sqrt{2} - 3\sqrt{5} - 2\sqrt{10}$

**26.** $\dfrac{3 - \sqrt{6} - \sqrt{3} + \sqrt{2}}{4}$

**27.** $\sqrt{3} + \sqrt{2}$

**28.** $\dfrac{90 + 37\sqrt{6}}{57}$

**29.** $\dfrac{6 - \sqrt{10}}{13}$

**30.** $\dfrac{13\sqrt{5} - 29}{2}$

**31.** $\dfrac{12\sqrt{6} + 3\sqrt{10} - 2\sqrt{15} - 30}{6}$

**32.** $\dfrac{7\sqrt{6} - 12}{10}$

**33.** $\dfrac{a^2x - 3ab\sqrt{xz} + 2b^2z}{a^2x - b^2z}$

**34.** $\dfrac{x - \sqrt{x^2 - y^2}}{y}$

**35.** $\dfrac{14a - 11\sqrt{a^2 - 2a} - 24}{18 - 5a}$

**36.** $\dfrac{a + \sqrt{a^2 + b^2}}{b}$

**37.** $a - \sqrt{a^2 - b^2}$

**38.** $\dfrac{2a - 2\sqrt{(a-2)(a-4)} + 5\sqrt{a-2} - 5\sqrt{a-4} - 4}{2}$

**39.** $\dfrac{(b+a)(b\sqrt{a} - a\sqrt{b})}{a^2b^2}$

**40.** $2x^2 - 2x\sqrt{x^2 - 1} - 1$

**41.** $-\dfrac{1 + \sqrt{1 - q^2}}{q}$

**42.** $\dfrac{1 - \sqrt{1 - x^4}}{x^2}$

**43.** $\dfrac{12x^2 + 13\sqrt{x^4 - y^4}}{5x^2 + 13y^2}$

**44.** $\dfrac{9 - 12a^2 + 11\sqrt{1 - 4a^2}}{36a^2 - 5}$

**45.** $\dfrac{(\sqrt{15} + 4)b - 2\sqrt{3ab - 3b^2} + 2\sqrt{5ab - 5b^2} - 4a}{9b - 4a}$

**46.** $\dfrac{3(\sqrt[3]{x^2} - \sqrt[3]{xy} + \sqrt[3]{y^2})}{x + y}$    **47.** $-\dfrac{97 + 24\sqrt[3]{12} + 36\sqrt[3]{18}}{65}$

**48.** $\dfrac{20\sqrt[3]{4} - 30\sqrt[3]{6} + 45\sqrt[3]{9} + 24\sqrt[3]{12} - 36\sqrt[3]{18} - 32}{97}$

**49.** $\dfrac{8a + 9\sqrt{ab} + b}{a - b}$    **50.** $-\dfrac{4\sqrt{ab}(b - \sqrt{a^2 + b^2})}{a^2}$

**51.** **19.** 0.268;  **20.** 0.425;  **21.** 9.899;  **22.** $-$ 4.949;  **23.** $-$ 5.000;  **24.** 0.084;
**25.** $-$ 7.204;  **26.** 0.058;  **27.** 3.146;  **28.** 3.169;  **29.** 0.218;  **30.** 0.034;
**31.** 0.189;  **32.** 0.515

## Exercises.  Pages 50–51

**1.** $-$ 20    **2.** $-$ 6    **3.** $22 + 7i$    **4.** $5 - 12i$

**5.** $-\dfrac{23}{25} - \dfrac{12\sqrt{3}i}{25}$    **6.** $-\dfrac{6}{13} + \dfrac{17i}{13}$    **7.** $\dfrac{11}{10} - \dfrac{7i}{10}$

**8.** 20    **9.** $\dfrac{10 + 35i}{53}$    **10.** $\dfrac{-1 + 18\sqrt{2}i}{59}$

**11.** $\dfrac{3 - 7i}{58}$    **12.** $\dfrac{3 - 4i}{25}$    **13.** $\dfrac{5\sqrt{3} - 5i}{4}$

**14.** $i$    **15.** $-\dfrac{3i}{2}$    **16.** $\dfrac{5 - 2i}{29}$

**17.** $7 - 9i$    **18.** $2\sqrt{5} + 3\sqrt{15} + (2\sqrt{3} - 15)i$
**19.** $-1 + 8i$    **20.** $48 + 3\sqrt{2}i$    **21.** 34
**22.** $-4\sqrt{3} + (\sqrt{5} - 4)i$    **23.** $\frac{7}{2}$    **24.** 0    **25.** 0
**26.** 0    **27.** $3 - \sqrt{3}i$    **28.** 6    **29.** 0    **30.** 0    **31.** 0; 0

## Exercises.  Page 54

**1.** No    **2.** Yes    **3.** Yes    **4.** No    **5.** No    **6.** Yes    **7.** No
**8.** (a) Equivalent    (b) Equivalent    (c) Redundant    (d) Redundant
(e) Redundant    **9.** $2 - x \neq 0$

## Exercises.  Page 56

**1.** $x = 2$    **2.** $x = -9$    **3.** $x = -4$    **4.** $t = \frac{4}{3}$

**5.** $-\frac{13}{6}$    **6.** $-25$    **7.** 9    **8.** 31    **9.** $\frac{11}{15}$

**10.** 17    **11.** 5    **12.** 0.5    **13.** 0.3    **14.** $\frac{5}{3}$

**15.** $a - b$    **16.** $\dfrac{ac}{a - b}$    **17.** $\dfrac{a - b}{a + b}$    **18.** $a - b$

**19.** $bc$    **20.** $\dfrac{a^2bc^2 + ab + c^2}{a^2 - bc}$

## Exercises.  Pages 58–60

**1.** $\frac{7}{10}$    **2.** $-5$    **3.** $-\frac{1}{2}$    **4.** $-3$    **5.** $\frac{1}{10}$    **6.** $-\frac{21}{11}$
**7.** $\frac{34}{25}$    **8.** $\frac{14}{13}$    **9.** $-40$    **10.** $-7$    **11.** $-1$    **12.** 8

| | | | | | |
|---|---|---|---|---|---|
| **13.** 2 | **14.** $-1$ | **15.** $-\frac{5}{3}$ | **16.** 1 | **17.** $-\frac{3}{2}$ | **18.** 3 |
| **19.** 0 | **20.** 6 | **21.** 1 | **22.** 2 | **23.** 2 | **24.** $\frac{1}{4}$ |
| **25.** 9 | **26.** 2 | **27.** $\frac{11}{6}$ | **28.** $-7$ | **29.** 6 | **30.** 2 |
| **31.** $\frac{1}{24}$ | **32.** 24 | **33.** $\frac{11}{2}$ | **34.** 3 | **35.** $\frac{153}{416}$ | **36.** 1 |

**37.** $\frac{2}{3}$     **38.** 11     **39.** $\dfrac{(a-b)^2}{a+b}$     **40.** $\dfrac{1}{2(a+b)}$

**41.** $a^2 - b^2$     **42.** $\dfrac{a-b}{a+b}$     **43.** $\dfrac{bx-a}{ax+2}$     **44.** $\dfrac{bm+an}{abc}$

**45.** $\dfrac{d}{c}$     **46.** $\dfrac{2ab}{ab+ac-4c}$     **47.** $\dfrac{ab}{a+b}$

### Exercises. Pages 61–64

**1.** 6 sq. ft.
**2.** Breadth = 4, length = 6
**3.** 60 sq. yd.
**4.** $B - 5$ yr. old, $A - 15$ yr. old
**5.** 6, 7, 8
**6.** Width = 5 ft., length = 7 ft.
**7.** Width = 2 in., length = 5 in.
**8.** $24\frac{1}{2}$ ft.
**9.** $1\frac{1}{2}$ ft.
**10.** 90 mi.; 30 mi. per hr.
**11.** 6 hr.
**12.** 50 mi.; 62 mi.
**13.** $1.00
**14.** 8, 27
**15.** 18, 19
**16.** 3
**17.** 6
**18.** 32, 40
**19.** 17, 68
**20.** 33, 72
**21.** 135, 150
**22.** 5
**23.** 34 days
**24.** $9\frac{81}{11}$ hr.
**25.** $600 at 4%, $400 at 5%
**26.** $8,333$\frac{1}{3}$
**27.** $100 per month
**28.** 150 miles
**29.** 40 mi. per hr.
**30.** 4 hr.
**31.** 7
**32.** 3
**33.** 7
**34.** 40 min.
**35.** 10:24 p.m.
**36.** 6 lb. of 65¢ tea, 12 lb. of 50¢ tea
**37.** 140 c.c.
**38.** 10 lb.
**39.** 66 eggs
**40.** 4.6 miles
**41.** $\left(\dfrac{100}{x} - 3\right)$ yd.
**42.** 8400 lb.

### Exercises. Pages 68–70

**1.** $x = -2, y = 0$
**2.** $u = 4, v = -2$
**3.** $w = 12, y = 8$
**4.** $m = \frac{15}{29}, n = -\frac{112}{29}$
**5.** $x = \frac{34}{23}, y = \frac{77}{23}$
**6.** $u = 6, y = 9$
**7.** $a = 9, b = 8$
**8.** $u = \frac{8}{3}, v = \frac{2}{3}$
**9.** $u = 20, v = 20$
**10.** $y = 2, z = 3$
**11.** $u = 5, v = 10$
**12.** $m = \frac{8}{3}, n = \frac{3}{2}$
**13.** $a = 3, b = 2$
**14.** $u = 4, v = -3$
**15.** $x = 10, y = 8$
**16.** $w = \sqrt{6}, z = 1$
**17.** $u = 4, v = 12$
**18.** $m = -\frac{3}{17}, n = \frac{55}{17}$
**19.** $u = \dfrac{ac}{a+b}, v = \dfrac{bc}{a+b}$
**20.** $x = \dfrac{2ab^2}{a^2+b^2}, y = \dfrac{b(b^2-a^2)}{a^2+b^2}$
**21.** $w = a + b, z = a + b$
**22.** $x = b - m, y = -(a+m)$
**23.** $u = \dfrac{a+1}{b+1}, v = \dfrac{a+b}{b+1}$
**24.** $u = \dfrac{a}{3}, v = \dfrac{b}{3}$
**25.** $x = 5, y = 1$
**26.** $x = 3, y = 4$
**27.** $x = -\frac{11}{40}, y = \frac{11}{70}$
**28.** $u = 6, v = -3$
**29.** $x = 2, y = 6$
**30.** $u = 6, v = 2$

**31.** $w = \dfrac{ad - bc}{md - bn}$, $z = \dfrac{ad - bc}{an - mc}$  **32.** $u = a$, $v = -a$

**33.** $u = \dfrac{c(a^2 + bc)}{a + c}$, $v = \dfrac{b(a^2 + bc)}{b - a}$  **34.** $x = \dfrac{1}{b}$, $y = \dfrac{1}{a}$

## Exercises. Pages 71–72

**1.** $x = 8$, $y = 4$, $z = 2$  **2.** $r = 3$, $s = 2$, $t = 7$  **3.** $u = \frac{11}{7}$, $v = 1$, $w = \frac{3}{7}$
**4.** $a = -3$, $b = 3$, $c = \frac{1}{2}$  **5.** $x = \frac{73}{7}$, $y = \frac{40}{7}$, $z = \frac{34}{7}$
**6.** $u = \frac{18}{7}$, $v = -\frac{2}{7}$, $w = \frac{10}{7}$  **7.** $x = -\frac{1}{13}$, $y = \frac{49}{13}$, $z = -\frac{14}{13}$
**8.** $m = 2$, $n = -6$, $p = -10$  **9.** $u = 3$, $v = -1$, $w = \frac{1}{2}$
**10.** $x = \frac{15}{14}$, $y = -\frac{27}{28}$, $z = \frac{11}{14}$  **11.** $a = 60$, $b = 60$, $c = 20$
**12.** $u = \frac{147}{41}$, $v = \frac{513}{123}$, $w = \frac{220}{41}$  **13.** $m = 1$, $n = 2$, $p = \frac{5}{3}$
**14.** $x = \frac{1}{2}$, $y = \frac{1}{6}$, $z = \frac{1}{12}$  **15.** $a = \frac{1}{8}$, $b = \frac{1}{12}$, $c = \frac{1}{16}$
**16.** $u = 2$, $v = \frac{2}{3}$, $w = \frac{2}{5}$  **17.** $r = 5$, $s = 6$, $t = 8$
**18.** $x = a + b$, $y = a - b$, $z = b - a$  **19.** $x = a$, $y = b$, $z = a + b$
**20.** $w = -2$, $x = \frac{1}{3}$, $y = \frac{1}{5}$, $z = \frac{1}{4}$  **21.** $p = -1$, $q = 1$, $r = -1$, $s = 1$

## Exercises. Pages 78–80

**1.** 5, 8  **2.** 7, $-2$  **3.** $\frac{6}{5}$  **4.** 96 sq. ft.
**5.** Width = 20 ft., length = 50 ft.  **6.** 6000 gallons
**7.** $800 at 6% interest  **8.** $A$ in 20 days, $B$ in 60 days
**9.** $A$ carries 40 gals. per min. and $B$ 30.
**10.** $A$, 72 days; $B$, 36 days; $C$, 12 days
**11.** Peaches @ 32¢ per basket, strawberries @ 51¢ per basket
**12.** 20% good wheat, 80% poor wheat
**13.** First grade, $1.05; second grade, 70¢
**14.** Original speed, 54 mi. per hr.; reduced speed, $33\frac{3}{4}$ mi. per hr.
**15.** Rate of rowing, 3 mi. per hr.; rate of current, 1 mi. per hr.
**16.** 80 men  **17.** 12 dimes, 16 nickels; other answer is in fractions.
**19.** $b = 760 - 0.1h$  **20.** $116,600 - 550w = h$

## Exercises. Page 83

**1.** $x = 7$, $x = -3$  **2.** 7, 2  **3.** $\frac{3}{2}$, $-\frac{7}{3}$
**4.** 14, $-2$  **5.** $\frac{4}{3}$, $-\frac{1}{2}$  **6.** $-2$, $-\frac{2}{3}$
**7.** $-1$, $-\frac{1}{3}$  **8.** $-3$, $-4$  **9.** 0, $-9$
**10.** 7, $\frac{4}{3}$  **11.** 2, $-12$  **12.** $-\frac{2}{5}$, $-\frac{2}{5}$ (double root)
**13.** 5, 5  **14.** 0, 7  **15.** 12, $-12$  **16.** 0, $\frac{5}{3}$
**17.** 2, $-5$  **18.** $\frac{3}{4}$, $-\frac{2}{5}$  **19.** $\frac{3}{2}$, $-7$  **20.** 3, $-\frac{1}{2}$

## Exercises. Pages 85–86

**1.** $\dfrac{1 \pm \sqrt{21}}{10}$  **2.** $\dfrac{3 \pm \sqrt{13}}{2}$  **3.** 0, $-3$

**4.** $\dfrac{1 \pm \sqrt{7}}{3}$  **5.** $\pm i$  **6.** $\dfrac{4 \pm \sqrt{10}}{3}$

**7.** $\frac{3}{2}, -\frac{1}{3}$          **8.** $-3 \pm \sqrt{13}$          **9.** $-\frac{3}{2}, -\frac{2}{3}$

**10.** 14, 23          **11.** $\frac{2}{7}, -\frac{3}{4}$          **12.** $\frac{8}{5}, -\frac{3}{11}$

**13.** $\dfrac{19 \pm \sqrt{3}i}{2}$          **14.** $\dfrac{1 \pm \sqrt{5}}{2}$          **15.** $\dfrac{-5 \pm \sqrt{65}}{2}$

**16.** $\dfrac{5 \pm \sqrt{119}i}{6}$          **17.** $\frac{3}{2}, -\frac{5}{7}$          **18.** $\dfrac{9 \pm \sqrt{181}}{10}$

**19.** $\dfrac{-a \pm \sqrt{a^2 + 4b}}{2}$          **20.** $b, \dfrac{1}{b}$          **21.** $-a, -c$

**22.** $b, 3b$          **23.** $\pm a\sqrt{2}i$          **24.** $a, \dfrac{a}{2}$          **25.** $4, -1$

**26.** $2, -1$          **27.** $3, -\frac{7}{2}$          **28.** $\dfrac{-24 \pm 2\sqrt{31}i}{35}$

**29.** $3, -\frac{4}{5}$          **30.** $-3$          **31.** $5, -7$          **32.** 6

**33.** $2y, -y$          **34.** $\dfrac{y}{2}, -3y$          **35.** $-2y, \dfrac{3-y}{2}$

**36.** $\dfrac{-y \pm \sqrt{y-2}}{2}$          **37.** $\dfrac{2y - 1 \pm \sqrt{13 + 8y - 44y^2}}{6}$

**38.** $\dfrac{3y^2 + 3y + 1}{7y + 2}$          **39.** 1.77, 0.57          **40.** 2.78, 0.72

**41.** $0.58, -2.58$          **42.** 18.27, 1.23          **43.** $-1.16, -0.22$

**44.** $-1.12, -0.18$          **45.** 0.34, 1.46          **46.** $0.88, -1.88$

**47.** $2.73, -0.73$          **48.** $1.41, -1.41$

### Exercises. Pages 88–89

**1.** 10          **2.** 7          **3.** $-1$, (9 ext.)          **4.** 15          **5.** $\dfrac{\sqrt{3}}{2}$

**6.** No solution, ($\frac{7}{3}$ ext.)          **7.** $-5$          **8.** $\frac{9}{4}$          **9.** $\pm 8$

**10.** $4, -2$          **11.** No solution, (4, 9 ext.)          **12.** No solution, (0, 4 ext.)

**13.** 5, (1 ext.)          **14.** 4, (64 ext.)          **15.** $\frac{9}{2}$

**16.** 8, ($-\frac{8}{5}$ ext.)          **17.** 1          **18.** 1, 9

**19.** 9, ($\frac{1}{5}$ ext.)          **20.** $6 \pm 6\sqrt{3}i$          **21.** 4, ($-9$ ext.)

**22.** $-\frac{113}{11}$, (1 ext.)          **23.** 5, ($-2$ ext.)          **24.** 3, ($-4$ ext.)

**25.** 5, ($-\frac{5}{6}$ ext.)          **26.** 9, ($-\frac{15}{2}$ ext.)          **27.** 5, ($\frac{13}{4}$ ext.)

**28.** $-\frac{1}{4}$, ($-2$ ext.)          **29.** $-\frac{4}{3}$, (2 ext.)          **30.** 4, ($-\frac{4}{7}$ ext.)

**31.** 5, ($-\frac{9}{11}$ ext.)          **32.** 5, ($\frac{45}{8}$ ext.)          **33.** $7, -\frac{7}{3}$

**34.** 9, (18 ext.)          **35.** $\pm 2i, \pm \sqrt{2}$          **36.** No solution, (0 ext.)

### Exercises. Pages 91–92

**1.** $\pm \sqrt{2}, \pm \sqrt{3}$          **2.** $\pm \frac{2}{3}, \pm \frac{1}{2}$          **3.** $-9$

**4.** $11, \frac{7}{2}$          **5.** 1          **6.** $\frac{4}{9}, \frac{9}{4}$

**7.** 3          **8.** $\pm 1, \pm \sqrt{5}i$          **9.** 1

**10.** $\frac{1}{16}$          **11.** 16          **12.** $6, \frac{12}{2}$

**13.** $-4 \pm \sqrt{15}, 1, 1$          **14.** $3, 4, -5, -6$          **15.** $3, -\frac{11}{2}$

**16.** $2, -7$          **17.** $\dfrac{3 \pm \sqrt{19}i}{2}, \dfrac{3 \pm \sqrt{7}i}{2}$          **18.** 625

**19.** $-1 \pm \sqrt{5}$     **20.** $-2$     **21.** 9     **22.** $-8, \frac{1}{8}$

**23.** $3, -1$     **24.** 2     **25.** $1, 3, -5, -15$

**26.** $0, 1$     **27.** $-\frac{1}{2}$     **28.** $1, 2, -2, -3$

## Exercises. Pages 93–95

**1.** 4 in.     **2.** 10 ft. and 24 ft.     **3.** 2     **4.** 2 ft.     **5.** 1 in.

**6.** 18 ft. $\times$ 20 ft.     **7.** 6 ft.     **8.** 50 mi. per hr.

**9.** Time $= 1\frac{1}{2}$ hr.; rate $= 4$ mi. per hr.     **10.** 4 mi. per hr.

**11.** $A$, 3 mi. per hr.; $B$, $2\frac{1}{2}$ mi. per hr.     **12.** 50 mi. per hr.

**13.** 24 per mi.     **14.** 25     **15.** 2     **16.** $\frac{3}{2}, 2\frac{1}{2}$     **17.** 35, 37

**18.** 8, 24; (also $-16, 48$)     **19.** 5, 6, 7; (also $-1, 0, 1$)

**20.** 64     **21.** $\frac{5}{7}$; $\left(\text{also } \dfrac{-7}{-5}\right)$     **22.** $\frac{5}{12}$; $\left(\text{also } \dfrac{-\frac{24}{29}}{\frac{10}{29}}\right)$     **23.** 12 men

**24.** 10 hr.; 14 hr.     **25.** Man, 18 days; boy, 36 days

**26.** 40 rows     **27.** 320 men     **28.** 32¢ per dozen

**29.** $A$, 4 days; $B$, 8 days     **30.** 50 gallons

**31.** 200 pigs     **32.** Equation has no integral solution.

**33.** $L = \dfrac{s}{2} + \dfrac{\sqrt{9s^2 - 96d^2}}{6}$; why use "plus" sign only?

**34.** $D = d\left(0.94 + \sqrt{\dfrac{n - 3.7}{.907}}\right)$, $D = 1.406$

## Exercises. Pages 99–101

**1.** $x = 1, y = 0$; $x = 3, y = 2$     **2.** $u = -5, v = 0$; $u = 4, v = 3$

**3.** $w = 15, z = 3$; $w = -15, z = -3$

**4.** $u = 4, v = 1$; $u = -\frac{11}{4}, v = -\frac{5}{4}$

**5.** $u = 8, v = 5$; $u = -5, v = -8$     **6.** $x = \frac{3}{2}, w = \frac{5}{2}$; $x = \frac{5}{2}, w = \frac{3}{2}$

**7.** $u = 2, v = 1$; $u = -4, v = 4$     **8.** $x = -\frac{4}{5}, w = -\frac{1}{5}$; $x = \frac{1}{5}, w = \frac{4}{5}$

**9.** $u = 1, v = -2$; $u = 1, v = -2$; [double root]     **10.** $u = 9, v = 1$

**11.** $x = \dfrac{-7 + 3\sqrt{377}}{19}, y = \dfrac{8 + 2\sqrt{377}}{19}$; $x = \dfrac{-7 - 3\sqrt{377}}{19}, y = \dfrac{8 - 2\sqrt{377}}{19}$

**12.** $x = \dfrac{-9 - 3\sqrt{57}}{4}, y = \dfrac{33 + 3\sqrt{57}}{8}$; $x = \dfrac{-9 + 3\sqrt{57}}{4}, y = \dfrac{33 - 3\sqrt{57}}{8}$

**13.** $x = -\frac{2}{3}, y = -\frac{1}{3}$; $x = \frac{1}{3}, y = \frac{2}{3}$     **14.** $u = \frac{1}{3}, v = \frac{1}{2}$; $u = \frac{1}{2}, v = \frac{1}{3}$

**15.** $u = 1, v = 2$; $u = -1, v = -2$; $u = 2, v = 1$; $u = -2, v = -1$

**16.** $u = 4, v = 1$; $u = -4, v = -1$; $u = 3, v = \frac{4}{3}$; $u = -3, v = -\frac{4}{3}$

**17.** $x = 2, y = -3$; $x = -2, y = 3$; $x = 3, y = -2$; $x = -3, y = 2$

**18.** $x = \dfrac{1}{d}, y = -\dfrac{1}{2c}$; $x = -\dfrac{1}{d}, y = \dfrac{1}{2c}$; $x = \dfrac{1}{2c}, y = -\dfrac{1}{d}$; $x = -\dfrac{1}{2c}, y = \dfrac{1}{d}$

**19.** $u = 2, v = 6$; $u = -2, v = -6$; $u = 6, v = 2$; $u = -6, v = -2$

**20.** $x = \dfrac{5 + \sqrt{7}}{2}, y = \dfrac{5 - \sqrt{7}}{2}$; $x = \dfrac{5 - \sqrt{7}}{2}, y = \dfrac{5 + \sqrt{7}}{2}$; $x = \dfrac{-5 - \sqrt{7}}{2}$,

$y = \dfrac{-5 + \sqrt{7}}{2}$; $x = \dfrac{-5 + \sqrt{7}}{2}, y = \dfrac{-5 - \sqrt{7}}{2}$

**21.** $x = 4, y = 3;\ x = 4, y = -3;\ x = -4, y = 3;\ x = -4, y = -3$

**22.** $u = 2\sqrt{\frac{7}{11}},\ v = 2\sqrt{\frac{3}{11}};\ u = 2\sqrt{\frac{7}{11}},\ v = -2\sqrt{\frac{3}{11}};\ u = -2\sqrt{\frac{7}{11}},$
$v = 2\sqrt{\frac{3}{11}};\ u = -2\sqrt{\frac{7}{11}}, v = -2\sqrt{\frac{3}{11}}$

**23.** $x = 0, y = 2;\ x = 0, y = -2;\ x = 2, y = \sqrt{5};\ x = 2, y = -\sqrt{5}$

**24.** $u = 4,\ v = \sqrt{6};\quad u = 4,\ v = -\sqrt{6};\quad u = -4,\ v = \sqrt{6};\quad u = -4,$
$v = -\sqrt{6}$

**25.** $u = \dfrac{8 + \sqrt{91}}{9}, v = \dfrac{\sqrt{59 + 4\sqrt{91}}}{3};\ u = \dfrac{8 + \sqrt{91}}{9}, v = -\dfrac{\sqrt{59 + 4\sqrt{91}}}{3};$

$u = \dfrac{8 - \sqrt{91}}{9}, v = \dfrac{\sqrt{59 - 4\sqrt{91}}}{3};\ u = \dfrac{8 - \sqrt{91}}{9}, v = -\dfrac{\sqrt{59 + 4\sqrt{91}}}{3}$

**26.** $x = 2\sqrt{2},\ y = \sqrt{2};\quad x = 2\sqrt{2},\ y = -\sqrt{2};\quad x = -2\sqrt{2},\ y = \sqrt{2};$
$x = -2\sqrt{2}, y = -2\sqrt{2}$

**27.** $x = \dfrac{\sqrt{14}}{4},\ y = \dfrac{\sqrt{3}}{2};\quad x = \dfrac{\sqrt{14}}{4},\ y = -\dfrac{\sqrt{3}}{2};\quad x = -\dfrac{\sqrt{14}}{4},\ y = \dfrac{\sqrt{3}}{2};$

$x = -\dfrac{\sqrt{14}}{4}, y = -\dfrac{\sqrt{3}}{2}$

**28.** $u = \sqrt{2}, v = \sqrt{3};\ u = \sqrt{2}, v = -\sqrt{3};\ u = -\sqrt{2}, v = \sqrt{3};\ u = -\sqrt{2},$
$v = -\sqrt{3}$

**29.** $x = \frac{3}{2}, y = 2;\ x = \frac{3}{2}, y = -2;\ x = -\frac{3}{2}, y = 2;\ x = -\frac{3}{2}, y = -2$

**30.** $x = \sqrt{70}, y = \dfrac{-7 + 4\sqrt{70}}{9};\ x = -\sqrt{70}, y = \dfrac{-7 - 4\sqrt{70}}{9}$

**31.** $u = 2\sqrt{5 + \sqrt{7}},\quad v = 2 + \sqrt{7};\quad u = 2\sqrt{5 - \sqrt{7}},\quad v = 2 - \sqrt{7};$
$u = -2\sqrt{5 + \sqrt{7}},\ v = 2 + \sqrt{7};\quad u = -2\sqrt{5 - \sqrt{7}}, v = 2 - \sqrt{7}$

**32.** $x = 3, y = 2;\ x = -3, y = 2;\ x = \dfrac{3\sqrt{3}}{2}, y = -\dfrac{5}{2};\ x = -\dfrac{3\sqrt{3}}{2}, y = -\dfrac{5}{2}$

**33.** $u = 1, v = -1;\ u = -1, v = 1$　　**34.** $x = \frac{1}{7}, y = \frac{1}{5};\ x = -\frac{1}{5}, y = -\frac{1}{7}$

**35.** $x = 2 + 3i, y = 1 + 2i;\ x = 2 - 3i, y = 1 - 2i$

**36.** $x = 7, y = -3;\ x = -\frac{9}{4}, y = \frac{28}{3}$

**37.** $x = 4, y = 1;\ x = 4, y = -1;\ x = -4, y = 1;\ x = -4, y = -1$

**38.** $u = 4, v = 3;\ u = 4, v = -3;\ u = -4, v = 3;\ u = -4, v = -3$

**39.** $u = 5, v = 3;\ u = 5, v = -3;\ u = -5, v = 3;\ u = -5, v = -3$

**40.** $u = 2, v = 2;\ u = 2, v = -2;\ u = -2, v = 2;\ u = -2, v = -2$

**41.** $x = 3, y = 2;\ x = -3, y = 2;\ x = \dfrac{\sqrt{39}}{3}, y = -\dfrac{8}{3};\ x = -\dfrac{\sqrt{39}}{3}, y = -\dfrac{8}{3}$

**42.** $x = 1, y = -1;\ x = -1, y = -1;\ x = \dfrac{\sqrt{89}i}{2}, y = \dfrac{27}{4};\ x = -\dfrac{\sqrt{89}i}{2}, y = \dfrac{27}{4}$

**43.** $x = 2, y = 1;\ x = 2, y = -1;\ x = -\dfrac{7}{2}, y = \dfrac{\sqrt{62}i}{2};\ x = -\dfrac{7}{2}, y = -\dfrac{\sqrt{62}i}{2}$

**44.** $x = \dfrac{-5 + \sqrt{249}}{4}, y = \dfrac{\sqrt{-278 + 14\sqrt{249}}}{4};$

$x = \dfrac{-5 + \sqrt{249}}{4}, y = -\dfrac{\sqrt{-278 + 14\sqrt{249}}}{4};$

$$x = \frac{-5 - \sqrt{249}}{4}, \quad y = \frac{\sqrt{-278 - 14\sqrt{249}}}{4};$$

$$x = \frac{-5 - \sqrt{249}}{4}, \quad y = -\frac{\sqrt{-278 - 14\sqrt{249}}}{4}$$

**45.** $x = 2, y = -3$; $x = \frac{32}{23}, y = \frac{1}{23}$     **46.** $x = 0, y = -5$; $x = \frac{5}{2}, y = -\frac{5}{2}$

## Exercises.  Pages 104–105

**1.** $x = 2, y = -3$; $x = -2, y = 3$; $x = 3, y = -2$; $x = -3, y = 2$

**2.** $u = \frac{1}{3}, v = \frac{1}{2}$; $u = -\frac{1}{3}, v = -\frac{1}{2}$; $u = \frac{1}{2}, v = \frac{1}{3}$; $u = -\frac{1}{2}, v = -\frac{1}{3}$

**3.** $x = 4, y = \frac{1}{2}$; $x = -4, y = -\frac{1}{2}$; $x = 14, y = -2$; $x = -14, y = 2$

**4.** $x = 1, y = -1$; $x = -1, y = 1$; $x = 3, y = 2$; $x = -3, y = -2$

**5.** $x = 8, y = 7$; $x = -8, y = -7$

**6.** $u = 3, v = 1$; $u = -3, v = -1$; $u = 2\sqrt{2}, v = \sqrt{2}$; $u = -2\sqrt{2}, v = -\sqrt{2}$

**7.** $u = 2, v = 3$; $u = -2, v = -3$; $u = 10, v = -9$; $u = -10, v = 9$

**8.** $x = 4, y = \frac{5}{2}$; $x = -4, y = -\frac{5}{2}$; $x = 5, y = 2$; $x = -5, y = -2$

**9.** $x = 4, y = -1$; $x = -4, y = 1$; $x = \frac{\sqrt{66}}{6}, y = \frac{\sqrt{66}}{6}$; $x = -\frac{\sqrt{66}}{6}, y = -\frac{\sqrt{66}}{6}$

**10.** $x = 1, y = 3$; $x = -1, y = -3$; $x = 3, y = -4$; $x = -3, y = 4$

**11.** $u = 1, v = -2$; $u = -1, v = 2$; $u = \sqrt{3}, v = 0$; $u = -\sqrt{3}, v = 0$

**12.** $x = 2, y = 4$; $x = -2, y = -4$; $x = 4i, y = -2i$; $x = -4i, y = 2i$

**13.** $x = 3, y = 1$; $x = -3, y = -1$; $x = \frac{4\sqrt{10}}{5}, y = \frac{-3\sqrt{10}}{5}$; $x = \frac{-4\sqrt{10}}{5}, y = \frac{3\sqrt{10}}{5}$

**14.** $u = 4, v = 6$; $u = -4, v = -6$; $u = \sqrt{3}, v = \frac{-2\sqrt{3}}{3}$; $u = -\sqrt{3}, v = \frac{2\sqrt{3}}{3}$

**15.** $x = 2\sqrt{5}, y = \sqrt{5}$; $x = -2\sqrt{5}, y = -\sqrt{5}$; $x = \frac{\sqrt{26}}{2}, y = -\frac{\sqrt{26}}{2}$; $x = -\frac{\sqrt{26}}{2}, y = \frac{\sqrt{26}}{2}$

**16.** $x = 1, y = -\frac{3}{2}$; $x = -1, y = \frac{3}{2}$; $x = 4, y = -1$; $x = -4, y = 1$

**17.** $u = 5, v = 2$; $u = -5, v = -2$; $u = \frac{\sqrt{5}}{5}, v = -\frac{12\sqrt{5}}{5}$; $u = -\frac{\sqrt{5}}{5}, v = \frac{12\sqrt{5}}{5}$

**18.** $x = 3, y = -1$; $x = -3, y = 1$; $x = \frac{5\sqrt{2}}{4}, y = \frac{7\sqrt{2}}{2}$; $x = -\frac{5\sqrt{2}}{4}, y = -\frac{7\sqrt{2}}{2}$

**19.** $u = 8, v = 5$;   $u = -8, v = -5$;   $u = 6\sqrt{3}, v = \sqrt{3}$;   $u = -6\sqrt{3}$, $v = -\sqrt{3}$

**20.** $y = 2, z = -1$;   $y = -2, z = 1$;   $y = \frac{17}{9}, z = -\frac{11}{9}$;   $y = -\frac{17}{9}, z = \frac{11}{9}$

**21.** $x = \dfrac{2\sqrt{35}}{7}$, $y = \dfrac{6\sqrt{35}}{7}$;    $x = -\dfrac{2\sqrt{35}}{7}$, $y = -\dfrac{6\sqrt{35}}{7}$;    $x = \dfrac{6\sqrt{65}}{13}$, $y = \dfrac{8\sqrt{65}}{13}$;   $x = -\dfrac{6\sqrt{65}}{13}$, $y = -\dfrac{8\sqrt{65}}{13}$

**22.** $u = 3, v = 2$;   $u = -3, v = -2$;   $u = \dfrac{\sqrt{2}}{6}, v = -\dfrac{7\sqrt{2}}{6}$;   $u = -\dfrac{\sqrt{2}}{6}$, $v = \dfrac{7\sqrt{2}}{6}$

**23.** $w = 3, z = 2$;   $w = -3, z = -2$

**24.** $x = 2, y = -5$;   $x = -2, y = 5$;   $x = \dfrac{\sqrt{3}}{3}, y = -\dfrac{8\sqrt{3}}{3}$;   $x = -\dfrac{\sqrt{3}}{3}$, $y = \dfrac{8\sqrt{3}}{3}$

**25.** $u = \sqrt{3}, v = -3\sqrt{3}$;   $u = -\sqrt{3}, v = 3\sqrt{3}$;   $u = 3\sqrt{3}, v = -\sqrt{3}$;   $u = -3\sqrt{3}, v = \sqrt{3}$

**26.** $u = 3, v = 3$;   $u = 5, v = 1$

**27.** $u = 7, v = 2$;   $u = -\frac{22}{3}, v = -\frac{83}{66}$

**28.** $x = 1, y = 2$;   $x = -1, y = -2$

**29.** $x = 3, y = -1$;   $x = \frac{8}{3}, y = -\frac{2}{3}$;   $x = -\frac{3}{2}, y = \frac{1}{2}$;   $x = -\frac{8}{5}, y = \frac{2}{5}$

**30.** $x = \dfrac{\sqrt{10 + \sqrt{91}}}{3}$, $y = -\sqrt{10 - \sqrt{91}}$;   $x = -\dfrac{\sqrt{10 + \sqrt{91}}}{3}$, $y = \sqrt{10 - \sqrt{91}}$;   $x = \dfrac{\sqrt{10 - \sqrt{91}}}{3}$, $y = -\sqrt{10 + \sqrt{91}}$;   $x = -\dfrac{\sqrt{10 - \sqrt{91}}}{3}$, $y = \sqrt{10 + \sqrt{91}}$

**31.** $x = 1, y = -2$;   $x = -1, y = 2$;   $x = \frac{1}{2}, y = \frac{1}{3}$;   $x = -\frac{1}{2}, y = -\frac{1}{3}$

**32.** $u = 2, v = 1$;   $u = -2, v = -1$;   $u = \dfrac{4\sqrt{3}}{3}, v = \dfrac{\sqrt{3}}{3}$;   $u = -\dfrac{4\sqrt{3}}{3}$, $v = -\dfrac{\sqrt{3}}{3}$

**33.** $x = 4, y = 1$;   $x = -4, y = -1$;   $x = \dfrac{7\sqrt{2}}{3}, y = -\dfrac{4\sqrt{2}}{3}$;   $x = -\dfrac{7\sqrt{2}}{3}$, $y = \dfrac{4\sqrt{2}}{3}$

**34.** $a = 0, b = 0$;   $a = 2, b = 2$;   $a = \sqrt{2}, b = 2 - \sqrt{2}$;   $a = -\sqrt{2}$, $b = 2 + \sqrt{2}$

**35.** $x = 1, y = 2$;   $x = 1, y = -2$;   $x = 2, y = 1$;   $x = -2, y = 1$

**36.** $u = 2, v = 1$;   $u = 1, v = 2$;   $u = -3 + \sqrt{2}i, v = -3 - \sqrt{2}i$;   $u = -3 - \sqrt{2}i, v = -3 + \sqrt{2}i$

### Exercises. Pages 107–109

**1.** $2 + \sqrt{7}$      **2.** $\sqrt{11} + \sqrt{5}$      **3.** $\sqrt{10} - 2\sqrt{2}$

**4.** $2 + 3i$      **5.** $\frac{1}{2}(5\sqrt{2} + \sqrt{14})$      **6.** $3 + \sqrt{2}$

**7.** $\sqrt{6} - 2$        **8.** $12\sqrt{3} - \sqrt{10}$        **9.** $5 + 2\sqrt{3}$
**10.** 50 ft., 120 ft.        **11.** 3 ft., 4 ft.        **12.** 7 in., 24 in.
**13.** 7 ft., 12 ft.        **14.** 20 min., 25 min.        **15.** 4 and 7

**16.** 5, 12, 13        **17.** \$155        **18.** 13, 12; also $\dfrac{\sqrt{2}}{2}, -\dfrac{25\sqrt{2}}{2}$

**19.** $\frac{3}{5}$        **20.** 8 days, 10 days        **21.** 168 sq. in.        **22.** 15 in.
**23.** 15 mi. per hr., 30 mi. per hr.        **24.** 1 hr.        **25.** 8, 9; also $-8, -9$
**26.** 7, 6; 8, 9        **27.** 7, 5; $-7, -5$        **28.** 16, 25
**29.** \$1000; 6 per cent        **30.** 4 per cent and 8 per cent
**31.** $a + b - \sqrt{a^2 + b^2}, \ a + b + \sqrt{a^2 + b^2}$
**32.** $h = r - \sqrt{r^2 - s^2}$        **33.** $\sqrt{r^2 + d^2} - r$
**34.** $x = \dfrac{2}{c} \sqrt{s(s - a)(s - b)(s - c)} = \dfrac{2}{c} \times$ area
**35.** 8 ft. per sec.

## Exercises. Page 111

**9.** 13; 5        **12.** (4, 3); $(-4, -3)$

## Exercises. Pages 114–115

**13.** 3.0, $-1.0$        **14.** 0.0, 1.0, $-1.0$        **15.** 1.0, $-1.0$
**16.** 0        **17.** 1.0, 0.7        **18.** No real roots
**19.** $-1.1, 4.1$        **20.** No real roots        **21.** 2.6, $-1.6$
**22.** 0.8, $-0.8$        **23.** 4.6, 0.4        **24.** $-2.6, 1.6$        **45.** $x = 4$

## Exercises. Pages 117–118

**1.** 36        **2.** 4        **3.** 1        **4.** $\pm 2(a + b)^2$        **5.** $ab$
**6.** $\frac{25}{2}$        **7.** $6c^2$        **8.** $\pm 18$        **9.** 209        **10.** $\frac{5}{4}$
**11.** $\pm \sqrt{(a^2 + b^2)(c^2 + d^2)}$        **12.** $5b^2$        **13.** $\pm 6a^2b$
**31.** 8, 4        **32.** 10 : 15        **33.** 3        **35.** $\pm 2$
**36.** 10        **37.** 18, 27        **38.** 5, 3
**39.** \$4000, \$8000, \$16,000        **40.** 4

## Exercises. Pages 120–122

**1.** $A = \pi r^2$        **2.** $P = 4s$        **3.** $V = \dfrac{4\pi r^3}{3}$        **4.** $S = \pi d$

**5.** $A = \frac{1}{2}bh$        **6.** $S = 2\pi rh$        **7.** $V = \dfrac{kx}{y^2}$        **8.** $z = \dfrac{kxy^2}{\sqrt{w}}$

**9.** $s = kt^2$        **10.** $w = \dfrac{kx^{\frac{2}{3}}}{\sqrt{y}}$        **11.** $s$ varies directly as $t^2$.

**12.** $A$ varies directly as $r^2$.        **13.** $P$ varies directly as $s$.
**14.** $w$ varies jointly as $x^2$ and $\sqrt[3]{z}$ and inversely as $\sqrt{u}$.
**15.** $S$ varies jointly as $r$ and $l$.        **16.** $v$ varies inversely as $p$.
**17.** $w$ varies jointly as $x$ and $y$ and inversely as $z^3$.
**18.** $A$ varies jointly as $b$ and $h$.

**19.** $A$ varies jointly as $h$ and the sum of $b_1$ and $b_2$.

**20.** 400 ft.;  144 ft.  **21.** 9 horsepower

**22.** 0.8 sec.  **23.** 12 cu. ft.  **24.** 2 ft.

**25.** $\dfrac{24\sqrt{93}}{961}$ yr. = 0.241 yr.  **26.** 19.753 lb., 62.5 lb.

**27.** $483.33\frac{1}{3}$  **28.** $3\frac{5}{7}$ ft.

**29.** $C = \dfrac{500}{s}\left(100 + \dfrac{10s^2}{144}\right)$  **30.** Increased 69.5%

**31.** $S = \dfrac{2000bd^2}{9l}$  **32.** 35,342.9 lb.

**33.** 187.5 cu. in.  **34.** 11.18 mi. per hr.  **35.** 0.273

**36.** An increase to four times the original value  **37.** A decrease of 23.6%

### Exercises.  Pages 124–125

**1.** $l = 12$, $S = 78$  **2.** $l = -7$, $S = -12$  **3.** $l = 80$, $S = 1107$

**4.** $l = -198$, $S = -4020$  **5.** $l = -65$, $S = -558$

**6.** $l = 120$, $S = 3660$  **7.** $l = 102$, $S = 1090$

**8.** $l = \frac{35}{2}$, $S = 162$  **9.** $n = 5$, $l = -8$; $n = 8$, $l = 4$

**10.** $a = -7$, $S = 425$  **11.** $a = 9$, $n = 11$; $a = -12$, $n = 4$

**12.** $d = \frac{5}{9}$, $l = 9$  **13.** $d = \frac{2}{3}$, $l = \frac{13}{3}$

**14.** $l = 81$, $S = 851$  **15.** $a = -72$, $n = 6$

**16.** No solution  **17.** $a = -13$, $d = 4$

**18.** $d = -\frac{88}{19}$, $n = 20$  **19.** $n = 79$, $S = 15,800$

**20.** $a = 3$, $d = \frac{5}{7}$  **21.** $d = -0.9$, $S = -11$

**22.** No solution  **23.** $l = -7$, $d = -2$

**24.** $a = 5$, $l = 75$  **25.** 2, 5, 8, 11, $\cdots$

**26.** 3, 5, 7, 9, $\cdots$  **27.** 4, 7, 10, 13; $-13, -10, -7, -4$

**28.** 3, 5, 7, $\cdots$; 7, 5, 3, $\cdots$  **29.** 3, 5, 7, $\cdots$

**30.** 2, 4, 6  **31.** 1, 3, 5, 7, $\cdots$  **32.** $n = 14$, $n = 68$

**33.** $\frac{345}{8}$  **34.** 5, 8, 11, $\cdots$  **35.** 6 sec.

**36.** $1450 salary for eleventh year; $14,575 total amount in eleven years

**37.** 2, 4, 6, 8  **38.** 780 ft.  **39.** $10.56  **40.** 57,600 ft.

### Exercises.  Pages 126–127

**1.** $l = 32$, $S = 62$  **2.** $l = 96$, $S = 189$

**3.** $l = 0.00002$, $S = 0.22222$  **4.** $l = 4\sqrt{6}$, $S = 7\sqrt{3}(\sqrt{2}+1)$

**5.** $l = 2048$, $S = 4095$  **6.** $l = -\frac{1}{4}$, $S = -\frac{11}{4}$

**7.** $l = -\frac{243}{4}$, $S = -\frac{410}{9}$  **8.** $l = -96$, $S = -\frac{129}{2}$

**9.** $r = 2$, $S = -62$  **10.** $l = 64$, $S = 43$  **11.** $a = 50$, $n = 4$

**12.** $a = 128$, $n = 8$  **13.** $S = 1022$, $n = 9$  **14.** $a = 3$, $l = 243$

**15.** $r = 3$, $S = 120$  **16.** $a = 25$, $n = 3$  **17.** $r = -3$, $n = 5$

**18.** $r = \frac{3}{2}$, $S = 633$  **19.** $r = 3$, $S = 242$  **20.** $a = 5$, $l = 320$

**21.** $r = 3$, $l = 162$  **22.** $r = -\frac{1}{2}$, $n = 5$  **23.** 3, 6, 12

**24.** $a = 16$, $t_6$ (sixth term) $= \frac{1}{2}$, $S = \frac{63}{2}$

**25.** $r = 3$, $S = 242$  **26.** 2, 6, 18, 54, $\cdots$  **27.** 3, 6, 12

# ANSWERS

**28.** 4092 or $-$ 1364 **29.** $r = \frac{1}{2}$, $S = 1\frac{89}{8}$ **30.** 12.6098 in.

**31.** $\left[1 - \left(\frac{5}{6}\right)^6\right]$ = part removed in first six strokes;
$\frac{1}{6}\left(\frac{5}{6}\right)^5$ = part removed in sixth stroke

**32.** \$10.23 **33.** \$126.68

### Exercises. Pages 132–133

**1.** $x^5 + 5x^4y + 10x^3y^2 + 10x^2y^3 + 5xy^4 + y^5$

**2.** $u^3 - 3u^2v + 3uv^2 - v^3$ **3.** $a^4 + 4a^3b + 6a^2b^2 + 4ab^3 + b^4$

**4.** $16x^4 - 96x^3y + 216x^2y^2 - 216xy^3 + 81y^4$

**5.** $x^6 + 6x^4 + 12x^2 + 8$ **6.** $1 - 10x + 40x^2 - 80x^3 + 80x^4 - 32x^5$

**7.** $a^7 - 14a^6 + 84a^5 - 280a^4 + 560a^3 - 672a^2 + 448a - 128$

**8.** $16x^4 + 96x^3 + 216x^2 + 216x + 81$

**9.** $\dfrac{64}{729} - \dfrac{32x}{27} + \dfrac{20x^2}{3} - 20x^3 + \dfrac{135x^4}{4} - \dfrac{243x^5}{8} + \dfrac{729x^6}{64}$

**10.** $x^{12} - 24x^{11}y + 264x^{10}y^2 - 1760x^9y^3 + 7920x^8y^4 - 25344x^7y^5 + 59136x^6y^6$
$- 101376x^5y^7 + 126720x^4y^8 - 112640x^3y^9 + 67584x^2y^{10} - 24576xy^{11}$
$+ 4096y^{12}$

**11.** $\dfrac{1}{a^5} + \dfrac{5}{a^4y} + \dfrac{10}{a^3y^2} + \dfrac{10}{a^2y^3} + \dfrac{5}{ay^4} + \dfrac{1}{y^5}$

**12.** $\dfrac{32x^5}{y^5} - \dfrac{240x^3}{y^3} + \dfrac{720x}{y} - \dfrac{1080y}{x} + \dfrac{810y^3}{x^3} - \dfrac{243y^5}{x^5}$

**13.** $\dfrac{x^8}{y^4} + \dfrac{4x^5}{y} + 6x^2y^2 + \dfrac{4y^5}{x} + \dfrac{y^8}{x^4}$

**14.** $\dfrac{a^{12}}{x^{18}} - \dfrac{6a^7y^{\frac{1}{2}}}{x^{15}} + \dfrac{15a^2y}{x^{12}} - \dfrac{20y^{\frac{3}{2}}}{x^9a^3} + \dfrac{15y^2}{x^6a^8} - \dfrac{6y^{\frac{5}{2}}}{x^3a^{13}} + \dfrac{y^3}{a^{18}}$

**15.** $32x^5 + 80x^{\frac{7}{2}} + 80x^2 + 40x^{\frac{1}{2}} + \dfrac{10}{x} + \dfrac{1}{x^{\frac{5}{2}}}$

**16.** $x^8 + 0.8x^7 + 0.28x^6 + 0.056x^5 + 0.007x^4 + 0.00056x^3 + 0.000028x^2$
$+ 0.0000008x + 0.00000001$

**17.** $\dfrac{32}{x^5} + \dfrac{80}{x^2} + 80x + 40x^4 + 10x^7 + x^{10}$

**18.** $x^{-\frac{3}{2}} + 3x^{\frac{1}{2}} + 3x^{\frac{5}{2}} + x^{\frac{9}{2}}$

**19.** $\dfrac{x^{\frac{8}{3}}}{16} + \dfrac{\sqrt{2}x^{\frac{3}{2}}}{2} + 3x^{\frac{1}{3}} + \dfrac{4\sqrt{2}}{x^{\frac{5}{6}}} + \dfrac{4}{x^2}$

**20.** $x^{\frac{7}{2}}\left(1 - \dfrac{7}{y^{\frac{1}{2}}} + \dfrac{21}{y} - \dfrac{35}{y^{\frac{3}{2}}} + \dfrac{35}{y^2} - \dfrac{21}{y^{\frac{5}{2}}} + \dfrac{7}{y^3} - \dfrac{1}{y^{\frac{7}{2}}}\right)$

**21.** $a^9 + 12a^7 + 60a^5 + 160a^3 + 240a + \dfrac{192}{a} + \dfrac{64}{a^3}$

**22.** 1.1262 **23.** 1030300 **24.** 92237000

**25.** 1015100 **26.** 97229000 **27.** 3280800

**28.** $- 1512x^5y^3$ **29.** $- 3432a^7b^7$ **30.** 252

**31.** $736281x^{12}y^{\frac{2.5}{9}}$ **32.** $- 496128b^{-\frac{1.5}{4}}c$ **33.** $3060x^{\frac{8}{3}}$

**34.** $\dfrac{11 \cdot 7 \cdot 3^7x^3}{2^{13}}$ **35.** $- \dfrac{35x^4}{y^{\frac{1}{2}}}$ **36.** $- \dfrac{7 \cdot 3^7}{2^7}$ **37.** $\dfrac{7 \cdot 3 \cdot 2^8x^3}{5^3}$

**38.** $- 20a^{\frac{3}{2}}b^{-\frac{9}{2}}x^{\frac{9}{2}}y^{\frac{1.5}{2}}$ **39.** $- 138567a^2b^{\frac{7}{6}}$

**40.** $7 \cdot 2^8$  **41.** $924$  **42.** $\dfrac{45a}{2^8}$

**43.** $-21x^2$  **44.** $35 \cdot 2^5 x^8$  **45.** $y = \pm \frac{1}{2}$

**46.** $\left( a = \dfrac{15 + 5\sqrt{3}}{6},\, b = \dfrac{15 - 5\sqrt{3}}{6} \right),\ \left( a = \dfrac{15 - 5\sqrt{3}}{6},\, b = \dfrac{15 + 5\sqrt{3}}{6} \right)$

**47.** $-\dfrac{7 \cdot 2^5}{3^2}$  **48.** $-252$  **49.** $\frac{1}{8}$  **50.** $\frac{21}{176}$  **51.** $5$

## Review Exercises

### Part A.  Page 134

**1.** $5y$  **2.** $2^{1-h}$  **3.** $\dfrac{3a}{b}$  **4.** $-\frac{1}{2}$  **5.** $\dfrac{x^{n+5}}{4^{4n}}$  **6.** $\dfrac{y^4}{x^5}$

**7.** $8xy$  **8.** $9ax$  **9.** $2\sqrt[6]{3}$  **10.** $x^4 y^{\frac{17}{2}}$  **11.** $\dfrac{b^{\frac{7}{3}}}{a^{\frac{3}{2}}c^{\frac{3}{2}}}$  **12.** $\dfrac{y^{\frac{1}{6}}}{x^{\frac{5}{8}}}$

### Part B.  Pages 134–136

**1.** $\dfrac{1}{x - a}$  **2.** $\dfrac{1}{x + a}$  **3.** $2\sqrt{9 - y^2}$  **4.** $\dfrac{1}{a - b}$

**5.** $\dfrac{3a^2 x^2}{(a^2 - x^2)^2}$  **6.** $\dfrac{2a^2 x + 3x^3}{(a^2 + x^2)^{\frac{3}{2}}}$  **7.** $2 + \dfrac{\sqrt{3}}{3}$

**8.** $\sqrt{ab}\left( \dfrac{4}{b} - \dfrac{6}{a} + \dfrac{5}{ab} \right)$  **9.** $\sqrt{ab}\left( \dfrac{4}{b} + \dfrac{5}{a} - \dfrac{3}{ab} \right)$  **10.** $\dfrac{105\sqrt{2}}{4}$

**11.** $3$  **12.** $2(a^2 - b^2)\sqrt{a^2 + b^2}$  **13.** $-6 + 5\sqrt{6}$

**14.** $17$  **15.** $\dfrac{-1 + 3\sqrt{3}}{2}$  **16.** $7\sqrt{6}i$

**17.** $\dfrac{6 + 17i}{13}$  **18.** $10 + 5i$  **19.** $3i$

**20.** $-\dfrac{1}{1 + 3x}$  **21.** $-\dfrac{3}{1 + x}$  **22.** $\dfrac{a + 2b}{2(b - a)}$

**23.** $\dfrac{x^2 + 3x + 3}{(x + 1)(x - 2)(x + 3)}$  **24.** $\dfrac{b^2}{a(b^2 - a^2)}$  **25.** $-\dfrac{(x - 2n)^2}{x + 3n}$

**26.** $-\dfrac{3a + b}{4a + b}$  **27.** $\sqrt{3}$  **28.** $5 - 4\sqrt{2}$  **29.** $5\sqrt{3}$

**30.** $\dfrac{-9 + 26\sqrt{3}i}{57}$  **31.** $7\sqrt{2}$  **32.** $3x^{\frac{1}{3}} y^{\frac{1}{3}} (x^{\frac{2}{3}} + y^{\frac{2}{3}})^{\frac{1}{2}}$

**33.** $\dfrac{13x + 6}{(x + 2)(2x - 1)(3x + 1)}$  **34.** $a^3 + 2a^2 b + 3ab^2 + 4b^3$

**35.** $1$  **36.** $\dfrac{x + a}{x - a}$  **37.** $\dfrac{2(x - 2)}{(x + 2)(x - 3)}$  **38.** $\dfrac{11a - 13}{17a - 20}$

**39.** $y$  **40.** $-3$  **41.** $0$  **42.** $-\frac{1}{4}$

## Part C. Pages 136–137

**1.** 0  **2.** $-\frac{4}{15}$  **3.** $\frac{1}{2}$

**4.** 2, 1  **5.** No solution  **6.** 10, 6

**7.** 4, 3, $-5$  **8.** $-\frac{27}{11}, \frac{9}{4}, -\frac{3}{2}$  **9.** $\frac{2}{11}$, 3

**10.** $\dfrac{2 \pm \sqrt{10}}{3}$  **11.** $\dfrac{b \pm \sqrt{b^2 - ac}}{2a}$  **12.** $y - 1, -\dfrac{3y}{2}$

**13.** 1, (Ext. $-\frac{3}{8}$)  **14.** 5  **15.** $\pm 4, \pm \frac{2}{3}$

**16.** $-1, \pm 2, 3$  **17.** 3, $-\frac{9}{2}$  **18.** $-3, 7$

**19.** $x = 0, y = 5;\ x = 3, y = 4$  **20.** $x = 6, y = -9;\ x = -9, y = 6$

**21.** $x = \pm 1, y = 0;\ x = \pm 3, y = -2$

**22.** $x = 0, y = 0;\ x = 2a, y = -4a$

**23.** $x = 3,\ y = -2;\ x = -2,\ y = 3;\ x = -2 + \sqrt{5},\ y = -2 - \sqrt{5};$
$x = -2 - \sqrt{5}, y = -2 + \sqrt{5}$

**24.** $x = 4, y = 3;\ x = -4, y = -3;\ x = 3, y = 4;\ x = -3, y = -4$

**25.** $A$, \$960; $B$, \$1200; $C$, \$1080; $D$, \$1760

**26.** Rate of rowing $= 4$ mi. per hr.; rate of stream $= 2$ mi. per hr.

**27.** 9 mi. per hr.  **28.** 40 yd.

## Part E. Pages 137–138

**1.** 5 and 11  **2.** $\frac{4}{3}$  **3.** $2, -\frac{2}{5}$  **5.** $\frac{8}{5}$

**6.** 8 in.  **7.** $-300$  **8.** 24 days

**9.** $n = 16, d = \frac{5}{6}$  **10.** $a = \frac{7}{2}, n = 7$  **11.** $a = 2, S = 728$

**12.** $r = -4$  **13.** 5, 8, 11 and 15, 8, 1  **14.** $7 \cdot 5 \cdot 3^4 \cdot 2^5 x^8 y^6$

**15.** $13 \cdot 11 \cdot 7 \cdot 5 \cdot 3^9$  **16.** 1.04060401  **18.** 50%

## Part F. Pages 138–143

**1.** 2  **2.** $x = -3, y = 4$  **3.** 6  **4.** $\dfrac{2x(2x^3 + 5)}{x^3 + 5}; -\dfrac{3}{2}$

**5.** $x = 2, y = 3, z = 4$  **6.** 1  **7.** $\dfrac{(x - y)^2}{xy(x + y)^2}$

**8.** $\dfrac{p + 2q + 3r}{p + q + r + 1}$  **9.** 2, (Ext. $-3$)  **10.** 30 min.

**11.** $x^5 - \dfrac{5x^4}{2y^2} + \dfrac{5x^3}{2y^4} - \dfrac{5x^2}{4y^6} + \dfrac{5x}{16y^8} - \dfrac{1}{32y^{10}}$

**12.** $\dfrac{3x - y}{2y}$  **13.** $\frac{13}{2}, -\frac{5}{4}$  **14.** 0.58

**15.** $u = \dfrac{1}{a}, v = \dfrac{1}{b - a}, w = \dfrac{1}{c - b}, z = \dfrac{1}{d - c}$

**16.** $2, -7$  **17.** $a$ and $5a$  **18.** $\dfrac{1}{y}$  **19.** $(2, 1);\ (\frac{1}{4}, -\frac{1}{6})$

**20.** 3978  **21.** $2, 1, -3$  **22.** $\dfrac{x^3}{y^5}$  **23.** 55 mi.

**24.** 4 and 10  **25.** $-\dfrac{2a}{3\sqrt{x}}$  **26.** 56

**27.** 13 ft. and 10 ft.    **28.** $5\sqrt{3} - 4$    **29.** $6 - 2\sqrt{3} - \sqrt{6} + \sqrt{2}$

**30.** $- 2.83$    **31.** $\frac{3}{2}$, (Ext. $- 1$)    **32.** 2500 lb.

**33.** $A - 3$ hr., $B - 4$ hr., $C - 6$ hr.    **34.** $2, -\frac{4}{5}$

**35.** 7    **36.** 2    **37.** $- 1, 3$

**38.** $3 - \sqrt{5}$    **39.** 1000 yr.    **40.** $S = \dfrac{n}{2}(2a + (n - 1)d)$

**41.** $\dfrac{1 \pm \sqrt{19}}{2}$    **42.** $\frac{35}{24}$    **43.** $1.4+$

**44.** 2 mi. per hr. and 3 mi. per hr.    **45.** $2\sqrt{3} - 1$

**46.** $(\frac{9}{10})^5$    **47.** $1.05+$ units    **48.** $13 \cdot 7 \cdot 5 \cdot 2^6 a^4 x^{-6}$

**49.** 18 calves at \$12, or 16 calves at \$14.    **50.** 1, 5

**51.** 3 mi. per hr.    **52.** 30 hydrants, 42 valves, 360 pipe sections

**53.** Man, 4 mi. per hr.; boy, 2 mi. per hr.; stream, 1 mi. per hr.

**54.** 15 ft. per sec. and 5 ft. per sec.